Nan Booth

Great Garden Sources
of the Pacific Northwest

A Sourcebook of
Design Ideas and Garden Suppliers
for Both Novice & Experienced
Northwest Gardeners

Portland, Oregon U.S.A.

First Edition
ISBN 0-9639879-0-9

Library of Congress Catalog Card Number
93-61869

☆DESTINATIONS

Throughout this book you'll find a select number of listings identified with the "Destinations" mark shown above. These have been designated by the author as special places in terms of quality, quantity, visual appeal, historical interest and/or the expertise of the folks involved with the source.

Bulk Sales

Copies of this book in quantities greater than two dozen, are available at discount for fund raising by garden clubs and non-profit support organizations. Contact the publisher for more information.

Forewarning

This publication is intended as a general guide. The subject matter deals with hundreds of independent businesses, nonprofit organizations and public agencies which are apt to change at any time. Therefore it is sold as is, and without a warranty of any kind, either express or implied.

Every effort was made to ensure that the information presented was accurate on the date of publication. Businesses do close, locations and hours often change, and companies alter their product mix. Therefore, neither the author nor the publisher shall be liable to the purchaser or any other person or entity with respect to any liability, loss or damage caused or alleged to be caused directly or indirectly by information appearing in this publication.

We neither expressly guarantee, warrant or endorse the businesses, locations and/or subjects to which this guide provides descriptions and other general information.

Printed in the United States of America.
Published by:

The **Authors** Communication Team
Post Office Box 25211
Portland, Oregon 97225 U.S.A.
Phone & Facsimile 503/297-0873

As an environmentally conscious publisher, we have printed this book and its cover on recycled paper.

Foreword

This book was not created to collect dust on your bookshelf. Rather, it is intended to be used until it falls apart or is replaced by the next edition.

This is a how-to and where-to workbook, a compendium of information for improving your garden and your skills as a gardener.

Reading this book from cover-to-cover is not required or even recommended. However, we think you'll find each chapter's introduction filled with wonderful bits of information along with many personal insights from its garden designer/author. The listings themselves are presented to help you in choosing the most appropriate supplier of goods and services. There really is no single best source for anything. This book can aim you in the right direction, but it's up to you to make the decisions.

Don't forget to take this book with you on your travels. The Northwest's best garden sources are dotted throughout the region. Visit and learn.

About the Author

Nan Booth Simpson, a native Texan, is a registered landscape architect specializing in the design of residential landscapes. In addition to designing gardens, she has spent her career writing about gardens for such prominent journals as *Southern Living, Garden Design* and *Landscape Architecture*.

Upon moving from Austin, Texas to Seattle five years ago, Nan longed for the many great garden sources she had uncovered and come to rely upon in her Texas practice. What began as a personal list of her favorite newly discovered sources in the Pacific Northwest, evolved into a two-year project to share this information with her fellow gardeners.

In addition to hundreds of great garden sources, you'll find lots of information and opinions gleaned from years of experience as a professional garden designer, home gardener and respected writer.

Today Nan resides in the Southwest hills of Portland, Oregon, a place she describes to her Texas friends as "a wonderful place to live, a gardener's paradise, and just a four-hour flight from home."

Using the Book

If you read only one section of this book, make it the introduction to Chapter Two. Nan has included important planning tips than can make your garden unique. Without a plan, the joy of gardening can quickly become a painful and costly experience. After first digesting this section, move on to the topic that interests you most and read all about it. Although this is primarily a sourcebook, the introductions to each chapter are full of timesaving, labor-saving and money-saving tips on design and maintenance.

Reader Feedback

A book of this type is an ever-changing data base of discovery and revelation. Your input can make it better, and your recommendations will most assuredly be considered. If you know of a "Great Garden Source" that doesn't appear in this edition, Nan would like to hear from you. We've reserved a page at the end of the book (page 431) for your comments and suggestions. Mail or FAX your recommendations to the publisher. Each will be reviewed carefully before the next edition is published.

The Editors

Contents

☆DESTINATIONS

Throughout this book you'll find a select number of listings identified with the "Destinations" mark shown above. These have been designated by the author as special places in terms of quality, quantity, visual appeal, historical interest and/or the expertise of the folks involved with the source.

Chapter 1

Inspiration & Information, 13

Chapter 2

Garden Construction, 41

Chapter 3

Garden Conservation, 79

Chapter 4

Ecologically Balanced Landscapes, 113

Chapter 5

The Garden's Green Foundation, 135

Chapter 6

The Flower Garden, 169

Chapter 7

The Edible Landscape, 203

Chapter 7 *(continued)*

Chapter 8

The Specialty Garden, 227

Chapter 9

Collector's Plants, 261

Chapter 10

Garden Furniture, 283

Chapter 11

Garden Accessories, 301

Chapter 12

One Stop Shopping:
The Region's Great Garden Centers, 329

See **Regional Index** page 401 to locate specific areas and cities.

Appendixes & Indexes, 401

Introduction

I got my first glimpse of the Pacific Northwest from the back of a motorcycle on a journey from Portland, up Mt. Rainier, and over to the southernmost island in Puget Sound. My children were horrified at the time. My grandchildren think the story is hilarious. For me, the trip was a life-changing experience. Having grown up in the rolling farmland of Central Texas, I was coming home, as they say, to a place I'd never been before. The dramatic seascapes and forested mountainsides were visions of paradise. I returned to my life and work in Texas carrying memories of six-foot-long fern fronds growing in a misty, mystical understory beneath the forest giants.

I ultimately married the man who introduced me to the Northwest. Persuading me to move in mid-career might have been difficult if I were not a landscape architect. For, nowhere else in North America is the environment more hospitable to garden-making than here in the temperate climes of western British Columbia, Washington and Oregon. Having gardened in Texas, I can also appreciate the difficulties of growing plants on the "dry side." I've come to admire the land forms and native flora of the high deserts and interior alpine regions as well as the wooded coastal hills, wetlands and fertile river valleys that outsiders usually associate with the Pacific Northwest.

After living in this vast and varied region, I've realized a second factor that makes gardening unique here. The best stylistic traditions of European and Asian settlers are being brought into harmony with the conservation ethic of the Native Americans, who lived within the region's inimitable environment for centuries without despoiling it. Out of this confluence of cultures has arisen a distinctive regional landscape style.

Why This Book?

A few years ago the editor of *Garden Design* magazine asked me and several other garden writers from across the country to research a proposed article entitled "Secret Garden Sources." I called some of the Northwest's most prominent landscape architects, who willingly shared information on the best places to find rocks and roses and garden tools. While I expected that the places where professionals shop would be "wholesale only," I was surprised to learn that many of the sources they mentioned are open to the public, if only the public can find them.

Later, at a planning session for my garden club, someone asked where to look for a certain plant. Having just completed the earlier project, I agreed to prepare a program on garden sources. I searched libraries and bookstores for a comprehensive regional guidebook and discovered that no single publication covered the gamut of materials that go into a garden. It also occurred to me that knowing *where* to shop does not equip garden consumers with everything they should know about *how* to shop.

So I decided to write this book, sharing not only "secret garden sources," but also everything I've learned (often the hard way) as a design professional on selecting the right plant for the right place, the best container for the best effect and the sturdiest landscape materials for the use intended.

You'll find **Money-saving tips** sprinkled throughout the text. I've tried to suggest economical ways for you to improve your garden, with enough advice to get you pointed in the right direction and enough horticultural information to ask the right questions. There are hundreds of excellent, highly specialized books that cover every aspect of gardening. (See pages 34-37.)

I have shared what I know about planting design in the chapters on plant sources. It is not enough to love plants – it is creating a pleasing composition of color and texture that makes a garden. In most cases, I have chosen to use the common names of plants in this text. It was a difficult decision. On the one hand, Latin botanical nomenclature is a universal language. On the other hand, many gardeners are scared off by *"Latinus grandiosus esoterica."* This book is not meant to intimidate novice gardeners. What I hope to convey is that gardening is a life-long avocation. Nobody knows everything there is to know about the vast world of plants.

To avoid unpleasant surprises, one does need to learn something about Latin names, if only to know how to read plant tags. Common names can present problems. A rose is a rose is a rose, but a Rose of Sharon (*Hibiscus syriacus*) is not a rose at all. To compound the confusion, this plant is commonly called "althaea" in some parts of the country. Furthermore, if you walk into a nursery looking for hibiscus, you could be directed to a tropical plant or a hardy garden perennial or one of several deciduous shrubs. *Hibiscus* tells us the genus. *Hibiscus syriacus* is the species name for a lovely flowering shrub. *Hibiscus syriacus* 'Albus' says that the shrub is a white-flowering variety.

It is my hope that *Great Garden Sources of the Pacific Northwest* will serve both the inexperienced gardener and the connoisseur. An increasing number of homeowners are no longer satisfied with setting out a flat of purple petunias and retiring to the deck with a cold beer. For some, gardening has become a competitive sport! If you are a gardener who would pursue to the ends of the earth a rare variegated form of English boxwood (*Buxus sempervirens* 'Aureo-variegata'), I've got your source!

I'm fairly certain that the largest category of gardeners this book addresses are those who truly enjoy their gardens, but have limited time to spend. Even homeowners who only mow the lawn to keep neighbors from complaining should find resources within these pages. I've laced the text with time-saving ideas and, hopefully, introduced you to products to make every aspect of gardening easier and more rewarding.

Nobody loves a fabulous garden more than I, but this book is not meant to fuel the fires of guilt or send over-achievers to a chiropractor's office. As a gardener, I fall into a middle-ground. My father, a devout and patient gardener, once gave me sage advice. When I asked him what to do about crabgrass, he said, "Learn to love it."

I'm less sanguine about volunteer blackberries. I confess to the occasional use of herbicide, but I'm willing to accept a few serendipitous surprises the birds bring in. I happen to believe gardening should be good for the environment as well as enjoyable for the gardener. And while I'm as guilty as the next person of impulse buying, once I've planted some new "horticultural marvel," I tend to take a *laissez faire* attitude. If I've carefully chosen its spot, given it reasonable care and it doesn't respond, I figure that the plant didn't "belong." Part of the fun of gardening is experimentation.

Good overall design is another matter. You can consign plant mistakes to a compost pile, but a misplaced patio, ugly retaining wall or drainage problem won't simply go away. As a landscape architect, I promise my clients that I'll save them money in the long run by preventing costly mistakes. It only seems fair that I share the same information with readers.

In Chapter One, I've listed places to look for visual inspiration and knowledge about good design and gardening practices. In Chapter Two, I have stressed a Master Plan for your garden. Then I've discussed the walls, walkways, fences and "follies", garden structures and lighting that are as important to a landscape design as plants. And, I've listed sources for the materials that go into this "hardscape."

Before getting into plants, Chapter Three takes up sound gardening practices. I've dwelled heavily on the topic of conservation. As the Pacific Northwest copes with an expanding population, we are seeing diminishing wildlife, depleting water resources, and increasing soil, water and air pollution. I've consulted a number of experienced gardeners in the region who have shared practical methods for improving the soil, feeding and pruning plants, and coping with pests in the most environmentally sensitive manner. The good news is that these techniques can result in reduced garden maintenance!

The sources for plant materials begin in Chapter Four with a discussion about the region's unique biological diversity, which can and must be maintained! This chapter includes sections on Northwest natives, backyard wildlife habitats, wildflower meadows, reforestation, wetland restoration and drought-tolerant plants. Having designed gardens in Austin, Texas where water conservation has been a "hot" issue for over a decade, I believe I bring some expertise to the subject. (Water-wise gardening tips that occur throughout the text are summarized at the end of the chapter.)

Chapters Five through Nine address planting design and list specialized sources for plant materials. The book is organized with specialty nurseries first, on the theory that everyone knows the location of their local garden centers, but few gardeners are aware of the vast number of small, specialized nurseries that contribute to the Northwest landscape. However, don't underestimate the garden centers of this region. Although they appear in the final chapter, they are wondrous places staffed by knowledgeable gardeners and stocked with everything from arbors to zinnias.

Before we get into one-stop shopping at the garden centers, Chapters Ten and Eleven deal with the furniture and decorative accessories that make a garden both livable and memorable. Basically, the book is arranged in the order in which my work as a landscape architect progresses: planning, constructing and conserving, planting and, finally, embellishing the garden.

At the end you'll find an appendix that summarizes the book's **Money-saving tips.** Another appendix contains twenty-five tips for the catalog shopper and a few words about U.S.-Canadian border protocol. Also check out the Geographical Index. You may discover some nearby source you didn't know existed. You'll certainly learn about special places to visit on your travels through the Northwest.

While this is an era for global thinking, there's much to be said for buying locally. It's good for the regional economy. But more importantly, plants grown in the Pacific Northwest are better adapted for Northwest climates than those grown on the East Coast or in Southern California. Don't be afraid to ask big chain stores where they obtain their plants. Do take a look at some of the "out-of-the-way" suppliers you'll meet in this book.

Many of the businesses listed began as backyard hobbies and remain labors of love. Please respect the privacy of those who are open by-appointment-only or deal strictly by mail-order. Some are one-person operations in residential neighborhoods. Others are large wholesalers who, although they are not set up to meet the public, will sell to homeowners under certain circumstances. A number of the manufacturers listed do not sell directly to the public, but will happily furnish the name of a dealer in your area. 🌿

Acknowledgments
On a Personal Note

I want to thank special people who encouraged and guided me through this two-year research project. Catherine Booth, Lynnette Claire, Betsy Fitzgerald, Roberta Green, Patricia McHargue, Martha Simpson and Carolyn Wiecks provided invaluable assistance as copy editors. Two good friends and good gardeners, Cindy Epsen and Dean Kirn, provided inspiration. My son, Michael Simpson, helped with the typing; my husband's son, Mike Green, and Jennifer Kimmey helped with the indexing. I can't name all the other friends and family members who forgave me when I forgot to return phone calls or failed to write thank-you notes. You know who you are; I hope you know I've appreciated your support.

Thanks also to landscape architects Thomas Berger, Bob Chittock, Kia Micaud, Robert Perron, David Roberts and Bill Talley for answering questions about garden sources in this region. I received help in Spokane from Debbie Clem-Olsen, in Boise from Claude Hansen, and in Vancouver, British Columbia from Wilf Nichols. Dan Borroff, Kenneth Moppins, Eric Nelson and Stephen Weedman freely offered advice in their areas of expertise. And, how could I not acknowledge all of the nursery professionals, garden shop owners and product manufacturers in the Northwest? Many not only shared their enthusiasm for the "green industry," but also shared the names of their competitors! We gardeners are in this together.

Most of all I want to thank my husband Ron Green, who guided every step of this book from concept to research to graphic production. He doesn't know barberry from bindweed, but I love him dearly! This book should be dedicated to him, but he understands why I want to bestow the honor elsewhere.

This book is dedicated to the memory of my father, Zachary A. Booth, Jr., whose love of gardening inspired my appreciation for all things green and growing.

Invitation to Readers

Let me know if you are familiar with other great sources that should be included in the next edition of the book. In two years of research I discovered how many garden-related businesses there are in the Northwest. I'm certain that I missed several that should have been included. A few companies asked me not to publish their names because the owners are getting up in age or they have more business than they can serve. I respected their wishes. By all means tell me if you disagree with anything I've said.

I've tried diligently to avoid mistakes like the one I found in a respected gardening book on the subject of manure: "For the same expenditure, far better results may be obtained from the use of domestic humans and commercial fertilizers."

To err is humus.

Chapter One

Inspiration & Information

"Gardens were before gardeners, and but some hours after the earth."

.....*Sir Thomas Browne 1658*

Public Gardens

Although young in comparison to the gardens of Asia, Europe and the East Coast, our Pacific Northwest parks and public gardens appear mature, having been designed at a time when garden-making was already a sophisticated art. They had additional advantages in the region's interesting topography and favorable climate. In many cases they were carved out of dense wilderness and designed to take in spectacular vistas. At their outer edges, however, all Northwest gardens dissolve back into the natural landscape, transcending any order imposed by man.

It must be borne in mind that in 1858, the year Frederick Law Olmsted designed New York City's Central Park, the English had just formed the Colony of British Columbia, Oregon was not yet a state, the Washington Territory (created in 1853) included Idaho and Wyoming, and settlers in what is now the entire Pacific Northwest numbered less than 100,000! Typical of the gardens of that time is the lovingly recreated **Hudson's Bay Gardens** (20)* at Fort Vancouver, which was established in 1825 to supply food for nearby forts.

The Northwest's great public gardens are the legacy of ardent conservationists and plant collectors. Many were originally private estates. Some were created, ironically, by sons and daughters of the timber barons, shipping magnates, railroad men and merchants who played a hand in laying bare great swaths of the landscape. Visiting area gardens, we can trace the various design influences on Pacific Northwest style. I've written this text not as a travelogue, but as a way of helping visitors see each garden in a historical context. From these examples, the reader may glean ideas appropriate for his or her own garden style. 🌺

* **Note:** *Beginning on page 26, you'll find numbered listings of all the gardens mentioned in the text, with addresses and hours of operation.*

English Landscape Gardens

Le jardin anglais was Britain's chief contribution to the art forms of the world. Wherever this romantic landscape was copied, it took with it curving entrance roads, vast rolling lawns and serpentine ponds surrounded by great sweeps of deciduous trees. The English countryside as we think of it today was "invented" in the mid-eighteenth century at a time when most of England's trees had been felled for lumber and the land had been terraced for strip farming. Avenues of clipped trees marked the approaches to the grand country homes, and walled gardens with geometrically patterned flower beds (in pale imitation of Renaissance gardens in Italy and France) shut out views of mundane agricultural land.

What the eighteenth-century designers created was actually no more natural than what they swept away, but they made the landscape appear natural. The notion of breaking up straight lines and co-opting the countryside was based, in part, on the aesthetics of Chinese and French landscape painting. This naturalistic revolution was also an anti-monarchist political statement, and as such, it greatly influenced Thomas Jefferson, whose vast greenswards at Monticello were the first in America in the style of the English Landscape Gardening School.

Frederick Law Olmsted, landscape architect, conservationist and devoted social reformer, was the spiritual successor to this soft, pastoral planting style. In 1903, Olmsted Brothers, the large, prestigious firm continued by Olmsted's son and nephew, was commissioned to design a number of parks, campuses, subdivisions and private estates in the newly affluent and rapidly developing Pacific Northwest. Schooled in an Americanized version of the romantic style, the Olmsteds influenced every designer who practiced here during the first half of the twentieth century. Their vision of what a public park should be is our treasured inheritance.

It must be remembered, however, that eighteenth-century landscape designers were working with acres and acres of countryside. Few facilities can support such vast expanses of mown grass; in fact, golf courses are the only landscapes being designed today that exemplify the eighteenth-century ideal of beauty. We can get a feel for the effect of open rolling lawns, sparkling ponds, belts of trees and picturesque vistas at Vancouver's **VanDusen Botanical Garden** (37), which, although relatively new as a public garden, was built on the grounds of an existing golf course.

Private properties are rarely large enough to produce a similar effect. One exquisite example is the centerpiece of Bainbridge Island's **Bloedel Reserve** (2), where the house overlooks a soft grassy meadow and two large swan ponds. Another is the thirteen-acre property in Portland now known as **The Bishop's Close**. Designed in 1905 by John Charles Olmsted for grain merchant Peter Kerr and originally called **Elk Rock** (22), its wide undulating lawn stretches out to meet curving boundaries of untrimmed vegetation, framing a view of the Willamette River and mountains beyond. In nearby Aloha, **Jenkins Estate** (26), which is smaller still, manages to evoke miles of countryside as the viewer's eye leaps from the foreground to "borrowed" vistas in the background, with clipped grass as the void between.

The most lasting consequence of the English Landscape Gardens Style, however, has been the ubiquitous suburban lawn. Grass takes on an entirely different appearance when rolling acreage is reduced to a small plot, but, for better or for worse, manicured front lawns remain as a cultural holdover from the country estate. 🌺

Victorian Taste

English garden design moved away from a naturalistic handling of outdoor space in the nineteenth century. If any legitimate criticism could be made of the eighteenth-century English designers, it would be that in bringing grass up to the doorstep, they failed to tie the landscape to the house. In both England and North America, "foundation plantings" returned. By the Victorian era, homes were surrounded by tight corsets of shrubbery.

The Victorian era also ushered in a taste for sentimental statues and flower beds cut into the lawns in the shapes of hearts, circles, fans and kidneys. When residential garden design began in earnest in the Pacific Northwest, the Victorian penchant for show-stopping color and fascination with "exotics" were at a zenith. City gardens were most often designed by nurserymen, who by the 1880s had discovered the Northwest's mild, rainy climate as an ideal place for growing what we now call "bedding plants" and propagating ornamental shrubs and trees from all over the world.

Remnants of the Victorians' cheerfully contrived approach to landscape design can be seen in old neighborhoods and in parks with floral clocks and town names spelled out in colorful displays. Although maintenance costs have diminished the exuberance of former times, such popular attractions as the **Butchart Gardens** (39) near Victoria and **Minter Gardens** (38) in Rosedale, B.C. are modern-day revivals of the style.

The region retains two remarkable Victorian glasshouses, Seattle's **Volunteer Park Conservatory** (8) and the **Seymour Conservatory** (16) in Tacoma. You'll also find splendid collections of palms, bromeliads, cacti, orchids and assorted exotica in such modern structures as Vancouver's **Bloedel Conservatory** (32) in Queen Elizabeth Park, Spokane's **Gaiser Conservatory in Manito Park** (18) and tropical rain forest exhibits in regional zoos. Such collections are progeny of the Victorians' passion for displaying horticultural rarities from all over the world.

Plant collecting took yet another form during this period as rock gardens became immensely popular. Usually tucked into a naturalistic edge of the garden and often associated with a small water feature, the dwarf and alpine plants associated with rockeries spawned large, active garden societies. Few public gardens today are without a rock garden and few in this country are more sensitively designed than **Ohme Gardens** (19) in Wenatchee, Washington, where thyme, phlox, iberis and dianthus carpet the hillside with soft colors in spring. This nine-acre landscape of rocks and grass is a study in rich textures throughout the remainder of the warm season.

Siskiyou Rare Plant Nursery (see listing on page 265) also maintains a fine display rock garden. The grounds feature the newly-completed "Mt. Halda" (named for the renown Czechoslovakian landscape architect and plantsman Joseph Halda who designed it), replete with a waterfall and rich plantings.

Roses have always had a place in English gardens, but devoting a separate section of the garden to roses and planting them in a formal arrangement seems to be a late-Victorian/Edwardian phenomenon, borrowed from the French and quickly picked up in this country. The American Rose Society, formed in 1899, is responsible for most of the rose displays and test sites we enjoy. Enthusiasm for single-species gardens has inspired other plant societies (chrysanthemum, iris, daylily, dahlia, etc.) to display their prize-winning blooms in parks and public gardens. 🌼

Neoclassicism

Elements of the garden design of Renaissance Italy and France briefly came back into vogue in the early decades of the twentieth century as classical architecture supplanted Victorian residential styles. Fanciful waterworks and parterres (patterned ornamental planting beds) illustrated a returning taste for architectural elements in the landscape. Charles Platt, who had written on Italian gardens in 1894 and whose work was widely respected on the East Coast, was one of an impressive roster of landscape architects brought to the Pacific Northwest to design homes and gardens in keeping with the grand Beaux Arts period.

Fir Acres (23), which was constructed in the mid-twenties in Portland (now the centerpiece of the campus of **Lewis and Clark College**), was perhaps the most ambitious project of its kind. It took thirty-two gardeners to manicure the lawns and Italianate planting beds of this 77-acre estate where five terraces built down an open axis reached out more than a thousand feet to take advantage of a view of Mt. Hood. The plantings have been simplified, but the magnificent axis remains. Another fine example of the style is the Italian-style terrace garden, complete with colonnades and statuary, attached to **Hatley Castle** (40) on Vancouver Island, now the campus of **Royal Roads Military College**.

Shore Acres State Park Botanical Garden (30), the restored gardens at the former estate of Louis J. Simpson near Coos Bay on the Oregon coast, offers yet another look at parterres employed to structure a landscape. The Simpson mansion was razed in 1948, which is a pity because formal gardens lose some of their reason for being when they are not connected to a formal building. Nevertheless, axial symmetry and regimented plantings were popular elements in the design of public parks of the period. The **Duncan Formal Gardens at Manito Park** (18) in Spokane and many of the region's fine rose gardens date from the "City Beautiful Movement" that swept the country.

Elements of neoclassicism are woven quite charmingly into the gardens at **Lakewold** (15) near Tacoma, which incorporates garden styling borrowed from several historical periods. The formal core of this magnificent garden features a long brick walk flanked by clipped boxwood parterres. Topiary swans and symmetrical rose beds lead to a lattice-domed summerhouse. A quatrefoil pool (actually a well-disguised swimming pool) lies in a cross axis balanced against a view of Mt. Rainier. What is surprising is that Lakewold took its present form in the 1950s under the guidance of California landscape architect Thomas Church, who is best-known for his modernist works. But here, with a full understanding of historical precedent in the art of garden-making, Church built upon the garden's existing symmetry.

Old English Revival and the Cottage Garden Style

One of Lakewold's most memorable features is an Elizabethan knot garden, executed in shades of green and gray around an antique well head. Other Tudor-inspired gardens worth exploring are the lovely **Physick Garden at the University of British Columbia Botanical Garden** (36) and the Hedge Maze at **VanDusen** (37), both in Vancouver, B.C. These clipped-hedge gardens are drawn from the middle ages, when people grew culinary and medicinal plants within the safety of castles, cloisters and fortified cities.

Embracing the open countryside only became possible in societies governed by rule of law; unfortunately civil disorder reigned throughout most of the history of Western civilization. The geometric patterns of medieval cloister gardens can be traced back to the courtyards of the ancient Egyptians and Persians, and indeed such gardens never disappeared entirely. Even after walls were no longer necessary for security, farmer's wives continued to grow their herbs, fruits and vegetables behind walls built to keep the livestock out. Out of this tradition came the tidy walled gardens of colonial America, which typically brimmed with a profusion of fragrant flowers as well as life-sustaining plants.

Before the turn of the twentieth century, English garden designer Gertrude Jekyll popularized the strong architectural forms of walled gardens softened with informal plantings. She made transitions between house and garden in rhythmic stages and wrote of "living pictures," which she executed with long drifts of bulbs and double flower borders flanking grassy paths. Trained as an artist, she painted with flowers in much the same way the impressionists applied oils to canvas. Her soft, harmonic hues could not have been more different from the bold color contrasts that typified urban Victorian style. And she accented her gardens with simple, classical garden furniture, pergolas and containers inspired by the arts and crafts movement, which stressed quality of workmanship.

We see her influence today at **Deepwood Estate** (29) in Salem, Oregon. This garden was designed in 1929 by the remarkable partnership of Elizabeth Lord and Edith Schryver, who met on a garden tour of Europe and settled in Salem to practice landscape architecture for forty years. At Deepwood they created intimate "rooms" where garden structures invite outdoor living and the intricately textured walls of boxwood, yew and holly are used as backdrops for soft, informal floral displays.

A love of old-fashioned plant materials – shrub roses and flowering vines and fruit trees and billowing perennials chosen for texture, color and fragrance – is at the heart of the English Cottage Garden tradition. It has been carried on by successive generations of English garden designers and writers, from Gertrude Jekyll to Vita Sackville-West to such prolific contemporary authors as Penelope Hobhouse, Rosemary Verey and Graham Stuart Thomas, whose gardens have thrilled North American gardeners. The grounds of a distillery in North Vancouver, B.C. seem an unlikely place to discover an example of the style, but the **Park & Tilford Gardens** (35) are full of surprises. Here, eight lovely little theme gardens, ingeniously separated by walls and hedges, display highly refined plantings set amid fountains, arbors and pergolas.

Gertrude Jekyll called her work "cottage garden style," but the English country homes she embellished are mansions by today's standards. The beguiling charm of the cottage garden lives on at a different scale in the lattice work, picket fences, rose-covered arbors and perennial borders that enhance the little bungalows so widely favored in the small towns and inner-city neighborhoods of Northwest cities. The **Hovander Homestead** (11) at the Tennant Lake Natural History Interpretive Center near Ferndale, Washington, is a good example of an early Northwest-style cottage garden, as are many of the area's small nurseries that have grown up around old homesteads. ✿

Modern American Gardens

The modernist movement of the 1920's in architecture brought changes in landscape design as well, although the changes were not felt on the residential level until after the Second World War. By 1955, when California landscape architect Thomas Church published his book, *Gardens Are for People*, landscape design had returned to an integration of buildings and landscapes, but what Church described – the melding of the home's interior with the garden – was revolutionary. His designs also sought to bring landscape designs in closer harmony with industrial-age materials and address new economic realities.

As Church noted in his book, indoor-outdoor living is not a new idea. Urban dwellers living in small homes on small lots are once again inclined to carry some of the functions of the house into the outdoors. Taking cues from the walled gardens of ancient Persia, Egypt and Rome, as well as medieval cloister gardens, modern designers began exploring old ways of preserving privacy. In Japan, they found inspiration for serene gardens in tiny spaces and learned new respect for materials.

Another factor that has affected modern garden design is that fewer people are trained to do garden maintenance (or fewer people are willing to pay garden laborers a living wage, as the case may be). Church, and the residential designers that followed him, began designing for lower levels of maintenance. Church used flowing swaths of concrete or pavers to replace lawns and elaborate planting beds. He introduced mowing strips and curbs to separate the lawn from planting beds, and he confined unclipped plants within easily accessible raised beds.

As we look at his book today, some of Church's work is a bit dated, especially the photos that include '50s-style garden furniture, but his ideas were truly ahead of their time. It's interesting to note that a photograph of his elegant formal swimming pool at Lakewold was chosen for the jacket photo of the second edition of the book rather than one of the "modernistic" California gardens. As he noted in the introduction, "Art Moderne strangled in the mesh of its own steel tubing... 'Modern' can be revived as an honest word when we realize that modernism is not a goal, but a broad highway."

For modernist ideas, we can look at new gardens such as the McVey Courtyard at the **Center for Urban Horticulture** (3) in Seattle, designed by landscape architect Iain Robertson. Here, ornamental grasses, rocks and fluid aggregate concrete paths are used as sculpture. We can draw inspiration from design details at other public spaces, such as the elegantly simple water rill at the entrance to the **Bellevue**

Botanical Garden (1), the handsome arbor structures at **University of British Columbia Botanical Garden** (36), or the elegantly sited contemporary sculpture and fine rock work at **VanDusen** (37). The splendid **Waterfall Garden** (10) in Seattle's Pioneer Square demonstrates how much can be made of a small space.

Today we borrow freely from every era of garden design. We've learned to produce visually interesting gardens by creating vistas. We've gained a new understanding of space and new skill in manipulating plant materials. We've put new emphasis on comfort, function and beauty. And, we have begun thinking about exterior and interior design as a unit. In the best modern gardens, the link between nature and the man-made environment appears effortless. 🪲

The Asian Aesthetic

As previously acknowledged, the Asian aesthetic indirectly influenced Northwest garden style through the eighteenth-century English landscape, which was based in part on the poetic Chinese vision of nature as seen in woodcuts and landscape paintings, and the "discovery" of Japanese landscape design by modern American designers. A direct, more important influence has come by way of our Asian settlers and the several master gardeners imported from sister cities in Asia to build Oriental gardens. These works of art have had a palpable influence on the Northwest aesthetic. While the symbolism and complex philosophical premises of two thousand years of garden-making in Asia may escape a non-Asian viewer, the gardens' pure visual impact does not.

Old Chinese art depicts mountains rising above a misty landscape, water cascading into shimmering lakes, craggy coastlines and wooded hillsides. The ancient Chinese saw the workings of universal forces and laws in their landscape, and their garden art was based on harmony between opposing forces. Their word for landscape is a combination of the characters for mountain and water.

Garden art flowed from China to Japan through Korea in the sixth century. While very different styles evolved out of these different cultures, all Asian gardens use rock and water to represent heaven and earth. Unlike Western landscape painters and garden designers, the Asian artist assumes the human is in the landscape, not viewing it from the outside. Asian gardens point out man's insignificance in relation to the majesty of untamed nature.

The diversity of Asian garden expression can be seen most vividly in the city of Vancouver, B. C. Within a few miles one can compare two totally different Asian garden concepts in the elaborate classical Chinese architectural space at **The Dr. Sun Yat-Sen Garden** (33) in downtown Vancouver and the naturalistic Japanese woodland setting of the **Nitobe Memorial Garden** (34) on the campus of the University of British Columbia.

In the ornate Dr. Sun Yat-Sen Garden, visitors encounter myriad patterns and textures in rock formations, paving, architectural details and gnarled old plants. Most of these treasured materials were brought from Suzhou, the premier garden city of China, and the workmanship here is impeccable. This Ming dynasty complex, which occupies two and a half acres in Vancouver's Chinatown, draws from a period of flourishing arts in China (from the mid-fourteenth to the mid-seventeenth century). Visually, the garden is almost overwhelming to Western eyes; to comprehend its intricate detailing requires several visits.

While Chinese gardens are rich in complexity, Japanese garden styles have become increasingly simplified over time. The earliest Japanese "paradise gardens" were similar to the Chinese, with elaborate adornment and concern for "correct" placement of stones, streams and waterfalls. Even the plant materials were aligned by rules of compass and astronomical instruments. The idea of a garden used for strolling was taken up in Japan during this first period of garden design, but the strolling gardens we find in Americanized Japanese gardens have more in common with later phases of Japanese design.

After Zen Buddhism flowered in the twelfth century, Japanese gardens increasingly focused on miniature landscapes. Simple compositions of rocks, evergreens and ground covers created intriguing textural contrasts. Layered plant materials conformed to the contours of the land, framing little vignettes or disclosing vistas to suggest limitless space. The art of bonsai was part of this trend toward miniaturization and understated elegance. One of the finest displays in North America can be viewed at **The Pacific Rim Bonsai Collection** (13) on the Weyerhaeuser Company grounds.

Drinking tea to prevent drowsiness during meditation was elevated to an art form in the sixteenth century. The tea gardens were meant to inspire deep contemplation, and with these gardens evolved familiar, utilitarian features such as stone pathways, wash basins and lanterns to light the way at night. Here, tranquillity and naturalness prevailed, with an increasing use of evergreen plants and stones employed as sculpture. Boulders were balanced asymmetrically, playing three small stones against a large one, for example. Rock was also used to represent flowing water, with different sizes of stones suggesting different sounds and velocities.

Unlike the gardens in Japan, which are generally the creation of a garden master working in a period style, the Asian gardens we visit in the Pacific Northwest borrow freely from the several schools of garden art. Portland's **Japanese Garden in Washington Park** (25), for example, employs five different styles. Its detailing is exquisite. The dramatic topography it scales and the distant vistas it enjoys are but two of the elements that make it the most admired Japanese garden outside of Japan. Here water, the elemental source of life and beauty, is shown in all its forms – cascading down a bluff, gurgling over rapids, standing still in large pools, or swirling symbolically in raked gravel. Structures, lanterns and bridges are used to represent human presence amid the symbols of heaven and earth. Paths guide a journey, and transitions between the gardens-within-a-garden are smoothly defined. The path may disappear enticingly around a corner, then a stone or lantern half-hidden in the foliage will mark the beginning of yet another sensory experience.

Two gardens that take visitors on great journeys of the imagination are Seattle's **Japanese Garden in Washington Park Arboretum** (5) and **Kubota Garden** (6), which is the oldest Asian garden in the region. In these contemplative places, the ideals of *wabi* (quietude) and *sabi* (elegant simplicity) are translated into Western experience. Both combine Japanese and Northwest native plant materials. They offer strolls along twisted paths that reveal scenes like landscape paintings.

What Northwest gardeners can borrow from Asian gardens are "tricks" practiced for hundreds of years. Asian gardens, it must be remembered, are no less man-made than Versailles. They employ special effects that are especially useful in small gardens. In the foreground, trees are pruned so as not to disrupt views, the middle ground is fully developed to give an illusion of distance. Smaller elements and small-leafed plants are placed in the rear to appear diminished. Here, a stone may represent a mountain, a clump of moss a forest, a pond the ocean. The background (which can simply be tree-tops "borrowed" from the landscape beyond) is used to suggest unlimited space. Streams and paths narrow as they get farther away.

The garden is composed of asymmetrically balanced interlocking parts, with materials shaped as mirror images of others nearby. Similar shapes and patterns are repeated to create a jig-saw puzzle effect. Where Western people most often respond to a straight axis (which allows them to know exactly where they are), the gardens in Japan devise ways to create mystery. Plants are used to create a feeling of enclosure; walkways are made difficult to negotiate; hidden secrets are revealed behind each bend in the path. There will be great distances hinted-at and the suggestion of things unsaid, all used to draw the visitor irresistibly into the experience. The French royals who commissioned Versailles would not have understood it at all.

An Asian garden is a display of nature's handiwork, and for Western man, this includes a lesson in humility. Perhaps after the environmental disruption created by the industrial revolution is analyzed, modern man will realize what Asian garden-makers have known all along – humans are not the center of the universe. 🌸

Northwest Style Defined

How different are the Oriental and Occidental approaches to a garden. Yet the concepts blend quite comfortably when merged in the Pacific Northwest and shaped by an inquisitive gardener. Like a Japanese garden master, a wise designer discovers the land's secrets in every season. The "real" Pacific Northwest garden is an exercise in conspicuous non-consumption. It may recall styles from other times and places, but it will be constructed of Northwest materials – simple wood structures, walls and pathways made of native stone or brick, and plants that grow without excessive maintenance.

The garden plan will be built the way a writer uses words – collecting, rearranging, editing and refining. When it is fully refined, the gardener will have removed everything unnecessary. It will be carefully balanced between the rustic and man-made. Its forms will be relaxed, but sophisticated. It will equally serve as a backdrop for quiet contemplation or for good conversation. And it will contain elements of mystery. What is only glimpsed at the entry is revealed fully from within.

The Bloedel Reserve (2) on Bainbridge Island may be the quintessential Pacific Northwest landscape. In 1951 Prentice Bloedel, who was untrained in the technical aspects of landscape design, began carving trails with a machete through dense brush on his 150-acre property, following fence lines and old logging roads to explore the woods, streams and swamps. He found incredibly varied topography and a "mosaic of plant life" that were to evoke what he termed "unexpected insight." His thirty-year process of discovery produced a sequence of alternately joyous and contemplative gardens orchestrated to illustrate man's relationship to nature.

Visitors can take a circular route through this landscape where man-made and natural areas are connected as a sequence of "events." The journey begins with a relaxing walk through a sunny hay meadow, past barns that serve as reminders of the island's agrarian past. Suddenly the meadow funnels into trees, and the trail meanders quietly downhill beneath giant conifers, opening again onto the banks of a marsh where islands host a community of water fowl and nesting birds.

The trail skirts the ponds and enters a majestic forest where even the second-growth trees are now a hundred years old. Then, a descent through heavily wooded wetlands across a boardwalk brings visitors to a romantic view of a chateau-style house standing on a rise beyond a shimmering lake. (The picture could have been taken in eighteenth-century England.) The handsome house is ringed with a simple, low boxwood border set in a manicured surround of grass enclosed by an outer row of small trimmed boxwoods. Two huge English elms punctuate the wide lawn.

Prominent landscape architects submitted sketch after sketch for grand Italianate terracing to address the precipitous north and west slopes as they fall away from the house, but baroque formality failed to move Mr. Bloedel. The bluff behind his home remained a problem area for thirty years. The elegantly simple solution he finally accepted involved cutting a slot through the center of a ridge that interrupted a view of Puget Sound and the snowcapped Cascades beyond. The cut was planted to resemble a river of closely mown turf grass. Meadow grasses that turn the color of straw by mid-summer cover the soft mounds that flank this undulating axis.

The actual trail continues with rustic wooden steps that descend from the side of the house and lead into a dimly lit glen. Here, two creeks lined with water-loving plants are dammed to form pools. Under the woodland canopy grow rhododendron and hardy cyclamen and scores of trillium, primroses and wild ginger. At the bottom of the glen, a chinoiserie bridge crosses a crystalline pool, serving as a reminder of man's presence in the garden. A dramatic magnolia stands sentry at the top of a waterfall, marking the beginning of an "orchid walk" and yet another transition.

A tori gate stands at the entry to a garden/guest house complex. Both the pavilion-like structure and the surrounding gardens are best described as "Japanesque" in intent. The north side of the guest house, the part of the garden visitors see first, is a Zen-inspired rock and sand garden set in a pattern of alternating squares of concrete and turf.

The contemporary Japanese-style guest house overlooks a garden lovingly built on the south-facing slope by Fujitaro Kubota. As it meanders down the hill, the path reveals a series of subtly framed focal points, tantalizing the viewer with elements of surprise in the compositions of stone and exquisite plant materials. A second gate signals the end of the built environment and the garden's final surprise.

Visitors enter an ethereal space created out of a tangled bog and paved with a thick, almost foreboding mat of moss. Huge decaying stumps, lush ferns and a lazy stream bed are sculptural elements beneath the opulent trees. By contrast, the simple formal garden that opens off this soft moss garden appears hard-edged until its long reflecting pool, which is boxed in with a precisely clipped hedge of Irish yews, elicits its magical response. Sitting on one of the benches within the cathedral form of this space, the visitor understands the double meaning of the word "reflection."

"The Reserve was conceived to be a place where man's power to manipulate has been used cautiously. Nature has a way of creating beautiful compositions that should be preserved," said Mr. Bloedel when he opened his home and garden to the public. Both he and his wife were born into families that had made fortunes in the timber industry. By the 1950s, Mr. Bloedel was promoting the cause of conservation. "Respect for trees and plants replaces indifference," he wrote. "One feels the existence of a divine order. Man is not set apart from the rest of nature – he is just a member of that incredibly diverse population of the universe, a member that nature can do without but who cannot do without nature."

A similar, though smaller, source of inspiration is the **Berry Botanic Garden** (21) developed by an extraordinary Portland plantswoman, Rae Selling Berry. She selected the property because its micro-habitats included springs and creeks, a ravine, meadow and a cattail marsh. She introduced new plants with a formidable knowledge of their cultural requirements, placing plants that like "wet feet" in moist areas and using the slopes for those that require good drainage. The rear garden is terraced to accommodate her extensive alpine collection. At the foot of a sloping front lawn, which is reminiscent of an English romantic garden, thickets of rhodo-dendron are naturalized in shrub borders. These borders are interlaced with lilies, primulas and Northwest natives, including rare and endangered species.

The approach that defines Northwest gardens begins and ends with a love of the land as nature designed it. Lilla and John Leach's former home in southwest Port-land, now open as the **Leach Botanical Garden** (27), overlooks the steep bank of a wooded creek. This nine-acre landscape capitalizes on hundreds of glorious ferns, trilliums and other native species. Its bogs, creek bank and forested hillside should provide ample inspiration for gardeners who inhabit shady, moist environments.

Here, nature is so provident it appears ready to reclaim the trails.

The **Cecil & Molly Smith Garden** (28) in St. Paul, Oregon and the **Meerkerk Rhododendron Garden** (12) on Whidbey Island are examples of other memorable private gardens carved out of peaceful woodland settings. Both gardens are now in the devoted care of Rhododendron Societies. Cecil and Molly Smith's choice collection of over 400 hybrid and species rhododendrons grows under the hushed canopy of tall firs and flowering trees. Collections of hardy cyclamen, trillium, lilies and primulas mingle with wildflowers in the understory. Much of Max and Ann Meerkerk's property is left to native woods, with two and half miles of nature trails. The 800 rhododendrons they planted bloom in informal drifts alongside dogwoods, camellias and magnolias.

In the luxuriant **Rhododendron Species Botanical Garden** (14) near Tacoma, 503 species are grouped according to country of origin, primarily Asian, with tropical species displayed in a greenhouse. The region's great arboretums offer further inspiration to gardeners seeking the look of untamed nature in an essentially man-made environment. Especially wonderful are the Winter Gardens within Seattle's **Washington Park Arboretum** (9), **Hoyt Arboretum** (24) in Portland and the Native Garden at the **University of British Columbia Botanical Garden** (36).

East of the Cascades, naturalism is defined in the context of mountains and prairie. Gardeners are years ahead of west-siders in learning to live with nature's more harsh disposition. The display areas at **Manito Park** (18) in Spokane (especially its Ferris Perennial Garden) and the **Idaho Botanical Garden** in Boise demonstrate the uncommon beauty that can be created in a sunny, dry landscape.

Visitors to the Tri-City area will enjoy the test/display areas at **Hillview Gardens** (18), a large wholesale nursery in Kennewick, Washington. One of the largest specialty growers in the region, Hillview lists over 2000 hardy perennials, ground covers, rock garden plants and natives in its catalog. Most can be viewed in the nursery's public gardens, which are organized by micro-climates.

Accustomed to a lush look and the luxury of planting without regard to summer drought, maritime Northwesterners are largely unfamiliar with the wide range of plant materials that require only a modest amount of water. Until recently, water has been cheap and plentiful. As we begin adapting to a smaller share of the region's water resources, we will learn to appreciate a different aesthetic.

Plantings suitable for wet-winter/dry summer climates are beautifully demon-strated in the big, bold perennial borders at the **Bellevue Botanical Garden** (1) and at **Children's Hospital** (4) in Seattle. You'll also find a mixed border of herbs, perennials and low-maintenance evergreens at **Seattle Tilth Association's Demon-stration Garden** (7), designed by Howard Stenn, who waters only the newly estab-lished plantings and leaves the rest to thrive on their own. I expect that we'll be seeing more drought-tolerant gardens established in the next few years.

Unlike Mr. Bloedel, few of us have two creeks to dam, nor do we enjoy the canopy of a second-growth forest, but even in our urban domain there's new interest in gardens designed to encourage wildlife. By planting shrubs and flowers suffi-ciently diverse to attract birds (especially songbirds), small mammals, reptiles, insects and butterflies, we may find the best of all worlds – a more relaxed look with fragrant, brightly colored flowering plants that tend to take care of themselves.

Such habitats as Yellow Island Preserve in the San Juans, which is maintained by the Nature Conservancy, the Nisqually National Wildlife Refuge and the Oak Creek Wildlife Area near Yakima are but three of the hundreds of public parks and refuge areas where you can see native plant species in varied, resplendent settings and observe the diversity of wildlife. The more we know of the Northwest's rich natural resources, the better we'll design with nature. 🐾

Gardens to Visit for Inspiration

Two books, *Garden Touring in the Pacific Northwest* by Jan Kowalczewski Whitner and *Public & Private Gardens of the Northwest* by Myrna Oakley, describe in great detail the gardens and wilderness areas open to the public in this region. I've devoted mere sentences to the forty gardens listed here. Each is worthy of days of study. Other wonderful gardens have not even been mentioned. It is my hope that when visiting beautiful, inspiring places you will observe the details, both man-made and natural, and take home ideas for your own garden. 🐾

Note: *The admission prices listed were in effect at the time of publication and are subject to change at any time.*

Washington

Seattle Metropolitan Area

1.

Bellevue Botanical Garden

12001 Main Street
Bellevue

☎ *206/462-2749*

Mailing address *16023 N.E. 8th Street*
Bellevue, Washington 98008

Hours *Daily 10-6 (May through Oct),*
10- 4 (winter)

Admission *Free*

Accessible *Yes*

2.

The Bloedel Reserve

7571 N.E. Dolphin Drive
Bainbridge Island, Washington 98110

☎ *206/842-7052*

Hours *By reservation only;*
Wed-Sun 10-4

Admission *$4*

Accessible *Partially*

3.

Center for Urban Horticulture

3501 N.E. 41st Street
Seattle, Washington 98105

☎ *206/543-8616*

Hours *Mon-Fri 9-5 (office hours);*
Elisabeth C. Miller Library open
Mon 9-8, Tues-Fri 9-5; Center open for
classes, workshops, plant sales, etc.
most evenings and weekends

Admission *Free*

Accessible *Yes*

4.

Children's Hospital and Medical Center

4800 Sand Point Way N.E.
Seattle, Washington 98105

Hours *Daily during daylight*

Admission *Free*

Accessible *Partially, some steep slopes*

5.
Japanese Garden in Washington Park Arboretum

Lake Washington Boulevard E.
Seattle, Washington 98112

☎ 206/684-4725; 324-1483 for tea
demonstration

Hours Daily 10-late afternoon (March
through November only); call for
closing times, which vary during the
season. Demonstration tea service,
third Saturday of each month at 1:30
p.m.

Admission Adults $2, Youth & Seniors
$1, children under 5 free

Accessible Partially, on gravel

6.
Kubota Garden

55th Avenue S. off Renton Ave S.
Seattle

☎ 206/684-4584

Mailing address P.O. Box 12646
Seattle, Washington 98111

Hours Daily during daylight; public
tours every fourth Saturday and
Sunday, 10 a.m. April through October

Admission Free
Accessible No

7.
Seattle Tilth Association Demonstration Gardens

4649 Sunnyside Avenue N.
Seattle, Washington 98103

☎ 206/633-0451
Hours Daily during daylight
Admission Free
Accessible Partially

8.
Volunteer Park Conservatory

1400 E. Galer Street
Seattle, Washington 98112

☎ 206/684-4743

Hours Daily 10-7 (May through Sept
15); 10-4 (mid-Sept through April)

Admission Free
Accessible Partially; narrow aisles

9.
Washington Park Arboretum

2300 Arboretum Drive E.
Seattle, Washington 98112

☎ 206/543-8800

Hours Daily during daylight; Graham
Visitor Center Mon-Fri 10-4; Sat, Sun
and holidays 12-4

Admission Free
Accessible Partially

10.
Waterfall Garden

Second Avenue S. at Main Street (in
Pioneer Square)
Seattle, Washington 98104

Hours Daily during daylight
Admission Free
Accessible Yes

Northwest Washington

11.
Hovander Homestead

5299 Neilsen Road
Ferndale, Washington 98248

☎ 206/384-3444 or 733-2900
(Whatcom County Park Department)

Hours Daily during daylight
Admission $3 per car for non-county
residents

Accessible Yes

12.
Meerkerk Rhododendron Garden

3531 S. Meerkerk Lane,
off Resort Road
Whidbey Island

☎ 206/321-6682
Mailing address P.O. Box 154
Greenbank, Washington 98253

Hours Daily 9-5
(mid-March through Labor Day)

Admission $2
Accessible Partially

South Sound

13. Lakewold

12317 Gravelly Lake Drive S.W.
Tacoma

☎ 206/584-3360
Mailing address P.O. Box 98092
Tacoma, Washington 98498

Hours By reservation only. Mon, Tues,
Thurs, Fri & Sat (April and May); Tues,
Thurs, Fri & Sat (June); Thurs, Fri & Sat
(July through Sept)

Admission Adults $5, Seniors $4, no
children under 12

Accessible Partially

14.
Pacific Rim Bonsai Collection

Weyerhaeuser Company Grounds
2525 S. 366th Street
Federal Way

☎ 206/661-9377
Mailing address P.O. Box 3798
Federal Way, Washington 98063

Hours Sat-Wed 11-4 (March through
Oct); Sun-Wed 11-4 (Nov through Feb)

Admission Free
Accessible Yes

15.
Rhododendron Species
Botanical Garden

2525 S. 336th Street
Federal Way

☎ 206/661-9377 (gift shop & general
information); 838-4646 (from Seattle),
927-6960 (from Tacoma)

Mailing address P.O. Box 3798
Federal Way, Washington 98063

Hours Daily (except Thurs) 10-4
(March through May), Sat-Wed 11-4
(June through Feb)

Admission $3.50 (adults), $2.50
(seniors and students), children under
12 free

Accessible Partially, with gravel and
some slopes

16.
W.W. Seymour Botanical Conservatory

*316 South G Street (in Wright Park)
Tacoma, Washington 98405*

☎ *206/591-5330*

Hours *Daily 8:30-8 (June through Labor Day); 8-4:20 (September through May)*

Admission *Free*
Accessible *Yes*

Eastern Washington

17.
Hillview Gardens

*120 S. Fillmore Street
Kennewick, Washington 99336*

☎ *509/783-2695*
Hours *Daily during daylight*
Admission *Free*
Accessible *Partially*

18.
Manito Park and Botanical Gardens

*21st Avenue
(between Grand and Bernard)
Spokane*

☎ *509/625-6622*
Mailing address *4 West 21st Avenue
Spokane, Washington 99203*
Hours *Daily 8-dusk; Japanese garden open April through October*

Admission *Free*
Accessible *Yes*

Central Washington

19.
Ohme Gardens

*3327 Ohme Road
Wenatchee, Washington 98801*

☎ *509/662-5785*
Hours *Daily 9-7 (summer); 9-6 (mid-April through late May and Labor Day until Oct 15)*

Admission *$5 (adults), $3 (ages 7-17), children under 7 free*

Accessible *No*

Southwestern Washington

20.
Hudson's Bay Gardens

*1501 East Evergreen Boulevard
Vancouver, Washington 98660*

☎ *206/696-7655*
Hours *Daily 9-5 (summer), 9-4 (winter)*
Admission *$2 (adults), children and seniors free*

Accessible *Yes*

Oregon

Portland Metropolitan Area

21.
Berry Botanic Garden
11505 S.W. Summerville Avenue
Portland, Oregon 97219

☎ 503/636-4112
Hours By appointment only
Admission $2 for non members
Accessible Partially

22.
Elk Rock/ The Bishop's Close
11800 S. W. Military Lane
Portland, Oregon 97219

☎ 503/636-5613
Hours Daily 8-7 (summer); 8-5 (winter)
Admission Free
Accessible Partially

23.
Fir Acres/ Lewis and Clark College
0615 S.W. Palatine Hill Road
Portland, Oregon 97219

Hours Daily during daylight
Admission Free
Accessible Yes

24.
Hoyt Arboretum
4000 Fairview Boulevard
Portland, Oregon 97221

☎ 503/228-8732
Hours Daily during daylight
Admission Free
Accessible Partially

25.
Japanese Garden in Washington Park
611 S.W. Kingston Avenue
(directly above the Rose Test Garden)
Portland

☎ 503/223-1321 or 223-4070
Mailing address P.O. Box 3847
Portland, Oregon 97208

Hours Daily 10-6 except New Year's,
Thanksgiving and Christmas;
9-6 (June 1-Aug 31)

Admission $4.50 (adults),
$2.50 (seniors and students),
free (children under 6)

Accessible No

26.
Jenkins Estate
209th at Farmington Rd,
off Grabhorn Road
Aloha, Oregon 97006

☎ 503/642-3855
Hours Mon-Fri 9-4
Admission Free
Accessible Yes

27.
Leach Botanical Garden
6704 S.E. 122nd Avenue
Portland, Oregon 97236

☎ 503/761-9503
Hours Tues-Sun 10-4
Admission Free
Accessible No

Willamette Valley	South Oregon Coast

28.
Cecil & Molly Smith Garden

5065 Ray Bell Road
St. Paul, Oregon 97137

☎ 503/771-8386

Mailing address P.O. Box 86424
Portland, Oregon 97286

Hours By appointment or 10-4 on the
third Sat in March and the first and
third Saturdays in April & May

Admission $3
Accessible Partially

29.
Deepwood Estate

1116 Mission Street S.E.
Salem, Oregon 97302

☎ 503/363-1825

Hours Sun-Fri 12-4:30 (May through
Sept); Sun, Mon, Wed & Fri 1-4 (winter)

Admission Free (note: gardens are
occasionally closed for private events)

Accessible Yes

30.
Shore Acres Botanic Garden

13030 Cape Arago Highway
(14 miles south of Coos Bay)

☎ 503/888-3732

Mailing address P.O. Box 1172
Coos Bay, Oregon 97420

Hours Daily during daylight
Admission Free
Accessible Partially

Idaho

Boise Metropolitan Area

31.
Idaho Botanical Garden

2355 Old Penitentiary Road
Boise, Idaho 83712

☎ 208/343-8649

Mailing Address P.O. Box 2140
Boise, Idaho 83701

Hours Mon-Fri 9-5 (office hours);
garden 12-8 Tues-Sun
(April through Oct)

Admission $3 adults, $2 seniors and
students

Accessible Yes

British Columbia

Vancouver Metropolitan Area

32.
Bloedel Floral Conservatory

West 33rd at Cambie
in Queen Elizabeth Park
Vancouver

☎ 604/872-5513

Mailing address 290 E. 51st.
Vancouver, British Columbia V5X 1C5

Hours Mon-Fri 9-8, Sat & Sun
10-9 (April 15 through September); Daily 10-5 (Oct through
mid-April)

Admission $3 (adults), $1.50
(seniors and students)

Accessible Yes

33.
Dr. Sun Yat-Sen Classical Chinese Garden

578 Carrall Street
Vancouver, British Columbia V6B 2J8

☎ 604/622-3207

Hours Daily 10-4:30

Admission $3.50 (adults),
$2.50 (seniors and students),
free (children under 5)

Accessible Partially

34.
Nitobe Memorial Japanese Garden

Gate 4, U.B.C. Campus
on N.W. Marine Drive
Vancouver

☎ 604/822-6038

Mailing address Same as U.B.C.
Botanical Garden

Hours Daily 10-6 (mid-Mar through
mid-Oct); Mon-Fri 10-3 (winter)

Admission $2 (adults);
1.25 (seniors and students)

Accessible Partially, on gravel paths

35.
Park & Tilford Gardens

440-333 Brooksbank Avenue
North Vancouver, British Columbia
V7J 3S8

☎ 604/984-8200

Hours Daily 9:30-dusk

Admission Free

Accessible Yes

36.
University of British Columbia Botanical Garden

6804 S.W. Marine Drive
Vancouver, British Columbia V6T 1Z4

☎ 604/822-3928

Hours Daily 10-6

Admission $3.75 adult, $1,50 senior
and students (free from Thanksgiving to
mid-March)

Accessible Yes

37.
VanDusen Botanical Garden

5251 Oak Street
Vancouver, British Columbia
V6M 4H1

☎ 604/266-7194

Hours Daily 10-dusk

Admission $4.50 (adults), $2.25
(seniors and students), $9 (family);
50% off in winter

Accessible Yes

Fraser Valley

38.
Minter Gardens

52892 Bunker Road
(Hwy. 1, exit # 135)
Rosedale, British Columbia

☎ 604/794-7191;
604/792-3919 (off-season)

Mailing address P.O. Box 40
Chilliwack, British Columbia V2P 6H7

Hours Daily 9-dusk (April through Oct)

Admission $7.50 (adult),
$6.00 (seniors), $3.50 students;
$20 (family)

Accessible Yes

Vancouver Island

39.
Butchart Gardens

Benvenuto Road
(13 miles northwest of Victoria)

☎ 604/652-4422

Mailing address P.O. Box 4010
Victoria, British Columbia V8X 3X4

Hours Daily 9-dusk
(call for exact closing times).
Open for night illumination
(June 15-Sept 15 and Dec 6-Jan 6)

Admission $11 Adults, $5.75
(ages 13-17), $1.50 (ages 5-12)

Accessible Yes; will provide free
wheelchairs and strollers if needed

40.
Hatley Castle/
Royal Roads Military College

Highway 1-1A
(7 miles east of Victoria)

☎ 604/388-1660

Mailing address F.M.O.
Victoria, British Columbia V0S 1B0

Hours Daily 10-4

Admission Free

Accessible Partially

Garden Books

The second best source of inspiration is a garden book. Long before I was able to spend three weeks crisscrossing the British Isles, Graham Stuart Thomas's *Great Gardens of Britain* took me to all the National Trust properties. From my armchair, I've visited other great gardens of the world – Georgina Masson's *Italian Gardens*, Bring and Wayembergh's *Japanese Gardens*, Schroer and Enge's *Garden Architecture in Europe*, to name a few. Griswold and Weller's *The Golden Age of American Gardens* introduced me to hundreds of private gardens I'll never be able to see; some are not open to the public, others no longer even exist.

My views on garden design have been influenced by such books as *Gardens are for People* by Thomas D. Church and *The Landscape of Man*, a wonderful history of landscape design by Geoffrey and Susan Jellicoe that describes the climatic, topographical, historical, social, economic and philosophical factors that shaped gardens from pre-history to modern times. From Anthony Huxley's *An Illustrated History of Gardening*, I've gained new appreciation for people who created uncommon beauty without the mechanization we employ today.

Since moving to the Pacific Northwest, I've worn out the pages of my *Sunset Western Garden Book* as I've learned (and put on computer) the vast palette of plants for Northwest climes. I'm also pouring over the *UBC Guide to Gardening in British Columbia*, published by The University of British Columbia Botanical Garden. It's hard to walk into a garden book section without adding a few more to my collection, and it's equally hard, even for a landscape professional, to choose from the plethora of titles.

The most unique bookstore I've encountered here is Flora and Fauna Books, located in Pioneer Square in Seattle. I'm giving the company a special listing because its owner, David Hutchinson, is the only bookseller in the Pacific Northwest who specializes in garden literature, both new and used, often old and rare. The company offers an excellent catalog and ships books all over the world.

⭐DESTINATION
Flora and Fauna Books

121 First Avenue South
Seattle, Washington 98104

☎ *206/623-4727*
Hours *Mon-Sat 10-5*
Accessible *No*
Mail Order
Catalog *Free*

Flora and Fauna's catalog is divided by sections: Specialized Garden Conditions; Garden History and Design, Regional and Cultural Styles; Garden Literature, Biography and Plant Collection; Edible Landscaping, Growing Fruits and Vegetables; Botany, Reference and Floras; Trees, Shrubs and Bamboo; Bonsai, Ikebana and Flower Arranging; Wildflowers, Herbs, Medicinal plants and Wildlife Gardens; Practical texts, Propagation, Pruning, Pests and Diseases; Perennials and Cottage Gardens; and Monographs of Plants, which are of interest to gardeners who specialize in a particular genus.

continued--

The books in Flora and Fauna's catalog have been selected for quality-of-content, importance as reference material and/or price. The store stocks a vast array of titles, and the owner can order most anything (in or out of print). He welcomes your "want-list." Beyond selling books, the knowledgeable staff at Flora and Fauna takes pride in finding the right book at the right value for each gardener's need.

"Over 700 new garden books are published each year, so it's overwhelming to edit them out, says David Hutchinson. "We attempt to steer people to the best of its kind, even if the book is a hundred years old. The things our grandparents knew are still valid." David is a keen gardener himself, and his employees include Susan Buckles, who is well-known in Seattle gardening circles for her landscape design work at Children's Hospital. David and Susan are both British, so gardening is "in their blood."

Basic Gardening Books

I asked the Flora and Fauna staff to recommend the best basic gardening books in print to supplement the topics covered in this source book. Here is their list:

General Gardening Encyclopedias

Sunset Western Garden Book

Encyclopedia of Garden Plants,
  American Horticultural Society

*Encyclopedia of Garden
  Plants and Flowers,* Reader's Digest

Right Plant, Right Place,
  Nicola Ferguson

The Complete Shade Gardener,
  George Schenk

Garden Design

The Book of Garden Design,
  John Brookes

Bold Romantic Gardens,
  Wolfgang Oehme &
  James van Sweden

Country Garden,
  John Brookes

Elements of Japanese Gardens,
  Isao Yoshikawa

The Art of Planting,
  Graham Stuart Thomas

Garden Construction

The Bamboo Fences of Japan,
  Osamu Suzuki & Isao Yoshikawa

Stonescaping,
  Jan Kowalczski Whitner

Trellising,
  Rhonda M. Hart

Pergolas, Arbors, Gazebos and Follies,
  David Stevens

Garden Conservation

*Landscape Design,
  Renovation and Maintenance,*
  Cass Turnbull

Rodale's Garden Problem Solver,
  Jeff Ball & Liz Ball

Pruning,
  Christopher Bricknell

Creative Propagation,
  Peter Thompson

Propagation,
  Phillip Browse

Ecologically Balanced Landscapes

*Gardening with Native Plants in the
  Pacific Northwest,*
  Arthur Kruckeberg

*Winter Gardening in the Maritime
  Northwest,*
  Binda Colebrook

The Natural Shade Garden,
  Ken Druse

Trees & Shrubs

*Trees and Shrubs for
Pacific Northwest Gardens,*
John A. and Carol L. Grant

Shrubs,
Roger Phillips & Martyn Rix

Hillier Manual of Trees and Shrubs

Manual of Woody Landscape Plants,
Michael Dirr

*Flowering Shrubs,
Step by Step to Growing Success,*
David Carr

*Ornamental Shrubs, Climbers
and Bamboo,*
Graham Stuart Thomas

Rhododendron Portraits,
D.M. Van Gelderen
& J.R. Van Hoey Smith

Roses,
Roger Phillips & Martyn Rix

Old Roses & English Roses,
David Austin

Climbing Roses,
David Austin

Encyclopedia of Ferns,
David Jones

Encyclopedia of Ornamental Grasses,
John Greenlee

The Flower Garden

Color in your Garden, Flower Gardens,
and *Garden Style,*
Penelope Hobhouse

The Random House Book of Perennials

The Green Tapestry,
Beth Chatto

Bulbs,
Roger Phillips & Martyn Rix

Bulbs, 2 volumes,
John E. Bryan

The Edible Landscape

*Designing and Maintaining your Edible
Landscape Naturally,*
Robert Kourik

Organic Gardening,
Dave Pike

Rock Gardens

Alpines,
Will Ingwersen

The Rock Garden and Its Plants,
Graham Stuart Thomas

Water Gardens

*The Complete Book of the
Water Garden,*
Philip Swindells and David Mason

Houseplants

The New Houseplant Expert,
D. G. Hessayon

Container Gardening & Bonsai

The Book of Container Gardening,
Malcolm Hillier

The Contained Garden,
David Stevens & Kenneth Beckett

Plants for Collectors

Hillier Guide to Connoisseur's Plants,
Alan Toogood

*Perennial Garden Plants:
The Modern Florilegium,*
Graham Stuart Thomas

Shrubs Through the Seasons,
Roy Lancaster

Garden Furniture & Accessories

Decorating Eden,
Elizabeth Wilkinson and
Marjorie Henderson

David Hutchinson introduced me to John Brookes' *The Book of Garden Design*, which details the basics of landscape design in simple language and reinforces the text with excellent illustrations. I also love *Bold Romantic Gardens: The New World Landscapes of Oehme and van Sweden*, which illustrates a new, naturalistic way of planting that incorporates grasses and great drifts of hardy perennials. These beautiful books are full of practical advice for do-it-yourself garden designers. Even if you're turning your garden over to a professional, I highly recommend them as tools for helping you communicate your ideas.

I would add to David's list the familiar paperback series on outdoor building from Sunset Publishing (*Decks, Fences & Gates, Outdoor Furniture, Walks, Walls and Patio Floors*, etc.). Sunset and other publishers, including Ortho, Random House, Penguin and Crowood, offer numerous, highly informative books on specific plant groups and basic gardening.

One of the most talked-about new books is *Noah's Garden: Restoring the Ecology of Our Own Back Yards* by Sara Stein, who came to realize that "fashionable plants" and conventional planting practices have devastated the rural ecology and created an "impoverished environment" hostile to wildlife. Her message is persuasive and beautifully written, but because she lives in suburban New York, the book's listings of symbiotic plants and animals apply to the Northeast. For our region, I highly recommend *Naturescaping: A Place for Wildlife*, which was published by the Oregon Department of Fish and Wildlife. (For information on ordering, see page 123.)

As you may have guessed, I'm addicted to garden books. Only the region's excellent libraries stand between me and credit card overload. The Elisabeth C. Miller Library at the Center for Urban Horticulture in Seattle helped me enormously in the preparation of this book. While this unique resource is not primarily a lending library, it's open to gardeners and researchers throughout the Northwest who come to use the reference facilities. I also availed myself of the Seattle Public Library and Multnomah County Library in Portland. Like most public libraries, their gardening collections are limited by lack of funding, but they have borrowing privileges from other public libraries in the country.

☞ **Money-saving tip: Ask your local public library about "inter-library loans," through which you can obtain almost any book in print.**

The libraries are also an economical way to keep up with all the garden-related magazines in print. I subscribe to *Sunset* and *Gardens West*, which is published in B.C., because they are filled with information specific to gardening in the region. I take advantage of the library's copies of *Horticulture, Pacific Horticulture, Garden Design, Fine Gardening* and *Organic Gardening*, to name a few. The fact is, there is more information out there than any one person can absorb! Every major newspaper features garden columns, and almost every "talk-radio" station and TV channel offers a gardening program. Ah, to have but a few more hours in each day....🌺

Personalized Sources of Garden Information

Gardeners learn by seeing, reading and questioning. I've always heard that a green thumb is equal parts knowledge, intuition and luck, but knowledge is the only thing that works for me. Luck I've never trusted, and the kind of intuition that allows a gardener to differentiate between weeds and precious seedlings is built on first-hand experience! Happily, the Pacific Northwest is replete with people trained to answer your gardening questions.

Landscape Professionals

Professionals in the fields of design, landscape construction, horticulture and maintenance provide knowledge and skill that can save you hundreds or thousands of dollars in the long run. But you should know that different types of professionals are trained in different, specific fields. The "green industry" is regulated to an extent by professional organizations, but not all landscape services are regulated. Within each area of "expertise," there are people who don't know what they are doing. No matter what kind of landscape service you employ, ask about credentials, check references, and look at examples of their work.

Among design professionals, landscape architects are the most highly trained. To be able to use the title "landscape architect," one must have graduated from an accredited university program, practiced for a number of years and passed a rigorous exam that covers design, construction techniques, plant materials, history and professional ethics. Most are members of the American Society of Landscape Architects (ASLA).

A number of people who call themselves "landscape designers" are graduates of university programs in landscape architecture who have not yet taken the registration exam. The yellow page listings for landscape designers also include anyone who has set up a business in garden design. Many are excellent designers, albeit self-taught, with years of practical experience and a real flair for aesthetics. Their emphasis is usually slanted more toward plant materials than structural design.

How does the average homeowner pick from the plethora of design professionals? Obtain recommendations from people whose gardens you admire and interview several firms. If you have major structural work to be done, a difficult site with steep slopes that will require retaining walls, serious drainage problems or a landscape in need of ecological restoration, you should consult a landscape architect or degreed designer. Most landscape architectural firms do not specialize in residential design, but most landscape architects enjoy garden design and are willing to take on a project, at least on a consulting basis.

Once the design work is complete, you may need the services of a landscape contractor. Landscape architects and designers normally prepare plans and written specifications that allow you to get construction bids from several different contractors, nurseries and/or specialists such as irrigation contractors or lighting contractors. Some landscape architects and landscape designers operate "design/build" firms, which include both design and construction services.

My best advice to homeowners is not to lock yourself into a contract that doesn't allow for the process of competitive construction bids unless you personally know the individual with whom you are dealing and highly respect the company's work.

☞**Money-saving tip: The lowest bid is not necessarily the best bid.**

Study every detail and make sure that the contractor carries liability insurance and is bonded. Ask for his or her registration number.

Certified Nursery Professionals are usually employed by nurseries. Their expertise is in horticulture, and the associations to which they belong provide continuing education through seminars and newsletters. Most area nurseries have professionals on staff who are highly qualified to give advice on plant selection and answer gardening questions. Some also provide design and landscape installation services. In the plant source chapters of this book, you'll find a number of nurseries that offer free classes and send out newsletters not only to promote products, but also to keep their customers informed about new developments in the field of horticulture. Ask to be added to the mailing list of every nursery where you trade.

Never trust your trees to anyone but an insured, licensed arborist. Unfortunately anyone who can afford a pick-up truck and chainsaw may call himself a tree trimmer. His handiwork is reflected in the misshapen forms of thousands of improperly trimmed trees all over the Pacific Northwest. Most competent arborists belong to the International Society of Arboriculture (ISA) or the National Arborist Association (NAA). You can contact either of these organizations to obtain a list of local member firms. Recently at a seminar in Seattle someone asked how to find a good tree-trimming company. An experienced arborist answered, "Call a company and ask if they top trees. If they say 'yes,' hang up!"✿

Extension Services

Cooperative Extension Services (so named because they are joint ventures between the United States Department of Agriculture, county governments and land-grant universities) were begun in 1914 to sustain farmers. As the population became more urban, the agencies widened the focus to include consumer affairs, food and water quality, home and family issues and gardening. In rural areas the extension agents still concentrate on the needs of farming and ranching families, but urban extension agents are responsible for answering the multitude of horticultural questions asked by homeowners, park departments, schools and city governments. The advice is always free, and most of the services are either free or modestly priced. Look for Cooperative Extension in the phone book under county listings.✿

☞ **Money-saving tip: Cooperative Extension Services are funded by your tax dollars. Tap into this gold mine!**

Master Gardeners & Other Sources of Continuing Education

The task of dispensing information in the large urban counties has become impossible for one agent to handle. The Master Gardeners Program was begun simultaneously in 1972 in Seattle and Spokane to train enthusiastic laymen to share the work of overburdened county agents. It has worked beautifully. Master Gardeners now answer garden questions, set up demonstrations, diagnose plant problems and make recommendations for the control of plant diseases, insect infestation and cultural problems. The program requires sixty hours of training and sixty hours of volunteer work the first year; it encourages continued learning and a minimum of twenty-five hours of community service in the following years. Over 40,000 Master Gardeners in the U.S. and Canada take part in the program today.

In the U.S., these volunteers conduct neighborhood clinics throughout the region during the gardening season. They offer taped messages on subjects from "apple varieties to zoysia grass," and participate in question-and-answer newspaper columns and frequent radio and TV appearances. If a Master Gardener doesn't know the answer to your question, he or she will contact the County Agent, who in turn can seek information from experts at WSU, OSU and University of Idaho or a nationwide network of information sources.

In Canada, Master Gardeners sponsor a nine-week garden lecture series each winter at the VanDusen Botanical Garden. This popular course, which covers all aspects of home gardening, from disease and pest control to propagation of hardy perennials, attracts people from throughout the Fraser Valley, Victoria and the Gulf Islands.

Master Composters is a new organization begun by Seattle Tilth Association (a group dedicated to organic gardening and urban ecology) to promote backyard composting. Its long-term goal is to prevent yard waste from reaching already-overburdened landfills. Like the Master Gardeners program, it is staffed by volunteers, and it provides "hot lines" and demonstration sites. The concept has already spread to Portland and Vancouver, B.C., and will be coming soon to smaller communities in the area. (Call your local waste management department or contact the Seattle Tilth Association at 206/633-0451.) Here's a way to improve your soil and save your tax dollars at the same time!

Many of the community colleges offer horticultural classes. Garden clubs and plant societies host hundreds of lecture series and gardening classes in the Northwest. They're eager to share information, and sometimes they'll even find mentors for enthusiastic novices. Watch local newspapers and regional magazines for times and dates. One Sunday, I counted 23 lectures and workshops slated for the coming week in the Seattle paper. So, let's get serious about gardening! 🌸

Chapter Two
Garden Construction

*"Nature does not complete things.
She is chaotic. Man must finish,
and he does so by making a garden
and building a wall.
Before I built a wall I'd ask to know
What I was walling in or walling out."*
.....Robert Frost

Master Planning

☞ **Money-saving tip (a.k.a. Rule #1): Work from a Master Plan!**

Good design is the difference between an ordinary landscape and a real garden. If you're establishing a new garden, take a designer's approach before spending a penny! If you want to improve an existing one, don't let the garden evolve "piece-meal." Look with a critical eye at the total picture. Is it attractive? Is it meeting your needs? Most gardens require major revision every five to ten years.

It's not enough to simply love your roses or rhodies. A garden is prime living space, worthy of as much thought as the arrangement of rooms within your house. The Northwest is replete with capable, creative garden designers, but you may prefer to draw your own plan. The process is the same either way.

Consider Function

Professional designers begin by examining how the property works. Is there adequate space for outdoor entertaining? A place for children to play? Good circulation? Adequate storage? Sufficient privacy? How does the garden look from inside the house? How does it feel at night? Are there drainage problems? Problems with soil erosion?

While visiting the homes of prospective clients, I've observed people who would never tolerate a clumsy kitchen or cluttered closet enduring all sorts of inconveniences in the landscape. Sometimes there's no way for guests to get from the front to the rear garden without encountering garbage cans or stepping in a mud puddle. Often the concrete patio poured by the contractor as a "selling feature" is too small for a table and chairs. There's no place to store hoes, hoses, bone meal or barbecue grills. The list goes on.

Create a "Wish-list"

Family members should talk about how they would like to use their outdoor space... *Mr. Smith has always wanted a vegetable garden, Mrs. Smith dreams of a shady spot to curl up and read, their teenage daughter demands a sunning deck and the son wants a basketball goal and a tree house. The dog needs a place to run...*

Site Survey

The garden plan starts with a drawing of what exists. You may have a property survey in your files or be able to obtain one from the city. It will probably be drawn at an engineer's scale (1 inch = 20 feet), but you can have it photo-mechanically enlarged to a quarter or eighth-inch scale. Or, you can take measurements and draw the house and grounds on a large sheet of ¼-inch graph paper, with each square representing one foot. The tools you'll use include graph paper, an architect's scale and a 50-foot tape for measuring the property. (If your lot is especially large, make the overall site plan at a smaller scale. Then enlarge each section of the garden to ¼-inch scale for construction drawings and planting plans.)

Locate all of your home's windows and doors and indicate the dimensions on the plan. Draw a north-pointing arrow on the plan and note which direction each side of the house faces. Locate existing trees and shrubs. Make note of sun angles and wind patterns, keeping in mind that each side of the house has its own micro climate.

Observe the vistas from every direction... *Nice view to the south, patio bakes in the afternoon sun, unsightly view of the neighbor's boat from the dining room window, wasted space in front, gorgeous tree beside the garage...*

Next, map the above-ground and/or underground utilities, as well as any utility easements. If you don't know where your buried lines run, ask the various service companies (gas, telephone, electrical, etc.) to come to your house and mark them.

☞ **Money-saving tip: Locate sewer, water, gas and any buried electrical cable lines before even thinking about building anything in the landscape.**

If the property has complicated drainage patterns, hire a professional surveyor to map changes in grade. You can use a rod and hand level to determine the slope of the land on a simple site. Assume the elevation of the ground floor of the house to be 100 and set elevations on the property accordingly. For example, an elevation of 98 would be two feet below the level of the floor of the house. If the lot is so steeply sloped that you have problems with erosion or so flat that you have potential drainage problems, call in a landscape architect to prepare a plan for re-grading the property.

Schematic Planning

After you have a drawing of what exists and you've analyzed how the garden is functioning, it's time to match your want-list with the property's potential. Designers call this the "schematic" phase; think of it as considering every option. Place a piece of tracing paper over the plan and sketch a proposed deck or a new retaining wall. Try various arrangements. Even the tiniest lot will yield myriad solutions.

☞ **Money-saving tip: It's a lot easier to erase pencil marks on a plan than it is to tear out a misplaced wall or walk!**

Every corner of the garden has a personality waiting to be developed. You may discover that the side yard has potential as a kitchen garden or a "secret garden" off a bedroom or a place for children to play. You'll want to select the most comfortable spots in the garden for the outdoor living areas, even if that means appropriating part of the front yard. There's no rule that says a patio must open off the back door. An entry courtyard might be an ideal place for dining outdoors or for reading the Sunday paper. Perhaps an open spot in the rear garden has potential for a sunning deck. Just for visual pleasure, you might decide to break up an expanse of lawn with a gazebo or a fish pond or to build a rose arbor over a gateway.

You'll also want to look at the landscape's effect on household energy consumption. Evergreen trees and shrubs planted on the north may serve as a windbreak to reduce heat loss in winter. Deciduous trees planted on the south and west sides of the property can help cool your house in summer. In winter, they will lose their leaves, allowing the sunshine in.

You may even consider alterations to the house itself, such as French doors to link the house and garden or floor-to-ceiling windows that frame a section of the garden and visually expand the interior living space. You might build a solarium addition out into the garden or extend the roof-line to create a covered outdoor seating area. At this point, you'll begin considering the choice of materials for decks, terraces, fences and retaining walls, possibly repeating the colors, textures and materials of the interior in the landscape.

The Master Plan

Now that you've considered all of your options, it's time to draw a Master Plan. This plan is usually a culmination of weeks or months of exploration. As the final blueprint for the garden's future, the Master Plan should reflect the owner's personality, the family's needs and the capabilities of the site. There will have been compromises along the way. If you, like most people, cannot immediately afford every improvement, divide the plan into sections (Phase 1, Phase 2, etc.) that allow you to build the garden at a pace and price you can manage.

After the Master Plan is complete, the designer prepares grading and construction drawings and specifications for soil preparation.

☞ **Money-saving tip: Be sure to check your local building codes before beginning any landscape construction project!**

The last step in the design process is the Planting Plan. Construction, which is messy, should be complete before any permanent planting begins.

☞ **Money-saving tip: Protect existing plants from the onslaught of the construction crew.**

I've seen left-over concrete dumped on tree roots, paint splattered all over hedges and perennials trampled to a pulp. If there's going to be major construction, build a temporary fence around the drip line of valuable trees, rope-off planting areas or be prepared to cover plants with clear, heavy plastic. ❀

Walks, Patios & Retaining Walls

Walkways are to a garden what hallways are to the house. I like to think of the entry walk as the home's first foyer; it sets the character of the landscape. A plain, straight concrete walk between the street and front door, although quite functional, doesn't hold the same welcoming appeal as a meandering pathway constructed of stone or brick. Walkways not only serve as connectors between the house and street, but also lead from space to space within the garden. They may delineate between different sections of the landscape or be used to separate the lawn from the planting beds.

Walkways eventually step up to a porch or widen into a patio or courtyard floor that connects directly into the house. Paved outdoor living areas have become essential elements in the landscape as more people rediscover the joy of entertaining and vacationing at home. Therefore, the materials you choose and the patterns you create in these transitional areas should be selected with an eye toward unifying the house and garden.

Materials

The Sunset book, *How to Build Walks, Walls and Patio Floors*, discusses the pros and cons of several different landscape materials. If you're designing your own garden, this book is a good starting point for making decisions. It offers practical information on relative costs and durability of brick, gravel, concrete, asphalt, tile, stone and wood. And, it provides good technical information on grading, drainage and foundation requirements.

The cost of paving depends upon the material and the labor involved in installation. Consider your options carefully. Each type of material carries the possibility of an infinite number of patterns and textures. Materials can be combined to create interest, but too many materials become confusing. I rarely use more than three. If I want to make a small garden seem larger, I'll use a single material, such as brick, for all of the walls, walks and patios.

Whatever your choice of materials, they should complement the architectural style of the house and garden. For example, wood decks or adobe-tile patios are attractive choices for a contemporary home, while brick or cut stone are more appropriate in a traditional setting. A raised planting bed constructed of rugged rock has a very different feel from a tidy timber box painted the same color as the house. The former suggests big, bold naturalistic plantings; for the latter, I picture a more orderly planting scheme.

Concrete is a good choice if you're planning large areas of terrace and/or curving shapes. It's durable, relatively inexpensive, and easily molded into intricate forms. However, large expanses of concrete can appear cold and monotonous. Exposed aggregate concrete is warmer than brush-finished concrete, and if it is combined with a brick border or stone insets, aggregate concrete takes on an even more friendly feeling.

I'm enthusiastic about the effects that can be achieved with colored, stamped concrete that simulates the feel of cobblestone, slate or brick. It "dresses up" the garden, yet it costs less than half as much as professionally installed natural stone or brickwork. You'll find companies that pour and form stamped concrete in the yellow pages under the heading, Concrete Contractors. The process is tricky, so ask to see completed examples of the company's work.

Brick and concrete pavers are versatile, but labor-intensive. Traditional mortared brick walkways and patios usually require the skills of a mason, but the average homeowner can lay a relatively durable walk or patio by placing the brick on a bed of compacted sand. Simply sweep dry mortar mix between the joints and moisten with a hose to set. You will need a solid edging, such as treated wood, concrete or mortared brick, to hold the loose bricks in place.

For residential use, I generally prefer the look of natural (fired-clay) brick over concrete paver bricks. At about $2 per square foot, the cost is the same. There's no real advantage in choosing concrete pavers for walkways and patios. However, if they are to be used for a driveway, interlocking concrete pavers need only a sand base while clay bricks require reinforced concrete underlayment. So, if you want to match the driveway and walkways, concrete pavers are the more cost-effective choice.

I was surprised to learn that Mutual Materials (see page 49) is the last remaining brick manufacturer in the Northwest. A number of companies in the area now manufacture concrete pavers and retaining wall blocks, and Mutual Materials sells these products in addition to their brick. As more companies enter the business, concrete products are becoming increasingly sophisticated and available in a wider variety of shapes and colors.

Tile is a nice choice for covering-over an unattractive old entry porch or small concrete terrace. It's the most expensive material you can choose for large-scale new construction. It runs two to four times more per square foot than brick or concrete pavers, plus it must be set on a concrete base. Not every retail tile store carries tile products suitable for landscape use. Exterior tile must be non-skid and frost-proof. In my search for handsome paving materials, however, I found several good possiblities, including clay paver tile, quarried stone cut in the form of tile, and even tile made of recycled materials.

Native stone is readily available and relatively inexpensive in the Northwest. If the stones are small enough to handle, they can be laid by a non-professional. The biggest difficulty with rock work, ironically, is making it appear natural. Many of the "decorative" rock retaining walls I've seen in the Northwest look hopelessly out-of-scale, as if the boulders were dumped on the site by the Jolly Green Giant!

There are secrets to successful rock work, which include choosing a color of stone that looks natural in the landscape, paying attention to the grain of the rock, and partially burying large boulders, as they would be found in nature. The book, *Stonescaping: A Guide to Using Stone in Your Garden*, written by Seattle author Jan Kowalczewski Whitner, is an excellent source of information. Also look at books on Japanese garden design. I've listed several regional sources for decorative rocks and paving stones, beginning on page 55.

Wood decking also has enormous appeal in the Pacific Northwest. It blends comfortably with the natural environment and achieves a "warmth" that no other material can match. At about $10 per square foot, wood decking is comparable to mortared brick or stone work in terms of cost. Wood decking allows you to build out over part of the landscape, in some cases doubling your gardening space, with container gardening on the deck and a shade garden beneath.

However, if you're building an outdoor living area close to ground-level and do not have sufficient space for good air circulation between the ground and the decking, choose another material. You'll see decking and wood walks built right on the ground in some of the national magazines, but they're susceptible to wood rot in the Northwest's wet-winter climate zones. If you need ground-level decking, look at the modular decking I've listed on page 52, which can be used for extra entertaining space in summer and then put in storage during the winter.

Design Tips

Walkways should be large enough for two people to walk abreast or for the gardener to maneuver a wheelbarrow or lawn mower. Three and a half feet is considered a minimum width for the garden's major connecting links. I prefer five-foot walkways wherever possible. Pathways that lead to seldom-used portions of the garden or just serve to allow weeding in a large planting bed may be constructed of stepping stones, bark or gravel, but, for reasons of comfort and practicality, the main passageways should be paved.

Steps require special attention. The proportions of garden steps are different from indoor stairs. They are most comfortable with deep treads and low risers. It's important to keep the riser heights constant throughout the landscape since unanticipated variations in height may cause people to trip and fall. A single step down also presents a danger in that it may not be immediately obvious. It's better to ramp the grade change if you need only one step down. And, if more than five steps are required, break up the staircase with a landing. All steps should be lighted at night.

In selecting a site for a patio or other outdoor living area, consider privacy, wind patterns, the path of the sun and the effects of rain. Good drainage is essential. You'll also need to consider proximity to running water and electricity, and you may want to provide a phone connection. Covered terraces that are usable in all weather are especially nice in this climate. I like to include an outdoor fireplace to warm the "room" on a chilly night. (If you install an outdoor fireplace, be sure to consider prevailing breezes to avoid a back-draft of smoke, and be careful of overhanging limbs that could pose a fire hazard.)

☞ **Money-saving tip: The most common error homeowners commit is in designing outdoor living spaces too small.**

It's a pity to go to the trouble and expense of construction only to discover that adding a few more feet would have made the living area more functional. Allow a minimum of eight by eight feet for an eating area. You'll want room for a barbecue grill and service bar, plus a four-foot transition area between the cooking and eating areas. Design spacious seating areas. Consider built-in benches to define space and take the place of deck railings.

Sunset's *How to Plan & Build Decks* is an excellent resource for the do-it-yourself deck builder. Even if you're hiring a contractor to build a deck, you should read the section entitled "Buyer's Guide to Building Materials," which not only explains lumber terminology, but also illustrates various types of substructures and attachment methods. The book's color photographs will spark your imagination, and the section, "Protecting Your Investment," will ensure additional years of enjoyment.

☞ **Money-saving tip: Seek professional help with the design and construction of structures that require complicated calculations and special engineering techniques.**

Such site amenities as driveways, freestanding masonry walls and retaining walls over three feet in height have special technical requirements. Freestanding walls require footings that will stand up to wind loads, and retaining walls are subject to tremendous forces of water. Walls of any significant height require reinforced concrete footings. Provision must be made for weep holes to ensure proper drainage. The factors that must be considered in the design of a driveway include angle of slope, turning radius and the weight of the vehicles that will be using it.

Construction Tips

Site preparation is the most time-consuming part of many landscape projects, especially if you are building a walk or patio over an existing lawn. Getting rid of grass is more difficult than getting it to grow, to put it mildly. You can smother it for a couple of months under black plastic or use herbicide to kill it quickly. In either case, it's prudent to remove the dead grass and its tenacious root system with a sod cutter.

If you're laying brick on sand, place a layer of polyethylene or roofing felt beneath the sand to reduce the chance of vegetation growing up between the cracks. Ed Hume's catalog offers a modular product that serves as a template for laying brick and also keeps grass and weeds at bay. (See page 223.)

There's usually some earth moving involved as well. Walkways should be laid with a slight "crown" along the center to shed water. Where walkways adjoin planting beds, raise the level of the walkway so that soil and mulches won't wash out onto the path every time it rains. Slope terraces away from the house.

☞ **Money saving tip: Always place a PVC pipe sleeve underneath new walkways or driveways.**

If you decide later to run electrical or irrigation lines, you won't have to tear out a section of the paving. A few dollars spent on a piece of pipe may save hundreds of dollars in the future! ❀

Northwest Manufacturers

Abbotsford Concrete Products Ltd.

3422 McCallum Road
Abbotsford, British Columbia V2S 4N3
☎ *604/852-4967 or 1-800-663-4091*

Hours *Mon-Fri 7-5*
U.S. Mailing address *P.O. Box 3046*
Sumas, Washington 98295-3046

Abbotsford's unique Hydra Pressed™ paving slabs are made of dense concrete with chamfered edges. These handsome 2"-thick pavers are strong enough to be laid on a compacted-sand base. The Yorkstone pattern convincingly emulates natural slate, and the sand-blasted aggregate patterns are offered in a choice of earth colors. Standard sizes are 18"x18", 24"x 24" or 24"x30", but the pavers can be ordered through the company's dealers in smaller squares and rectangles. The company also makes interlocking pavers in several patterns and colors. While Abbotsford's products are not sold directly to the public, you'll find them in many of the region's large garden centers and home improvement stores. You're welcome to call the company to get the name of the nearest dealer or request a free brochure.

Keystone Pacific Northwest

10445 S.W. Canyon Road #111
Beaverton, OR 97005
☎ *503/644-6248 or 1-800/733-7470*

Hours *Mon-Fri 8-5*
FAX *503/626-1755*

Keystone's interlocking blocks are suitable for tree rings, raised beds or retaining walls up to three-feet in height. A blessing for the do-it-yourselfer, the lightweight Garden Wall™ blocks weigh only 27 pounds and can be laid out in straight or curved lines. The company makes larger, heavier styles of block for massive retaining walls and shoreline applications. Keystone products are available from licensed dealers through-out the U.S. and Canada. Call the manufacturer at the number above for a brochure and the name of the distributor nearest you.

"Mutual Materials Company has been producing and distributing quality masonry products since 1900," wrote the company's spokesperson. In addition to clay brick and concrete block, they manufacture brick pavers, stair treads and coping brick, stepping stones, lawn edging, and Keystone Retaining Wall Systems. Mutual also distributes the wares of other Northwest manufacturers, including Westcon interlocking concrete pavers, Hydra-Press™ slabs by Abbotsford Concrete and stepping stones made by Pacific Concrete. Retail customers can buy some products directly from the sales branches. For certain products that the company markets only through retail outlets, Mutual's sales personnel will direct you to the nearest dealer. Free catalog sheets from manufacturers are available on request. Their products are available in virtually every region of the Northwest, and you can get job-site delivery. Occasionally, you'll find small quantities of discontinued lines, "seconds" or returned products available at reduced prices.

Mutual Materials Co.
605 119th N.E.
Bellevue, Washington 98005
☎ *206/455-2869*

Hours *Generally, Mon-Fri 7-5*
Accessible *In most instances*
Mailing address *P.O. Box 2009*
Bellevue, Washington 98009
FAX *206/454-7732*

Other Washington Locations:
Auburn, ☎ *206/939-7854*
Bremerton, ☎ *206/377-3939*
Bothell, ☎ *206/486-1918*
Everett, ☎ *206/353-9677*
Redmond, ☎ *206/881-6700*
Tacoma, ☎ *206/537-0288*
and ☎ *206/474-0885*
Tumwater, ☎ *206/357-3343*
Spokane, ☎ *509/922-4100*
Vancouver, ☎ *206/693-4766*
or 285-3336 (toll-free from Portland)

Oregon Locations:
Portland, ☎ *503/624-8860 or*
Toll-free 1/800-477-7137
Clackamas, ☎ *503/655-7167*
Hillsboro, ☎ *503/640-4731*
Salem, ☎ *503/375-6050*

This company manufactures "gourmet" bricks and stepping stones. All of its products are poured by hand, cast in rubber molds and colored with oxides to capture the texture of natural stone. Their random flagstones are offered in 100 different patterns. Their Burnaby pavers, for example, are reproductions of old cobblestones from the city of Burnaby, Scotland. Hart Nurseries very effectively used their keystones (which were originally made for archways) as steps in a display at the 1993 Northwest Flower and Garden Show. The company does a lot of custom work; they were making molds to build a stone bridge when I talked with the owners. They ship to homeowners all over the West Coast.

Northwest Stone and Brick
19503 63rd Avenue N.E.
Arlington, Washington 98223
☎ *206/435-8099*

Hours *Mon-Fri 7:30-4, Sat 8-noon*
(Saturdays by appointment only
Oct through March)
Accessible *Yes*
Mail Order
Catalog *Free*
FAX 206/435-4535

Pacific Concrete Products

303 26th Street N.E.
Auburn, Washington 98002
☎ *206/852-9120*

Hours *Mon-Fri 8-4:30*

Most large garden centers carry Pacific Concrete's stepping stones and patio pavers. These two-inch-thick paving materials come in several sizes and colors, including a particularly nice terra cotta. You'll find 12", 16" and 20" rounds; 12", 16", 20" and 24" squares; 16" hexagons and free-form shapes. Their *Walk Stones* (16" crescents) are designed to form a contiguous pathway. They also make a handsome interlocking edging material suitable for bordering straight or curved planting beds. Write or call the company for brochures and the name of your nearest dealer.

Retaining Wall Systems

8501 12th N.W., Suite 108
(office only; no showroom)
Seattle, Washington 98107
☎ *206/783-8967*

Hours *Phone answered 24 hours a day*
Catalog *Free*
FAX *206/782-3690*

This company's highly-textured interlocking concrete blocks stack up as an attractive, affordable alternative to natural stone or poured concrete retaining walls. The blocks require no mortar and will conform to convex and concave curves. The company will deliver to any location in the Pacific Northwest, and the individual blocks can easily be lifted and set in place by one person. Because electrical cable slots are cast into each block, you can install landscape lighting on the face of the wall and/or route cable for sprinkler systems within it.

Rocktile Specialty Products

220 S. Ave A
Boise, Idaho 83702
☎ *1-800/545-7735*

Hours *Mon-Fri 8:30-5*
Accessible *Yes*
Catalog *Free*

Rocktile cuts natural Idaho quartzite into tiles of various dimensions. Unlike marble and granite, this pretty sparkling stone is slip-resistant. It's dense structure makes it impervious to salts and acids. Quartzite varies in color from off-white to golds, greens and grays. As it is processed into tile, each slab is graded by color. Ask for samples showing typical color ranges. These durable tiles can be laid as squares or in rectangular patterns or in random lengths and widths. The company maintains a sales yard, but if you don't live in the area, a phone call will get you in touch with a nearby dealer. If there's no dealer available, the company will sell directly to homeowners and ship the product.

Westcon manufactures handsome concrete pavers and materials for concrete retaining walls. Their Manor Square Pavers, for example, replicate the appearance of slate, but they are made with a tough "Dura-Finish" that's more practical than the natural stone, which tends to water-stain. Available in a range of colors and compatible modular shapes, Westcon pavers can be laid in interesting patterns to personalize your walkways, patios and driveways. In British Columbia, call the manufacturer for the distributor nearest you. Distributed by Mutual Materials in the United States. See page 49.

Westcon Pavers
19675 98th Avenue
Langley, British Columbia V3A 4P8
☎ *604/888-0555*

Hours *Mon-Fri 8-4*
Accessible *No*
Catalog *Free*
FAX *604/888-0014*

Retail Sources for Pavers, Tile & Decking Materials

Note: In addition to the sources listed below, see Landscape Supplies, page 107.

Washington

Although the company's focus is on interior tile applications, Pratt & Larson offers several good-looking lines for landscape use. There's an imported Italian glazed tile with a slip-resistant finish. They carry frost-proof 12"x12" and 10"x10" squares that resemble stone in mottled hues of beige, terra cotta, white and gray. They also offer 50 kinds of natural slate (domestic and imported), plus colored and sandblasted concrete pavers in sizes up to 12"x12". For decorative fountains and pool surrounds, Pratt & Larson has an unusually varied selection of beautiful hand-painted ceramic tile ranging in size from 2"x2" to 12"x12". Free catalog sheets from manufacturers are available on request.

Pratt & Larson
207 Second Avenue
Seattle, Washington 97214
☎ *206/ 343-7907*

Hours *Mon-Fri 9-5, Sat 9:30-12*
Accessible *Yes*

Oregon

Cascade Block

1559 Dowell Road
Grants Pass, Oregon 97527
☎ *503/479-1323*

727 W. McAndrews
Medford, Oregon 97501
☎ *503/773-4575*

Hours *Mon-Fri 8-5, Sat 8-12*
Accessible *Yes*
FAX *503/479-6331 (Medford)*

Cascade Block has created a "Mason's Park" in which customers can see various paving materials used for pathways. The company manufactures concrete block for walls, but also markets concrete stepping stones and interlocking pavers from several manufacturers in all shapes and sizes. They also stock clay bricks and various kinds of natural stone for walks and walls.

Central Oregon Tile

1269 N.W. Wall Street
Bend, Oregon 97701
☎ *503/389-4740*

Hours *Mon-Fri 9-5, Sat 9-12*
Accessible *Yes*

Central Oregon Tile stocks exterior products from two different manufacturers, Ro-Tile and Coronado, giving customers a wide choice of concrete pavers with the look of stone or clay. Additionally, they carry several kinds of granite and slate, and they offer handsome tile for pools and fountains.

Kwik Deck Systems

P.O. Box 467
Woodburn, Oregon 97071
☎ *503/634-2712*

Hours *Daily 9-5*
Accessible *No*
Mail Order
Catalog *Free*

This company's 23-inch-square prebuilt cedar decking modules offer interesting design possibilities. They are available with either diagonal or straight board surfaces. The diagonal modules can be laid in diamond patterns; the straight modules can be alternated to create a basket weave design. With these squares you can construct a deck or walkway that may be easily moved to another part of the garden or stored during the winter. Or, you can use the product to floor a permanent deck, surround a spa or make simple, attractive benches. Because of the modular construction method, no surface nails are exposed.

See text for Seattle store, page 51. The Portland store is in a nice old building with several rooms full of fabulous tile.

Pratt & Larson
1201 S.E. Third
Portland, Oregon 97214
☎ *503/231-9464*

Hours Mon-Fri 9-5, Sat 9:30-12
Accessible Yes
FAX 503/231-4139

Idaho

Maintaining both wholesale and retail businesses, Mountain Tile carries a huge stock of landscape paving materials. They offer Ro-Stone™, a man-made paver with an unpolished natural stone appearance and Ro-Brick™ from a company in California. The company stocks Westcon and Abbotsford interlocking concrete pavers, which are made in B.C., and a native Idaho quartzite tile, which can be cut into planking or randomly shaped. They also carry Vermont cobble slate made from recycled roofing material and a Southwestern-looking ceramic stoneware made of recycled windshield glass. Free catalog sheets from manufacturers are available on request; the company ships its wares throughout the region.

Mountain Tile Distributors
415 Yellowstone Avenue #B
Pocatello, Idaho 83204
☎ *208/232-6696 or 1-800/677-6696*

Hours Mon-Fri 8-5:30, Sat 9-3
Accessible Yes
Mail Order
FAX 208/232-6694

British Columbia

Bricks 'N' Blocks carries a large supply of patio slabs and stepping stones, plus several brands of interlocking pavers and retaining wall materials. The staff provides patient instruction for homeowners as well as installation service throughout British Columbia. "We're willing to consult on-site if the customer just needs a little help, which is a money-saving compromise between full installation and do-it-yourself," says owner Graham Thomas. You'll also discover that they've a good selection of tools, garden ornaments, soils, mulches and filter fabrics here. Write or drop by for a free brochure.

Bricks 'N' Blocks
1371 McKeen Avenue
North Vancouver, British Columbia
V7P 3H9
☎ *604/984-3008*

Hours Mon-Fri 7:30-6,
Sat 9-5, Sun 10-5
Accessible Yes

Tile Town

901 E. Hastings Street
Vancouver, B.C. V6A 1R9
☎ 604/253-1211

6468 King George Highway
Surrey, B.C. V3W 2Z4
☎ 604/590-3183

100-1180 Bridgeport Road
Richmond, B.C. V6X 1T2
☎ 604/273-6721

3098 Nanaimo Street
Victoria, B.C. V8T 5A6
☎ 604/385-2141

Hours Mon-Fri 9-5, Sat 10-5, Sun 11-4
Accessible Yes
FAX 604/590-3183 (main office)

Tile Town stocks Ro-Stone™ and imports other frost-proof tiles from Portugal and Italy. The company maintains sample boards of tile suitable for pools and fountains; they will loan samples to customers. The inventory is large. What they don't have in stock, they'll custom-order from a wide source of manufacturers.

Van Isle Bricklok Surfacing and Landscape Supplies Ltd.

893 Van Isle Way
Victoria, B.C. V9B 5R8
☎ 604/478-5012

This neighborhood garden centre is a large distributor of Westcon Pavers, so its paths and patios are done in different styles and colors to inspire customers. The company also has an extensive "gravel mart," with washed rock, bark mulch, soils and soil amendments. See complete listing on page 398.

West Coast Tile & Marble

670 Gorge Road E.
Victoria, B.C. V8T 2W6
☎ 604/383-2990

Hours Mon-Fri 8-5, Sat 9-4
Accessible Yes
FAX 604/383-4664

West Coast Tile imports its own line of hand-crafted floor and wall tiles from Mexico three times a year. The staff prides itself on expertise in the area of installation procedures for patios, pathways, fountains and wall features. Watch for periodic inventory reduction "specials."

Retail Sources for Natural Stone

Washington

Interstate has five quarries from which it mines Camas Gray and black basalt. For walkways and patios, the company imports flagstones from all over the country. They carry lots of decorative river rock and moss rocks. You can see their "heather stone" at the Nike campus. In addition to piles and piles of stone suitable for a multitude of purposes, you'll find demonstration retaining walls and ponds at the company's sales yards. They will build your water feature or provide all the materials, including pumps and liners, for you do the job yourself.

Interstate Rock Products, Inc.
Highway 14 at Old Evergreen Road
(Old Fisher Quarry)
Camas, Washington
☎ *206/253-4992 or 285-6342*
(from Portland)

Hours Mon-Fri 8-4:30
Accessible Partially
Catalog Free
Mailing address 18480 S.W. Pacific Dr.
Tualatin, Oregon 97062

From massive displays like Waterfall Park in Seattle's Pioneer Square to little winding footpaths, Marenakos has defined rock gardening in the Pacific Northwest. They draw from quarries at the end of remote switch-back roads high in the Cascades, the distant reaches of the Rockies, the wild river country of Canada and Idaho and places as far away as Mexico. The company stocks rock of remarkable diversity and beauty – cobblestones, slate pavers, granite boulders and skillfully cut slabs of basalt. Their place of business is a bit hard-to-find on first try. Call for directions.

Marenakos Rock Center
30250 S.E. High Point Way
Issaquah, Washington 98027
☎ *206/392-3313*

Hours Mon-Fri 7:30-5, Sat 8-2 (summer);
Mon-Fri 7:30-5 (winter)
Accessible Partially
FAX 206/222-7292

For the "well-dressed" landscape, this company offers square and rectanglar patterns of cut sandstone, quartzite, basalt, granite, bluestone, and Vermont and Pennsylvania slates. They have a good selection of granite cobblestones and big irregular flagstones for casual paths and patios. You'll find crushed marble aggregate for pathways, river rock for dry stream beds, and large monument boulders suitable for driveway entrances.

Terrazzo and Stone
Supply Company
13162 S.E. 32nd
Bellevue, Washington 98005
☎ *206/644-5577*

Hours Mon-Fri 7:30-4
Accessible Yes
FAX 206/644-8754

Oregon

Interstate Rock Products, Inc.

18480 S.W. Pacific Drive
Tualatin, Oregon 97062
☎ *503/625-3258*

6242 Portland N.E.
Salem, Oregon 97305
☎ *503/390-6337*

Hours *Mon-Fri 8-5*
Accessible *Partially*

These Oregon outlets sell rock from the company's Camas quarry and numerous other sources. See page 55.

Interstate Stone

3300 Crater Lake Avenue
Medford, Oregon 97504
☎ *503/772-7173*

Hours *Mon-Fri 7-5, Sat 8-1*
Accessible *Yes*
Catalog *Free*

Here you'll find a large selection of natural paving stone, landscape boulders and rock for retaining walls. Additionally, the company offers concrete stepping stones, clay brick and interlocking concrete pavers. The staff will lend advice to the do-it-yourself crowd or provide a list of competent contractors for the installation.

Oregon Decorative Rock Co.

11050 S.W. Denney Road
Beaverton, Oregon 97005
☎ *503/646-9232*

1716 N.E. Columbia Boulevard
Portland, Oregon 97211
☎ *503/653-7412*

Hours *Daily 8:30-5 (March through Oct);*
Mon-Sat 8:30-5 (Nov through Feb)
Accessible *Partially*
Catalog *Free at site, $1 by mail*
Mailing address *4473 Aldercrest Road*
Milwaukie, Oregon 97222
FAX *503/644-1660 (Beaverton),*
503/653-7412 (Portland)

"Our unique niche," says Al Hawkins, "is that we have always catered to individual homeowners, small garden shop operators and landscapers. All of our materials are displayed on open pallets or bins. You can stroll through with one of our wheelbarrows and select flagstone or a piece of gray lava moss rock. We even have 'loaner gloves'. If you drive your vehicle onto our scale to get an empty weight, we will load all the stone you need for a do-it-yourself retaining wall, patio or waterfall. You drive back across the scale to pay for your selection. Call for directions."

Idaho

Since 1950, this company has been a source for sandstone, rhyolite, basalt and quartzite. The company cuts five colors of quartzite into 3/4"-thick paving tiles in a variety of sizes up to a 12" square. While they do not have a catalog, they will send samples and ship products to customers.

Boise Stone
5106 Fairview Avenue
Boise, Idaho 83706
☎ *208/376-4731*

Hours Mon-Fri 7-5, Sat 9-2
(closed Sat in Jan & Feb)
Accessible No
Mail Order

British Columbia

"We are a natural stone company supplying granite from our own quarry for retaining walls or other landscape projects. We also offer decorative terra cotta tile, bluestone, various types of random slate and much more," says Eric Kerkhof.

Adera Natural Stone Supply Ltd.
2525A Skeena Street
Vancouver, B.C. V5M 3Y6
☎ *604/436-0204*

Hours Mon-Fri 7:30-5
Accessible Yes
FAX 604/436-0555

Fences & "Follies"

Before simply slapping a fence around the perimeter of your property, consider coordinating the fences with other garden structures – you may save money *and* achieve a more pleasing environment at the same time. For example, fence posts might double as supports for a decorative arbor or as part of a covered deck. An enclosed gazebo at the rear corner of a property may serve in lieu of a section of fence. A combination of evergreen shrubs and a lattice summerhouse might be used instead of a fence to screen off an unpleasant view as well as providing a cool place to enjoy the outdoors.

Fences

The strongest visual elements in the landscape, fences not only accommodate the functions of privacy and security, but also make an architectural statement. Run along the perimeter, a handsome fence provides a backdrop for an interesting planting scheme. Within the property, fences create intimate spaces or separate the garden's functions. Fencing may allow you to utilize a heretofore unused portion of the landscape. For example, you might convert part of an open front yard into an entry court or reclaim a side yard as a secure play area. It must be remembered, however, that a high, tight fence built as a visual screen will also act as a wind-break, which may be an asset or a liability.

Don't settle for a plain, off-the-shelf fence until you've looked at the many textural patterns possible with wood fencing – vertical, horizontal, diagonal, basket weave, lattice and louvered. The Sunset book, *Fences and Gates*, is filled with pictures that inspire creative thinking. Look at it in tandem with another Sunset book, *Patio Roofs and Gazebos*. Ideally, the fence and other garden structures will harmonize with one another. Attention to detail will make them special.

Consider the architectural style of your home. For a traditional cottage, I might select a picket fence punctuated with a rose-covered trellis arching over the garden gate. A diagonally patterned fence would better serve a contemporary residence, and here I might incorporate a handsome arbor with strong diagonal bracing. For an Oriental effect, I would choose a bamboo fence and might weave-in such features as an arched bridge or a teahouse pavilion.

In my professional opinion, chain-link fences detract from a residential landscape unless they are completely hidden with hedges or evergreen vines. New vinyl-clad chain link fencing, which is available in black, brown or green, tends to "disappear" within a leafy background. At about $8 a lineal foot, vinyl chain link fencing compares favorably to a wood fence in the right setting, with the added advantage of increased durability.

Ornamental iron fencing, which was widely used to surround Victorian homes, is making a strong comeback in garden design today. An airy iron fence is especially nice where you have a view. To surround a large landscape, I've used a combination of ornamental iron and vinyl-coated chain link. Because even the simplest ornamental iron fences run close to $30 per foot, I use the iron work only for highly visible portions of the fence.

Speaking of vinyl, there's new vinyl lattice available. I've used it extensively for fencing and trellis work. It never needs painting and doesn't rot. It's available in a multitude of colors, various thicknesses, several patterns and different panel widths. It is as attractive as wood lattice and far more durable (albeit more expensive) than the thin wood lattice sold in sheets at building supply stores. Vinyl lattice used atop a wood fence "dresses-up" the fence, allows greater air circulation in the garden and provides a place for lacy vines to twine.

Whatever the style and material of the fence, the garden gate should make a good first impression. It should be different from the pattern of the fence, yet compatible. Often, I'll pick up an architectural detail from the house and repeat it in the gate design. To make the gate even more distinctive, I like to set off the gateposts with finials or lights.

Construction Tips

Properly designed and built, a wood fence should last without repair for fifteen or twenty years. Its posts are the critical element for ensuring durability; I specify pressure-treated wood or metal posts, with pointed, rounded or beveled tops to shed water.

Be sure the depth of the post hole is sufficiently deep and wide to accommodate a stout concrete footing. Depth of burial should equal one-third of the height of the post above ground (i.e. the post for a six-foot fence should be no less than eight-feet long). The width of the footing should be three times greater than the diameter of the post. Set the bottom of the post in four or five inches of gravel so that the wood or metal does not stand in water or come in contact with earth. The concrete footing is then poured on top of the gravel.

I hire a free-lance carpenter to custom-build fences for my most discriminating clients, but many of the fencing companies listed in the yellow pages are willing to do custom-quality work. It's up to homeowners to know what they want and to demand the best workmanship possible within their budget. In fencing, like most other things, you get what you pay for.

☞ **Money-saving tip: Before signing a contract for installation, ask to see samples of a company's work.**

Beware of mass-market companies that assemble fences with staples rather than ring-shank galvanized nails. If you're building down a slope, insist that the fence be designed to step down in increments, with the top of each section horizontal. (The cheap and easy way is to saw off the tops at an angle.) Be sure that gates are constructed with extra-sturdy posts and diagonal bracing; otherwise, they will begin to sag within a few months.

☞ **Money-saving tip: If you're handy with a hammer, you can have a fence company set the posts and construct the face of the fence yourself.**

Setting the posts is the really backbreaking part of the job. I know a homeowner who completed a decorative double-sided fence in a day with boards purchased pre-cut from a lumber yard. There are a number of books that illustrate various construction methods. Bamboo Gardens of Washington and Tsugawa Nursery (see index) offer workshops on Japanese fence building. ✿

Garden "Follies"

Modern gardeners are rediscovering romantic garden structures. Arbor, belvedere, bower, gazebo, grotto, hermitage, kiosk, lath house, mew, pagoda, pavilion, pergola, summerhouse, temple or trellis are but a few of the names we apply. Such "follies" have existed in every culture throughout the history of garden design. They remain popular because they are practical! Wonderful vine-covered arbors are still used to provide cooling shade in summer. Pavilions continue to make lovely places to escape for al fresco dining, relaxing or sleeping. Beyond shelter, decorative garden structures are important as focal points in the landscape.

Today's garden structures may be traditional or contemporary in design. An old-fashioned gazebo might incorporate a spa, with benches that double as storage compartments. A summerhouse may include a built-in barbecue grill, a wet bar and under-the-counter refrigerator. A fanciful pergola might be used to camouflage the side of a garage as well as support a collection of climbing roses. Lattice lath houses can be designed to screen off a dog run while providing a place for potting and propagating new plants. ✿

Sources for Specialty Fence Materials & Decorative Structures

Note: The listings that follow are for pre-fabricated or custom-made garden structures. Most offer free catalogs and ship their products throughout the Pacific Northwest. You'll find small garden structures, such as trellises and rose arbors in all the home improvement stores and large garden centers. Also see Retail Sources for Garden Décor, page 312.

A-1 Quality Pickett Fence

7956 S. E. 17th
Portland, Oregon 97202
☎ 503/224-4041

Hours Mon-Fri 7-6, Sat 9-2
Accessible Yes
Mail Order
Catalog Free

As the name implies, this company makes ten styles of Old English and Victorian pickets, plus they'll custom-make pickets to match existing fences or new versions of historically based patterns. The fence parts are smoothly finished fir, meant to be painted. What the name doesn't tell you is that the owners, Gene and Karen Scrutton, also make elaborate arched-wood arbors, gazebos and pergolas, as well as special custom lattice. The products exemplify the kind of workmanship "you can't find anymore."

Brauck's Specialty Building

5432 S.E. Hawthorne
Portland, Oregon 97215
☎ 503/234-2949

Hours By appointment only
Accessible No

Wes Brauckmiller specializes in upper-end woodworking, mostly custom designed. Judging by the pieces displayed at the Portland Garden Show, it's no wonder that Wes and his team are sought after by the top designers in the region. "If it can be made out of wood," says Wes, "I can do it." Simply put, his decks, fences, arbors, bridges and custom-made garden furniture are works of art.

Chateau Conservatories Ltd.

3955 Myrtle Street
Burnaby, British Columbia V5C 4G3
☎ 604/433-0979

Mail Order

Greenhouses are this company's main focus, but they also make elegant gazebos with ornately turned columns and spindles and roofs made of transparent "Acrylite," to let the sun shine in. See complete listing page 66.

Bill Honcoop's workshop fabricates fan, panel and espalier trellises and graceful rose arbors. Although light-weight, they are well-crafted from clear cedar, assembled with galvanized nails or screws and available finished or unfinished. He does a lot of custom work too. The day I visited, he showed me a sturdy, handsome arbor and swing structure he had made from a picture submitted by a client. He also makes beautifully constructed folding picnic tables and benches, Adirondack chairs and a rolling nursery cart.

Garden Cedar Inc.

699 E. Wiser Lake Road
Lynden, Washington 98264
☎ *206/354-0525*

Hours *Mon-Fri 8-5*
Accessible *Yes*
Mail Order
Catalog *Free*

Garden Classics fabricates modular Gateway Trellis™, a system of panels and posts that can be configured in hundreds of different combinations. They can be used to create gorgeous fences, gates, curved arches, arbors, benches and planter boxes. This sturdy modular treillage allows homeowners and land-scape designers to put together one-of-a-kind garden structures without the expense of custom design and construc-tion! They make components both in the style of English cottage gardens and in a straight-lined, Craftsman-style to work with contemporary or Japanese gardens. You'll receive an order form that serves as a design tool. If you need assistance, Tim Magee and his staff work with clients to help determine the configura-tion that will most effectively comple-ment your garden. The pieces come with a booklet that illustrates installation techniques.

Garden Classics, Inc.

1701 First Avenue South
Seattle, Washington 98134
☎ *206/343-2824*

Hours *Mon-Fri 8-5*
Accessible *Yes*
Mail Order
Catalog *Free*
FAX *206/343-7559*

This company's copper arbors and trellises are "Old World," but the idea is quite new – these graceful wall and garden accessories are fabricated of modular copper tubing and shipped in easy-to-assemble kit form. They last for years and weather to a rich verdigris patina. You'll find them in upscale garden shops, or you can order from the company's attractive catalog.

Garden Ventures

P.O. Box 448
Oregon City, Oregon 97045
☎ *503/650-8776*

Hours *By appointment only*
Mail Order
Catalog *$1*

Gazebo Woodcrafters

P.O. Box 187
Bellingham, Washington 98227
☎ 206/734-0463

Mail Order
Catalog Free

Gazebo Woodcrafters is a national mail-order company that offers gazebos in three standard models and four sizes. This family-owned business, now in its eighth year of operation, also does custom work. Their gazebos are made of western red cedar with 4x4 posts and inch-thick lattice, which is hand-crafted in their factory. "The structures are very sturdy and easy to put together, no building skills needed," says Kay Langford. "We offer lath roofed structures with the option of factory-installed shingles. They can be ordered with or without floor decking, so the structures can be set on an existing patio or floored with stone or brick, if the customer prefers. They can be left natural or painted."

Gazebos 'N' Gardens

8424 S.E. Barbara Welch Road
Portland, Oregon 98236
☎ 503/760-2322

Hours Daily 8-5
Accessible Yes
Mail Order
Catalog Free

Gazebos 'N' Gardens makes gazebos in modular kits that can be shipped anywhere and assembled in about six hours. The components are designed for easy relocation, if you wish. They offer a choice of railing types (lattice, tongue and groove or decorative dowel) and either octagonal or straight flooring. For entertaining, you can order handsome built-in benches and tables. Finish the gazebos with doors, skylights and windows to create a real "room-in-the garden" for summer guest quarters or to enclose an outdoor spa.

Nichols Bros. Stoneworks

20209 Broadway
Snohomish (Maltby), Washington 98290
☎ 206/668-5434

Nichols Bros. Stoneworks manufactures handsome finials for masonry gate posts. See complete listing on page 305.

Hinoki means white cedar in Japanese. Utilizing Port Orford cedar and employing a tradition of craftsmanship that dates back hundreds of years, this company manufactures a diverse range of products. They offer aromatic Japanese soak tubs in a range of sizes with covers, heaters and other accessories. They fabricate wall and ceiling kits, trim kits and floor grates, as well. In addition to complete bathing environments, Oregon Hinoki Products makes graceful garden bridges from strong Alaska yellow cedar. All of their products are finished to a "knife burnished polish" that seals the wood.

Oregon Hinoki Products, Inc.

P.O. Box 358
Molalla, Oregon 97038
☎ 503/829-4524

Hours Mon-Fri 8-5
Accessible Yes
Mail Order
Catalog Free
FAX 503/829-4100

Oregon Timberframe fabricates handsome gazebos, spa enclosures and bridges, using all mortise and tenon joinery. These Western cedar or fir structures feature strong 6x6 uprights. They'll will ship the pieces or help homeowners assemble the structures anywhere on the West Coast. You can order catalog models, or they'll build your custom design.

Oregon Timberframe

2078 Dewey
Eugene, Oregon 97402
☎ 503/344-6809

Hours Mon-Fri 8-5
Accessible Yes
Mail Order
Catalog $5
FAX 503/334-6809

Keith Riehl's metal fences and gates add a touch of class to the landscape. See complete listing on page 310.

Riehl Industries

16076 S.E. Evelyn Street
Clackamas, Oregon 97015
☎ 503/655-7632

Jandon's cedar swings and arbors grace gardens throughout the Northwest. See complete listing on page 289.

Swings by Jandon

18595 N.W. North Star Drive
Banks, Oregon 97106
☎ 503/324-7154

Mail Order

Greenhouses & Garden Sheds

While the primary appeal of a greenhouse may be to indulge an interest in orchids or cacti, it also allows you to raise food crops in winter, hold over patio plants, and get a head-start on spring. Or it may simply be a quiet place where rain-or-shine greenery offers solace for the soul. Greenhouses have often been used as visual features in the garden, but tool shed/storage buildings have rarely served any purpose other than function. A well-designed storage structure can be an attractive element in the garden. It can also serve multiple purposes.

Greenhouses and storage buildings take up a considerable amount of space on a small lot, however. With a bit of imaginative design, a homeowner might join the two together and even extend the roof-line of the structure to create an arbor. The possibilities for creativity are unlimited. Whatever the size and shape, such buildings should be incorporated into the landscape as part of a Master Plan. Optimally, they will be designed in conjunction with the fencing and other decorative structures.

Greenhouses

Greenhouses range from a $200 window greenhouse to the $20,000 solarium that may serve as a breakfast room, a spa enclosure or even an entrance hall. There are so many options today! If it's to be attached to your house, you'll want a unit with glass glazing and nicely detailed framing. If it will be screened off from the living areas of the garden, one of the less expensive, more utilitarian fiberglass or plastic models may work well for you. A third option is a beautifully detailed free-standing greenhouse that functions as focal point in the garden.

Attached greenhouses are generally less expensive to heat than free-standing models because they share a wall with the house, and they are easier to hook up to utilities. By placing an attached greenhouse on the south side of the house and selecting energy-efficient high-performance materials, the structure may actually be used to collect solar energy for the house. Before you attach a working greenhouse, however, consider the moisture factor and the heat-load on your home furnace.

Many of the greenhouses available in the Northwest come in kits, which the manufacturers assure me are easy-to-assemble if you're handy with tools and able to read instructions. Sources for greenhouse lighting can be found at the end of this chapter. 🌺

☞ **Money-saving tip: Be sure to check local building codes before ordering any greenhouse.**

Catalog Sources for Greenhouses

The functional, efficient Addco Greenhouse is constructed of one-inch-square aluminum tubing and clad in commercial greenhouse fiberglass. The company offers factory-direct pricing and after-sale assistance, including monthly workshops, a videotape and newsletters. It's greenhouses are made at the factory and then delivered and set up for customers in Oregon, Washington and Idaho. The structures come with evaporative cooler, heater, electric board, convection tube, water system, shade cloth and vinyl-coated growing benches.

Addco Home Greenhouse

23215 N.E. Sunnycrest Road
Newberg, Oregon 97132
☎ *1-800/227-4136*

Hours *Mon-Sat 8-3*
Accessible *Yes*
Mail Order
Catalog *Free*
FAX *503/537-1010*

Therma-Gro™ greenhouses are made of rigid PVC framing with eight-m/m, double-walled acrylic covering and 4x4 treated-wood bases. In addition to the simple gable-roofed freestanding model that has been the company's mainstay, there's now a beautiful new curved Gothic style. All of the greenhouses come with two full-length, 24"-wide aluminum tables, two full-length vents with automatic solar-controlled openers, full length gutters and down pipes. The company also offers Therma-Gro™ cold frames. In the U.S.A., contact Charley's Greenhouse Supply (see listing on page 66).

Advanced Greenhouse Mfg. Ltd.

120-12820 Clarke Place
Richmond, British Columbia V6V-2H1
☎ *604/276-8060*

Hours *Mon-Sat 9-5*
Accessible *Yes*
Mail Order
Catalog *Free*
FAX *604/276-2944*

Incorporated in 1951 and known as a one-stop greenhouse shop, this company manufacturers single glass and double-walled acrylic hobby greenhouses and carries a full line of accessories. Their retail outlet shares space on the property with the manufacturing facility, offering fourteen basic models, plus custom designs that work as "patio extensions." The two most popular sizes are 6x8 and 8x12; curved glass or shed-roof models are available as free-standing or lean-to units. The framing is heavy duty aluminum alloy. They offer installation in the greater Vancouver area and ship throughout Canada. Charley's Greenhouse Supply in Mt. Vernon, WA is their U.S. agent.

B. C. Greenhouse Builders Ltd.

7425 Hedley Avenue
Burnaby, B.C. V5E 2R1
☎ *604/433-4220*

Hours *Mon-Sat 9-5 (closed Christmas through New Year)*
Accessible *Yes*
Mail Order
Catalog *Free*
FAX *604/433-1285*

Charley's Greenhouse Supply

1569 Memorial Highway
Mount Vernon, Washington 98273
☎ 206/428-2626

Hours Mon-Fri 8-5, Sat 9-2
Accessible Yes
Mail Order
Catalog $2
FAX 206/428-0310

Charley's is the only mail-order firm in the U.S.A. that specializes in serving the hobby greenhouse gardeners. The company offers a 48-page catalog of hard-to-find greenhouse accessories and supplies. The retail store displays structures that range in size from window units to full-size greenhouses. The owners, Carol and Charley Yaw, offer consultation on design and equipment. Their catalog is a treasure-trove of information. You'll find building materials, heating and ventilating systems, benches, lighting and much more. Many of the products will be of interest to outdoor gardeners and lovers of house plants as well as to greenhouse owners – books, hand tools, seed starting supplies, meters of all descriptions, pest controls, watering accessories and fertilizers.

Chateau Conservatories Ltd.

3955 Myrtle Street
Burnaby, British Columbia V5C 4G3
☎ 604/433-0979

Hours Mon-Fri 8-4:30,
Sat by appointment
Accessible Yes
Mail Order
Catalog Free
FAX 604/433-0974

Conservatories, solariums, barrel-vault walkway covers, skylights and greenhouses are fabricated in this company's Burnaby factory. Their room-size conservatories borrow design details from Elizabethan England. For gardeners with limited space, the company has introduced a tall, thin portable cold frame suitable for apartment balconies. They also make curved glass garden windows ideal for baths and kitchens.

Imperial Systems, Inc.

17615 Bentley Road
Summerland, British Columbia V0H 1Z0
☎ 604/494-3226

Hours Mon-Fri 9-5
Accessible No
Mail Order
Catalog Free
FAX 604/494-3131

No foundation is required for this fully assembled, ribbed fibreglass greenhouse, which is shaped like a Quonset hut. The base is an integral part of each of the eight-foot-high, eight-foot-wide modules, and the structures can be built to any length in five-foot increments. Multi-layered glass fibres conduct light like a prism, and the interior is polished to resist fungus, bacteria and dirt. Units come with solar-powered automatic roof vents.

"We manufacture custom-designed greenhouses constructed of Sunwood™ framing, cedar exterior siding and bar cap," say Nick Moore and Rae Lawrence. They offer a choice of glass or acrylic glazing, plus a number of accessories, including automatic watering systems and heaters. While their custom work is confined to the Portland metropolitan area, the company offers a new kit for decks or patios called "The Complete Garden." This height-adjustable cold frame and potting box is available by mail-order.

Moore/Lawrence
Greenhouse Mfg., Inc.

11919 S.E. Brookside Drive
Portland, Oregon 97266
☎ 503/761-6026

Hours Mon-Fri 9-6
or by appointment
Accessible Yes
Mail Order
Catalog Free
FAX 503/761-6026

For almost twenty years Seattle Sun has specialized in living space/greenhouses. They make both curved-eaved and straight-line models in a range of sizes from large pool enclosures down to window extensions. The company offers finely crafted wood structures, pre-fab kits, and a Conservatory line of custom-made structures, which are available with fanned rafters, leaded glass windows and gingerbread trim. Their Bentwood Solarium™ features well-proportioned arches made of laminated fir combined with a color-coated aluminum glazing system for durability and ease-of-maintenance.

Seattle Sun Systems

1701 First Avenue. South
Seattle, Washington 98134
☎ 206/343-2822

Hours Mon-Fri 8-5
Accessible Yes
Mail Order
Catalog Free
Mailing address P.O. Box 84484
Seattle, Washington 98124

Since 1968 Sturdi-built has manufactured redwood and glass greenhouses, which the company sells factory-direct to customers from Alaska to Florida. A family-owned business, they take pride in personal service. Their product line ranges from a lovely little eight-foot octagonal Flower Gazebo™ to a large Garden-Sunroom™. They offer a wide range of lean-to and free-standing models, including a handsome new English Tudor design. They also customize units to fit special situations. All of the company's greenhouses and accessories are shipped in large sections. Inquire about a winter discount. "When customers call, they usually speak to one of the owners," says Rick Warner.

Sturdi-built
Greenhouse Mfg. Co.

11304 S.W. Boones Ferry Road
Portland, Oregon 97219
☎ 503/244-4100, 1-800/334-4115
or 1-800/722-4115 (within Oregon)

Hours Mon-Fri 8-5;
weekends by appointment
Accessible Yes
Mail Order
Catalog Free

Sunglo Solar Greenhouses

4441 26th Avenue W.
Seattle, Washington 98199
☎ *206/284-8900 or 1-800/647-0606*

Hours *Mon-Fri 8-5 or by appointment*
Accessible *Yes*
Mail Order
Catalog *Free*
FAX *206/284-8945*

Sunglo explains that it chose D.R. Acrylic (clear or bronze-tinted) for its greenhouses because this plexiglass product carries a special ultraviolet-inhibitor that resists yellowing and breakdown caused by the sun's harmful rays. The double-walled "thermal truss" construction is designed to prevent hot spots and plant scorching. Available in both free-standing and lean-to forms, the company's aluminum-framed greenhouses can be shipped as kits or may be factory installed. They also offer roof sections to be used as patio covers. For $10 you can get a video and product samples; the cost is refundable upon purchase. Inquire about their seasonal coupons and look for specials during the regional home and garden shows.

Garden Sheds/Storage Buildings

Rather than let lawn mowers, wheelbarrows and other tools of the trade clutter your garage or sit in a side yard to rust, consider an attractively designed storage shed. You may want to provide space for built-in benches and work tables as well as tools. Ideally the shed will have a water source and ample space to organize items by the season in which they will be used. A free-standing structure, such as the ones offered by the sources listed below, can be positioned to screen-off unsightly compost piles, cold frames and such garden debris as old pots and trash containers. 🌺

Sources for Storage Buildings

Cedar Chest Storage

3200 Dayton Bypass
Dayton, Oregon 97114
☎ *503/864-2354*

Hours *Mon-Fri 9-4:30, Sat 9-3*
Accessible *Yes*
Mail Order
Catalog *Free*
Mailing address *P.O. Box 40*
Dayton, Oregon 97114

Available in sizes from 6'x8' to 10'x20', these double-wall, gambrel-roof storage sheds are made and shipped in kit form. "You don't have to be a master carpenter to assemble one of our user-friendly kits," says the owner. "Trusses and wall panels are pre-manufactured. There's no sawing involved, so a couple of reasonably handy people can put the product together in a day." Skylights, windows and "doggie doors" are among the standard options available, and the company will build to your custom order.

Folks within a hundred miles of either Seattle or Portland can call the nearest Yard Barn™ dealer for information about sturdy, attractive wood storage structures built nail-by-nail on your lot. The sizes range from 6'x6' to 16'x24'. Designed in the form of a mini-barn, these attractive double-doored wood structures are available with ramps, windows, vents, loft sections and shelving. The company will furnish a drawing if required for a building permit.

Heartland Industries

2150 N.E. Columbia Boulevard
Portland, Oregon 97211
☎ *503/282-0541*

117 Frontage Road N.W., Bldg. B.
Pacific, Washington 98047
☎ *206/931-8082*

Hours *Mon-Fri 7-5*
Accessible *No*
Catalog *Free*
FAX *503/282-0613 (Portland)*

Sports & Play Equipment

My happiest childhood memories are of building playhouses out of cardboard boxes, dragging the garden hose to a sandbox to make castles, skating on sidewalks, playing hide and seek in the garden shrubbery... So, when my own three children were small, I turned our entire backyard into a play space. I surrounded the lawn with a curving concrete pathway for tricycles, built a huge sandbox and bought the sturdiest swing set on the market. Under the branches of an old tree, we built a playhouse with a "lookout" platform on top. When the children grew into their teens, the playhouse became my garden storage shed, the tricycle path served as an edging for flower beds, and the sandbox and swings gave way to a pool.

I wouldn't trade for having provided a special place for child's play. Children who are lucky enough to grow up in the country have access to creeks, trees, hills, rocks and animals. We urban-dwellers must create settings where kids can build strong bodies and develop imagination. They need space for running and playing games, and they should have the freedom to make a mess!

In the past twenty-five years, there has been a revolution in manufactured play equipment. It began in the Northwest with wonderful wood structures developed for city parks. As a landscape architect, I have designed numerous public and private playgrounds. I had a role in the development of safer equipment, having partici-pated in hearings at the Consumer Product Safety Commission, which set Federal Safety Guidelines. I've seen new wood and metal climbing structures replace the dangerous see-saws, monkey bars and merry-go-rounds I knew as a child. Even the swings are different. Gone are the wooden seats that knocked out teeth, and merci-fully, gone is the asphalt beneath the swings that caused more than a few broken bones.

The backyard play equipment available today is also far improved over what was on the market a few years ago. You'll find in the listings below a number of sources for well-designed structures that incorporate climbing, sliding and swinging activi-ties. Some of the companies also offer playhouses for pretend-play and equipment for games.

Backyard play areas have an advantage over parks and schoolyards, which must be kept tidy. At home you can include activities that stimulate creativity – sand-boxes, outdoor art easels, workbenches with scrap lumber and small garden plots.

Home playgrounds should be every bit as safe as the ones mandated on public property. To prevent eye injury and abrasions, the equipment you buy or build should be constructed with recessed bolts. Be sure the structures are sturdy. Install the equipment over a soft cushion of sand or bark chips. The surfacing under and around any piece of climbing equipment should be at least ten-inches deep and should extend six-feet beyond the equipment to prevent injury from falls.

Regular maintenance is critical. Check the depth and cleanliness of the surfacing material and replenish it as needed. Keep sandboxes covered when not in use. Check the bolts every couple of months to make sure they remain tight. Keep a close watch for splinters, frayed rope and open S-hooks. 🐾

Northwest Manufacturers

BigToys

7717 New Market Street
Olympia, Washington 98501
☎ *1-800/426-9788;*
in Canada call 604/888-3222

Hours *Mon-Fri 7:30-4*
Accessible *Yes*
Mail Order
Catalog *Free*

Backyard BigToys feature many of the same components found on the company's commercial-grade structures. The uprights are constructed of pressure-treated lodgepole pine logs. The play decks can be personalized with a number of different accessories, including plastic or metal slides, rope-climbs, polynet climbers and slidepoles. "Activity panels" serve as enclosure walls. These include bubble windows, wheels, chalkboards and kitchenettes. The structures may be fitted with baby swings, belt swings, hand rings and/or trapeze bars.

Columbia Cascade Company

1975 S.W. Fifth Avenue
Portland, Oregon 97201
☎ *503/223-1157*

Hours *Mon-Fri 8-5*
Accessible *No*
FAX *503/223-4530*

The playground revolution began here with TimberForm & PipeLine play structures. Columbia Cascade supplies top-quality wood and metal equipment to park departments all over the world. Movie stars and Arab sheiks have bought it for their children's backyard play, but it is most often used for school and community playgrounds. Basic structures start at $2,500. This company's equipment meets all national and international safety standards. If you must have the very best, look no further. Sales representatives are located throughout the U.S. and Canada. Call Columbia Cascade's headquarters for the name of the one nearest you.

The original Sport Court Company began in Seattle in 1976. Now dealers worldwide construct mini-courts for fifteen sports and games, including badminton, pickle-ball, paddle tennis, shuffleboard, hop-scotch and basketball. They also offer rebounders for soccer, tennis and softball. Designed for healthy family fun, the courts are individually customized to fit your lot and surfaced with a modular resilient material that drains well. The most popular size is 28'x66'.

Sport Court

12811 N.E. 126th Place
Kirkland, Washington 98034
☎ 206/ 822-3801

2704 S.E. Brookland Street
Portland, Oregon 97202
☎ 503/235-2192

2012 Eyre Road
Campbell River,
British Columbia V9W 354
☎ 604/337-5795

Hours *Mon-Fri 8-4:30*
Accessible *Yes*
FAX *206/822-3913*

This company's "Backwoods" catalog offers homeowners several options. You can buy playground parts to create a structure of your own design or buy a kit for one of several standard redwood units. Wildwood's *U-Build-It Kits* come with plans, hardware and parts (swings, slides, rope ladders, trapeze bars, etc.), and you supply the wood, tires and roof material from local sources.

Wildwood Playgrounds

811 E. Burnside #116
Portland, Oregon 97214-1231
☎ 503/232-3211 or 1-800/875-PLAY

Hours *Mon-Fri 8-5*
Accessible *Yes*
Mail Order
Catalog *Free*
FAX *503/232-1753*

Retail Sources for Sports & Play Equipment

Washington

Here you'll find an outside display area for wood equipment from Natural Structures of Sherwood, Oregon and metal units from American Playworld out of Utah.

ABC Campbell's Children USA

13724 S.E. Newport Way
Bellevue, Washington 98006
☎ 448-0782 or 1-800/726-0031

Hours *Mon-Fri 8-5, Sat by appointment*
Accessible *Yes*
Mail Order
Catalog *Free*

Backyard Adventures

10228 Main Street
Bothell, Washington 98011
☎ *206/488-1234*

Hours *Mon-Fri 10-6, Sat 10-5, Sun 12-5*
(Feb through Sept); Mon-Sat 10-5 (winter)
Accessible *Yes*
Mail Order
Catalog *Free*

Backyard Adventures carries pre-cut and drilled wood play structures from four nationally known manufacturers and a complete line of playhouses. The company maintains indoor and outdoor displays, where they welcome children to "sample" the wares. They ship to customers throughout the Northwest U.S. and British Columbia. They're also a good source for above-ground swimming pools, peddle boats and trampolines.

Northwest Viking Playworld

32003 Reata Road
Kennewick, Washington 99337
☎ *509/627-3785*

Hours *Daily 7-10*
Accessible *Yes*
Mail Order
Catalog *Free*

This company's swing sets, monkey bars, gym sets and slides are made of commercial-quality galvanized steel. Priced reasonably for backyard use, these items can be delivered anywhere in the Northwest. They maintain a display at the Reata Road address, where they also sell trampolines.

The Playground Store

22415 S.E. 231st Street
Maple Valley, Washington 98038
☎ *206/432-8000*

Hours *Mon-Fri 9-5, Sat & Sun 11-4*
(March through Labor Day);
Mon-Fri 9-5, Sat 11-4 (winter)
Accessible *Yes*
Mail Order
Catalog *Free*
Mailing address *P.O. Box 26*
Maple Valley, Washington 98038
FAX *206/432-2600*

The Playground Store is an outdoor showroom for Playsystems, a local manufacturer of "new generation" backyard equipment. Their colorful Timber TreeHouses, Timber Castles and Timber Fortresses hold plenty of play options. The company offers specials during regional Home Shows and several weekends throughout the year. Canadian customers can telephone for the name of a dealer in Vancouver B.C.

Oregon

Creative Play Structures, Inc.
7400 S.W. Macadam, suite J
Portland, Oregon 97219
☎ *503/246-0056*

Hours Mon-Sat 10-5, Sun 12-4
Accessible Yes
Mail Order
Catalog Free

A dealer for Krauss Craft, which is made in Southern Oregon, this company offers a number of special services, including free site evaluation and custom designs that allow you build around an existing tree or accomodate a difficult site. They'll install both equipment and safety surfacing or provide a kit if you want to build a structure yourself. Children are encouraged to play on and explore the several models on display at the store. Creative Play Structures also sells finished playhouses and playhouse plans.

Ludeman's, Inc.
12675 S.W. Beaverdam Road
Beaverton, Oregon 97005
☎ *503/646-6409*

Ludeman's sells equipment manufactured by Creative Playgrounds. Designed to appeal to a child's imagination, the structures are made of pressure-treated Southern Yellow Pine. Their catalog offers about 15 different configurations, and you can inspect displays at the store. Play equipment is included in the Annual Anniversary Sale in early August. See full listing on page 296.

British Columbia

Backyard Adventures, Ltd.
123 W. 3rd Street
North Vancouver,
British Columbia V7M 1E7
☎ *604/987-7776 or 534-7779*

Hours Mon-Sat 10-6
Accessible Yes
Mail Order
Catalog Free
FAX 604/984-4143

Not to be confused with the company in Washington, Backyard Adventures in British Columbia is the manufacturer's representative for several companies that make play and sports equipment. They maintain an indoor showroom to display basketball equipment, wood swinging and climbing structures and a line of galvanized steel swing sets. They offer *Swing-N-Slide* kits and accessories for building your own play structures, plus an unusual above-ground *Funny Pool*.

Lighting

Many homeowners think of outdoor lighting as something reserved for the wealthy, but in fact you can make an impact for as little as $200. With a budget of $1,000 you can achieve a sophisticated lighting system in an average-size garden. If you consider that it adds refinement and value to the house, enhances safety, and extends your hours of enjoyment in the garden, outdoor lighting is a bargain. A few well-placed fixtures allow you to reveal the garden's best features while hiding others. Lighting can make a large garden seem intimate or create an illusion of depth in a small space.

☞ **Money-saving tip: Light only the areas you use at night.**

Painting the landscape with light can create magical effects. Use soft uplighting to play a sculptural plant in silhouette against a wall or to define the trunk and branching pattern of a graceful tree. Employ downlighting to create a dance of shadows on lawn and terraces beneath the tree canopy. Tuck a string of low-voltage lights into ground covers to illuminate pathways and define the edges of planting beds. Mark the entrance to a driveway or frame a garden gate with handsome post lights.

Good lighting design involves controlling not only the direction but also the color and intensity of the light. It's best done by a professional who is trained to place the right fixtures and the right lamps in the right spot. Twice as many of the wrong fixtures may give half the impact, so assistance from a lighting designer can save you money in the long run. Many of the retail lighting stores listed in this section offer moderately-priced design services.

As a "picture book" source of ideas for how different lighting effects appear at night, the *Ortho* paperback, *How to Design and Install Outdoor Lighting* is top-notch. Even if you're bringing in a professional lighting designer or planning to work with a lighting dealer, its color photographs will enable you to visualize and communicate what you want. If you're installing a system yourself, the book contains a wealth of information on planning, installation techniques and maintenance.

For the longest-lasting lighting system, Bruce Cline, manager of Lighting Supply in Seattle, recommends a commercial-grade line-voltage system that runs on household current. He notes, however, that such a system should be laid in metal conduit which is more expensive to buy and install than plastic. (With plastic conduit there is a dangerous potential for cutting through the conduit with a shovel or spading fork.)

Low-voltage systems eliminate the need for conduit altogether. These systems offer a wider choice of small, unobtrusive fixtures and are more easily moved as the garden grows and changes. The main disadvantage to low-voltage systems is that they cannot be strung more than 50' without losing candlepower at the end of the line. And surprisingly, low-voltage systems are not necessarily less expensive to operate than a well-designed line-voltage system (It's the watts that count.)

Twelve-volt systems available at local hardware stores are safe, easy to install and quite inexpensive. I recently found a kit of four plastic low-voltage pathway lights for $34.99. The same store had attractive shell-shaped cast-metal lights for under $25 apiece and all of the wiring and transformers necessary to devise your own twelve-volt system. Inexpensive kit-form fixtures are better than no lighting at all, but I always suggest to my clients that they buy the highest quality fixtures they can afford and add lighting in phases if necessary.

Be sure any lighting equipment you buy bears a label that indicates approval by Underwriters Laboratory (UL) or the Canadian Standards Association. In terms of durability, I would choose die-cast or heavy-gauge metal over any plastic material. Look for neoprene gaskets. If vandalism might be a problem, buy a fixture with Lexan™ lenses rather than glass. If the fixture is brass, it should be triple-lacquered.

By day you want fixtures that complement the architectural style of the house. At night, the most important visual aspect is the color effect created by the lamp inside the fixture. For natural-looking color in the landscape, florescent or halogen lamps (such as MR 16 or PAR 36) are more effective than high-pressure sodium lamps, which have the poorest color-rendering characteristics.

There are a number of "bells and whistles" you can add to a lighting system, including photocells that turn the light on at dusk. You can also get motion detectors that sense intruders or turn lights on as you come in late at night. Many systems come with timers that turn off certain lights at a specified time. For example, you may want the security lighting left on, but choose not to burn decorative lighting all night. Remote controls that allow you to turn on security lights from inside.

If you seek professional help, ask to see several of the firm's completed projects and talk to homeowners who have used their services. Don't be afraid to request a demonstration in your own garden. ✻

☞ **Money-saving tip: Try various fixture arrangements before you decide on permanent placement. Get it right the first time!**

Northwest Manufacturers

Architectural Forms makes graceful cedar postlights, bollards and wall-mounted fixtures designed to complement contemporary or traditional residences. The company's owner, Stan Oliver, says that approximately a third of his business is custom-made lighting fixtures, so if you or your lighting designer have an idea for something unusual in your landscape, he can probably fabricate it for you.

Architectural Forms

P.O. Box 70
Kirkland, Washington 98083
☎ *206/827-5599, 1-800/255-5145*

Hours Mon-Fri 7-6
Mail Order
Catalog Free
FAX 206/880-4444

Since 1975 Idaho Wood has produced outdoor light fixtures rendered in rustic-looking cedar and red oak. Their catalog shows round, octagonal and square forms in post and wall lights. They also offer low-voltage lighting strips to be tucked under deck rails and stair treads and a 14"-high "Lite-Stik," which can be used in series to mark pathways.

Idaho Wood

P.O. Box 488
Sandpoint, Idaho 83864
☎ *1-800/635-1100*

Hours Mon-Fri 7-4:30
Mail Order
Catalog Free
FAX 208/263-3102

LiteForm Designs

9705 N.E. Colfax Street
Portland, Oregon 97208-3316
☎ *503/257-8464 or 1-800/458-2505*

Hours *Mon-Fri 8-5*
Accessible *Yes*
Mail Order
Catalog *Free*
FAX *503/253-9626*

Known for "enlightened" design and fine workmanship, this company crafts a full range of outdoor lighting products in California redwood or Western red cedar, and cast stone. LiteForms are scaled and priced for residential use. Professional designers respect the quality of materials and hand-finished appearance of the fixtures, which include wall sconces, pendants, path lights and post lights. Many models can be ordered with low-voltage lighting capacity for the do-it-yourself buyer. "We are always pleased to consult with customers concerning the correct placement of their fixtures. If in doubt, ask us," says owner Don King.

Retail Sources for Outdoor Lighting

Washington

Builders Lighting

7811 N.E. St.John's Road
Vancouver, Washington 98665
☎ *206/574-2636*

Builders Lighting is affiliated with Seattle Lighting. See facing page.

Lighting Supply

2729 Second Avenue
Seattle, Washington 98121
☎ *206/441-5075*

Hours *Mon-Fri 8-5*
Accessible *Yes*

Lighting Supply stocks fixtures from a number of nationally known manufacturers, including Kim, Adjusta-Post, Focus and Hadco. They feature beautifully designed fixtures from Arroyo Craftsman in the style of early-twentieth-century bungalows. The showroom bookshelf contains hundreds of catalogs from other manufacturers. With three lighting designers on staff, they offer considerable expertise in choosing the best combination of fixtures for your individual needs. Free catalog sheets from manufacturers are available on request.

Cast aluminum reproduction turn-of-the-century street lights are the specialty here, and they'll ship anywhere in the region. State and federally certified for restoration projects, these charming lights complement old houses. Use them to mark the entrance to a driveway or cast a warm glow on terraces and gazebos. The company also sells reproduction Victorian furniture and garden ornaments. The place is hard to find; call for directions.

Old Main Street

6306 16th Street E.
Tacoma, Washington 98424
☎ *206/922-3822*

Hours Mon-Fri 10-6, Sat 10-5, Sun 12-4
Accessible Outdoor display only
Mail Order
Catalog Free
FAX 206/926-1774

Seattle Lighting stocks the products of several nationally known outdoor lighting manufacturers including Kichler, Hadco and Progress. In addition, they order fixtures from many others. Free catalog sheets from manufacturers are available on request. The company offers free layout and design services at the showrooms. They'll let you check out "lighting loaner kits" to try various lighting arrangements in your own garden. A landscape lighting specialist out of the Aurora store will come to your home for on-site design in the Puget Sound area. If you're interested in doing-it-yourself, you can attend one of their free landscape lighting seminars. Note: some locations keep later hours and are open on Sundays. Call to confirm hours. In Bellingham, the store is called **Village Lighting**.

Seattle Lighting Fixture Company

222 Second Avenue
Seattle, Washington 98104
☎ *206/622-4736*

14032 Aurora Avenue N.
Seattle, Washington 98133
☎ *206/362-4444*

12828 N.E. Bel-Red Road
Bellevue, Washington 98005
☎ *206/455-2110*

1616 N. State Street
Bellingham, Washington 98227
☎ *206/734-3780*

5611 196th S.W.
Lynnwood, Washington 98036
☎ *206/778-1124*

349 Tukwila Parkway
Tukwila, Washington 98188
☎ *206/431-8602*

6710 Tacoma Mall Boulevard
Tacoma, Washington 98409
☎ *206/475-8730*

1811 Hewitt Avenue
Everett, Washington 98201
☎ *206/252-4151*

Silverdale Plaza
Silverdale, Washington 98383
☎ *206/692-1551*

Hours Generally, Mon-Fri 9-6, Sat 10-5
Accessible Yes
FAX 206/477-1660

Oregon

Builders Lighting, Inc.

17571 S.W. 65th
Tualatin, Oregon 97062
☎ 503/639-8816

2425 25th S.E.
Salem, Oregon 97302
☎ 503/364-2715

Hours Mon-Fri 9-6, Sat 10-5, Sun 12-5
(Salem store closed on Sunday)
Accessible Yes

Builder's Lighting, now owned by Seattle Lighting Fixture Company, stocks Kichler path lights, well lights, tree lights and deck lighting. They carry a particularly nice selection of wall lanterns and post lights. A company sales representative will lay out lighting on-site for customers. There's a $50 fee for the service, which is refundable when the homeowner purchases fixtures. Inquire about outdoor lighting seminars.

British Columbia

Robinson Lighting

2285 Cambie Street
Vancouver, British Columbia V5Z 2T5
☎ 604/879-2494

Hours Mon-Fri 8-6, Sat 9-5
Accessible Yes, via back door

Robinson's offers low voltage as well as line voltage lighting systems. Among the products they carry are such familiar names as Lightolier and Kichler. (Kichler makes especially attractive flower and shell-shaped path lights.) The company offers a booklet on outdoor lighting and sends catalog sheets to out-of-town customers. They'll recommend contractors to install your lighting or help you with do-it-yourself projects.

Catalog Sources for Greenhouse & Indoor Plant Lighting

Charley's Greenhouse Supply

1569 Memorial Highway
Mount Vernon, Washington 98273
☎ 206/428-2626

Mail Order

Charley's catalog includes two pages of indoor lighting, plus timers and light meters. See full listing on page 66.

Discount Garden Supply

E. 14109 Sprague
Spokane, Washington 99216
☎ 1-800/444-4378

Hours Mon-Sat 9-6
Accessible Yes
Mail Order
Catalog Free

Here's a mail-order source for getting a head start on spring or keeping patio plants happy throughout the winter. The company's specialty indoor lighting is ideal for greenhouses or houses filled with greenery! Its catalog also offers drip irrigation supplies, soil additives, organic fertilizers, insecticides and propagation aids for the greenhouse.

Chapter Three
Garden Conservation

"Nothing endures but change."
.....Heraclitus c.540 - c.480 B.C.

A Plea for Maintenance

More than any other art form, a garden is subject to change – through varying patterns of light each day, from season-to-season and from year-to-year. Unlike the architect's building, the artist's painting or the playwright's words, a garden designer's best efforts exist in a state of evolution. Designers rarely even live to see their work at full maturity; the sapling I plant today will not become the oak tree I envision for another fifty years. From the moment it is installed, the garden I've created will either be improving or deteriorating. This is where proper preparation and maintenance come into the picture.

Before listing sources, I've attempted to share everything I know about building up the soil, managing pests, watering and pruning. *Please* read these sections! The final section in this chapter, "Tools, Apparel and Landscape Supplies," is included to make lighter work of the previously named garden tasks. ✄

Soil and Soil Amendments

☞ **Money-saving tip: Before even thinking about establishing a new landscape or a garden renovation, improve the soil. It's a total waste to put good plants in poor soil!**

Soils in the Pacific Northwest range from remarkably rich river valley loams to thin, rocky clays. They are poorest in areas where glaciers stripped away the topsoil like giant bulldozers. Most could stand improvement. While it's possible to keep plants alive in wretched soil by pouring on fertilizer, a better solution is to build-up the natural health of the soil.

Good soil is a combination of weathered rock, decaying organic matter (humus), air, water (which holds dissolved minerals in solution) and living organisms (microbes). "Treat your piece of earth with respect as you would any living thing, for that is what it is," says my organic gardening friend, Stephen Weedman. "Within a handful of healthy soil are millions of living, breathing, growing organisms, most of them beneficial to plants." (You'll find some of Stephen's helpful hints in Chapter 7, The Edible Landscape.)

Soil Fertility

The factor most important to plant health is soil fertility. Inexpensive color-chart kits available at local garden centers allow you to measure fertility with some degree of accuracy, but professional soil testing is the best way to determine your soil's chemical make-up. (Ask your county extension agent or a trusted nursery owner to recommend a laboratory.) Soil tests normally analyze the three primary nutrients that plants need: nitrogen, phosphorus and potassium. You can also request lab tests that measure secondary nutrients: calcium, sulfur and magnesium and such trace elements as iron, boron, manganese and zinc. Other tests measure acidity (pH) and/or determine if there are toxic substances in your soil.

The pH scale runs from 0 (acid) to 14 (alkaline), with 7 the neutral point. Most plants thrive in a slightly acidic environment (6 to 7). Rhododendrons and other members of the heath family require acidic soil (4.5 to 5.5). If your soil tests extremely acid (below 4), you can neutralize it with finely ground limestone. Overly-alkaline soil, which is common in dry climates, is more difficult to correct. It responds to the generous addition of sphagnum peat moss, oak leaf mold and cottonseed meal. Alkaline soils (including those that have been over-limed) tend to become iron deficient. Yellowed leaves with dark green veins are tell-tale symptoms of iron depletion.

Soil Texture

The ideal soil is a friable sandy loam (about 40% sand, 40% silt, 10% clay and 10% organic matter). Soil that's too sandy doesn't retain water; soil that contains too much clay won't drain properly. Squeeze a handful of damp soil. If it will hold together, but not clump into a tight ball, you probably have pretty good soil texture. You can get a better handle on the texture of your soil by performing a couple of easy tests.

The "Mason jar" test for soil texture:

To learn the proportions of sand, silt, clay and organic matter in your soil, take random samples from the areas where you're going to plant. Put a cup of soil and four cups of water in a large jar with a lid. Shake well and allow to settle overnight. The bottom layer will be sand, then silt, then clay. The organic matter will rise to the top. Compare to the ideal proportions listed above.

The "coffee can" test for drainage:

Cut both ends from a one-pound coffee can and force the can into your garden soil to a depth of four inches. (If that's impossible, you *know* you have a problem!) Fill the rest of the can with water and let it drain through. Then fill it again and measure how long it takes the water level to drop an inch. If it drops immediately, the soil is too porous; if it takes more than four hours, plants are likely to drown.

Surprisingly, the addition of organic matter (cottonseed meal, blood meal, manure, composted garden debris, etc.) is the remedy both for soils that are too porous and for those that are too heavy with clay. Clay soils are also improved by the addition of sharp sand and pulverized gypsum. Enriching the soil is a labor of love. The project consists of loosening the soil to improve aeration and amending it to improve structure and fertility.

There's no substitute for good old-fashioned cultivation to aerate compacted earth. It's relatively easy to work an empty bed, where you can use a mechanical tiller to loosen the soil and then fork-in lots of organic matter. If possible, work the soil to a depth of 18 inches. Never cultivate wet soil – you'll eliminate the air spaces and compact it even more. If necessary, wait until late spring. Work from one end of a bed to the other so that you won't step on the soil you've just loosened.

Building up the soil in a bed with existing plants is a bit more difficult. Here, you'll need to work carefully around the roots, cultivating organic matter into the soil between the plants, by hand if necessary. In spots where you're adding new plants, add organic matter within as large an area as possible.

Fertilizers and Mulches

Fertilizers, both the synthesized and the commercially produced organic varieties, are labeled according to their content of nitrogen (N), phosphorus (P) and potassium (K). For example, a 10-10-10 contains 10% of each; the other 70% is filler. Plants can't tell the difference between organic and synthesized nutrients. So why are we hearing so much about organics these days? Let me explain.

Most synthetic fertilizers are designed to be rapidly absorbed into the roots of the plant, and many of these fast-acting products contain more nitrogen than the plants can actually use. What's not absorbed is flushed out by rain and wasted. Organic fertilizers, which are derived from by-products of once living organisms and rock powders, are released gradually into the soil, where the plants can extract them as needed.

I can attest to the effectiveness of a chemical fertilizer as a "quick-fix" for tired plants. But, we're setting up a vicious cycle when we rely on it to keep plants healthy. The real problem with chemical fertilizer is that microbes can't use it, so they take their nutrients from the organic matter (humus) in the soil. As this humus is depleted, microbes, which "stir" the soil and help make nutrients available, begin to disappear.

Another problem is that without humus, water-soluble nitrogen leaches even more rapidly into the water table. Additionally, salt residues from some synthetic chemicals tend to build up in the soil. The poorer the soil becomes, the more fertilizer it takes to keep the plants healthy.

Organic fertilizers, on the other hand, feed the soil as well as the plants. Organic materials help hold soil granules together, permitting the renewal of moisture, microbes and nutrients. The bad news about organic fertilizers is that they are more expensive than synthetics, and they are generally lower in nutrients per pound, so they must be applied liberally to be effective.

What has discouraged a lot of gardeners from "going organic" is that shoveling manure is harder work than broadcasting a granulated product. For some of us older folks, especially those with a lot of garden to keep, bagged fertilizers are the only feasible alternative. Happily, there are several sources for organic fertilizers in easy-to-apply liquid and granular forms.

☞ Money-saving tip: Reduce the amount of fertilizer you use.

I've found a manageable way to wean the garden away from excessive dependency on "store-bought" fertilizers. I apply a two-inch layer of organic mulch twice each year – in late-fall to protect plant roots from winter cold and in late-spring to preserve soil moisture during periods of heat and drought. By forking the old mulches into the soil and adding new mulch and a little fertilizer year after year, I've reclaimed some pretty poor patches of earth.

The first year into an organic approach, its best to fertilize very generously. In subsequent years, you can begin reducing the amounts. After the second year I apply a slow-release blended fertilizer under the mulch at about half the recommended rate. As the mulch breaks down, it is also adding some nutrients. (Remember, too, that the mulch has served to inhibit nutrient-robbing weeds and retain soil moisture.)

It has been my experience that plants tend to grow at a reasonable rate with this regimen. In the long run, plants are hardier and more pest-resistant if they are not fed excessively and encouraged to put on great spurts of growth. Continue to monitor the soil pH and fertility, however, and add nutrients as needed.

☞ Money-saving tip: Make your own mulch.

A one-and-a-half cubic foot bag of mulch costs about $4.50 at the garden center. Assuming you apply a three-inch layer, one bag will cover about thirteen square feet. This gets pretty pricey, so it makes a lot more sense to make your own mulch out of recycled yard waste. By composting the leaves and grass clippings that collect, you also reduce the cost of trash removal. Libraries and bookstores are replete with books that tell you how to compost. City governments are publishing free pamphlets on the subject and setting up demonstration sites, in an effort to reduce the need for landfills.

Well-composted yard waste mixed half-and-half with bagged composted manure makes an excellent mulch, and it stretches both materials twice as far. The addition of manure makes the compost more nitrogen-rich. Used alone, manure is too fine to serve as a mulch; it compacts and forms a pancake layer that won't let water in. If you have access to pine needles, they make excellent additions to a mulch mix for such acid-loving plants as rhododendrons, azaleas and blueberries.

I'm not especially fond of uncomposted bark mulch. Not only does it look unnatural in a refined garden, but also raw bark, wood shavings and sawdust rob the soil of nitrogen as they decompose. If you use bark mulch, apply a nitrogen-rich fertilizer before you spread the product. Do not use uncomposted wood products as soil amendments.

A three-inch layer of mulch is sufficient; if it's too thick, the mulch may prevent water from penetrating and inhibit gas exchanges. Be aware that uncomposted manure or straw may contain weed seeds, and that any mulch may attract slugs and rodents. Keep mulch away from the plant's trunks and low branches.

☞ **Money-saving tip: Stock-up on bagged soil, mulch and fertilizers when they are marked down.**

You'll find excellent organic soil amendments from the Northwest manufacturers listed below at regional garden centers and home improvement stores. Several of the manufacturers listed sell by mail order through their catalogs.

☞ **Money-saving tip: Be sure to ask questions about the source of any bulk soil you bring in – landscapes have been ruined by a load of bad soil filled with weed seeds.**

When you need large quantities of soil, sand or mulch, ask your local garden center owner for a recommendation or call one of the sources listed under Retail Sources, beginning on page 86. ✿

Northwest Manufacturers

"Coventry Gardens is committed to providing home gardeners with an all-natural choice for garden nutrients – minerals mined from the earth, organics collected from the sea, animal wastes, and the rich cast-offs from other indus-tries. Using these by-products from other processes, gardeners can not only feed their plants, but also can build up the soil. It works....naturally," says Elleen Hart, product manager. You'll find the company's soil amendments in ware-house clubs and home improvement chains.

Coventry Gardens
7737 N.E. Killingsworth
Portland, Oregon 97218
☎ *503/256-4600*

Hours Mon-Fri 8-5
FAX 503/255-7552

Down To Earth

532 Olive
Eugene, Oregon 97401
☎ *503/485-5932*

Hours *Mon-Fri 9-5*

Down To Earth produces several blended organic fertilizers and offers bulk ingredients for making your own fertilizer. Their all-purpose 4-6-2 (a blend of blood meal, bone meal, cottonseed meal, fish meal, kelp and other ingredients) is the most popular. The company makes an acid blend for rhododendrons, a lawn mix, and another blend for bulbs. They offer the products at their delightful store in Eugene (see page 376) and at other retail stores throughout the Northwest. If you don't see Down To Earth in your neighborhood garden center, you can call to get the name of a dealer in your area.

Ed Hume Seeds

P.O. Box 1450
Kent, Washington 98035

Mail Order
Catalog *$1 (U.S.), $2 (Canada)*

Ed Hume's bagged organic fertilizers are available in regional garden centers. You can order liquid kelp concentrate through his seed catalog. For vegetable gardens or areas where you plant annuals, the catalog offers a cover crop that's a mix of Austrian winter field peas, hairy vetch, winter cereal and crimson clover. A two-pound bag will cover 600-square-feet, acting to suppress weeds, fixing nitrogen in the soil, and contributing organic matter when it is tilled back into the soil in spring.

Growers and Associates

8608 S. 134th
Seattle, Washington 98178
☎ *206/271-1388*

Hours *By appointment only*
Accessible *Yes*

Look for Growers and Associates products in garden centers and hardware stores. If you are buying in quantity you may go directly to the manufacturer for any of its three potting mixes, pure earthworm castings or bottles of refined castings (excellent for fertilizing house plants). All of the soil mixes are pH neutral and all are available in bags or bulk. A price list is available upon request.

IFM offers soil audits and plant tissue analysis. Phillip Unterschuetz, the company's tree and soil expert, says, "In our view, soil tests are essential for the serious grower." This retail, wholesale and mail-order business serves the entire United States and Canada. Their reports include recommendations for organic amendments in per-acre or per-1000-sq.-ft. increments. The catalog contains a wide variety of soil amendments and foliar sprays. "Our whole business is structured to promote the use of organic materials. We take pride in excellent service and products, and we mark down products when we ourselves purchase for less," he explains.

Integrated Fertility Management
333 Ohme Gardens Road
Wenatchee, Washington 98801
☎ *1-800/332-3179*

Hours Mon-Fri 8-5;
open Sat 8-12 (April through July)
Accessible *No*
Mail Order
Catalog *Free*
FAX *509/662-3179*

In 1984 the Garden Grow Company began producing Whitney Farms™ fertilizers and soil amendments to serve the organic gardener. Their products (lawn mixes, all-purpose and specialized blends for shrubs, trees and flowers, a compost starter, mulches and potting soils) are sold throughout the region at select garden centers. Their product guide is packed with information to help gardeners "carefully manage their finite resources and reintroduce the inherent balances of nature." The owner, John Graham, invites customers to call or write for the catalog and name of the nearest dealer.

Whitney Farms
P.O. Box 278
Independence, Oregon 97351
☎ *1-800/531-4411*

Hours Mon-Fri 8-5
Catalog *Free*

Retail Sources for Bulk Soil & Soil Amendments
Washington

Cedar Grove Compost Co.

17825 Cedar Grove Road S.E.
Maple Valley, Washington 98038
☎ *206/764-1236*

Hours Mon-Fri 8-4 (April through Oct),
Mon-Sat 8-5 (November-March)
Accessible Yes, at scale window
FAX 206/764-1234

A cooperative venture between the City of Seattle and private enterprise, Cedar Grove takes yard waste and turns it into rich black compost. Puget Sound homeowners who do not have curbside pickup can deliver grass clippings, sod, leaves and/or brush to the company and take home recycled soil. (There's a fee for dumping, but it is less than at public "transfer stations.") They offer a free users' guide. The company will deliver a minimum load of ten cubic yards. The product is also available in bags or bulk at many area garden centers and hardware stores.

Pacific Topsoil, Inc.

14002 35th Avenue S.E.
Bothell, Washington 98012
☎ *206/337-2700*

Hours Mon-Fri 7 a.m.-10 p.m., Sat 8-7,
Sun 10-3; close at 8 on weekdays in
winter
Accessible Yes
Catalog Free
FAX 206/337-3056

Although it's a large operation, Pacific Topsoil is a family-owned business. Judging from the hours they keep, it's a hard-working family! "We learned years ago, when we were in the middle of a landscape project at home, how important it is to be able to get materials delivered after hours or on a Sunday," says owner Sandy Forman. In addition to topsoil, the company supplies potting mix, bark, mulch and compost (ground and screened) sand and gravel. They offer expert advice on soil amendments for problem areas. But there's more here than the name reveals. You'll also find railroad ties, paving stones, drainage pipe and fittings, grass seed and sod (year-around), plus construction-grade tools.

The landscape contractors I worked with when I moved to the Northwest raved about "Steerco" and "Groco." I quickly found out that these soil amendments made by Sawdust Supply Company worked wonders when mixed into the heavy clay soils at my clients' homes in Seattle. Steerco is composted manure. It's slightly acidic (pH 6.5), with a nitrogen content of 5%. Groco, with an 11% nitrogen content is made of biosolids from local treatment plants and sawdust. The company also sells "Play Chips," which are used for safety surfacing under children's play equipment.

Sawdust Supply Company

15 S. Spokane
Seattle, Washington 98134
☎ *206/622-4321*

Hours Mon-Fri 7:30-5;
open Sat 8-4 (March through June)
Accessible Yes
Catalog Free
FAX 206/622-9661

"Sunland Bark and Topsoil Co. is a family-owned business serving Skagit County and other counties from Seattle to Bellingham, including the San Juan Islands," say owners Ed and Jennifer Little. "We manufacture and deliver our own topsoils, compost and beauty bark. The products are laboratory-tested and approved for government jobs. We also do grading, excavating and trucking and have a variety of rock for driveways and decorative purposes." In business since 1972, they've relied on "word-of-mouth" as their best advertisement. Their products are marked down in spring and early summer. "We offer information on all products and advice as to which soils and compost are best for each garden."

Sunland Bark and Topsoils Company

1244 Reservation Road
Anacortes, Washington 98221
☎ *206/293-7188 or 206/293-0619*

Hours Mon-Sat 8-4:30
Accessible No
FAX 206/293-1355

All of the topsoils from this company contain recycled compost to give new landscapes a healthy start. Of the four mixes available, their Garden Mix is the most economical, and the moderately priced Landscape Mix is the most popular. For lawns, they have a Turf Mix and a Greens Mix, which are composed of sand and compost. "Our mixes have been tested for nutrient content and growth-promoting qualities," says the owner. The company also carries gravel products and sod.

Valley Topsoil, Inc.

35019 West Valley Highway
Algona, Washington 98001
☎ *206/839-5384 (from Seattle)*
or 939-0886

Hours Mon-Sat 7:30-5:30,
Sun 9-3; Mon-Sat 8-4 (winter)
Accessible Yes
FAX 206/931-0515

Wittkopf Enterprises

N. 1718 Fairview Road
Spokane, Washington 99207
☎ 509/467-0685

Hours Mon-Fri 7-5, Sat 8-3
Accessible No
Catalog Free

Wittkopf supplies a wide range of topsoils and potting soils. You'll also find four kinds of bark mulch, drainage rock, pea gravel, crushed rock, ten kinds of decorative rock and sands in a variety of colors.

Woodland Park Zoo

5500 Phinney Avenue North
Seattle, Washington 98103
☎ 206/625-POOP

Hours By appointment only; pick-up times on Wed, Fri & Sat
Accessible Yes

"Woodland Park Zoo is proud to provide Seattle area gardeners with Zoo Doo," says the pamphlet (printed on recycled paper, of course). "Zoo Doo is a fully composted blend of animal manures mixed with straw bedding, grass, leaves and wood chips from the grounds." Which animals contribute to the cause? Elephants are the most generous, followed by ponies, hippos, bison, elk, llamas, wallaroos and many other herbivores. "Adding this rich, dark Zoo Doo to your soil will enhance water and nutrient retention and will improve soil texture. It is completely organic and smells slightly sweet." Go to the main zoo parking lot at 50th and Fremont and follow the Zoo Doo signs to the horticultural nursery.

Note to readers: I called the Tacoma Zoo to see if they, too, sell Doo. They don't. But what they told me was interesting! They use it all in the city's public parks, where, they claim, it keeps deer out. Now, having tried almost every other home remedy for discouraging deer from eating plants, I'm curious to see if this works. It makes sense – the smell of lions and tigers would frighten even the most brazen buck. But, I'm skeptical. Please let me know if it works in your backyard!

Oregon

Cities and individual homeowners bring grass clippings, brush and stumps to Grimm's, which recycles landscape wastes into a rich Garden Mix. The company also blends the Garden Mix with sandy loam to make an excellent topsoil. They offer mushroom compost and bark dust too. It's a busy place, but the owners try to take time with homeowners, explaining the best product for the application intended.

Grimm's Fuel Company
18850 S.W. Cipole Road
Tualatin, Oregon 97062
☎ *503/692-3756*

Hours Mon-Sat 7-5, Sun 9-5
Accessible Yes
Catalog Free

McFarland's also makes a good compost out of decomposed yard debris. They turn out several different textures of rich, nutritious humus that can be worked into the soil or used as mulch.

McFarland's Bark, Inc.
13345 S.E. Johnson Road
Milwaukie, Oregon 97222
☎ *503/659-4240*

Hours Mon-Sat 8-6, Sun 9-6;
close at 5 during winter
Accessible Yes
Catalog Free

Pachyderm poop is available at Portland's zoo. It's a bargain at $10 per truck load, and you can get a bagful for a buck. You must make a reservation; eight lucky customers are served each Saturday between 7:30 and 7:45 a.m.

Metro Washington Park Zoo
4001 S.W. Canyon Road
Portland, Oregon 97221
☎ *503/220-2786*

Hours By reservation only
Accessible Yes

North American Soil markets quality potting soil and organic compost under the product name, Garden Care™. Finely textured and ideal for use as mulch or as a soil amendment, the product is made of composted sewage sludge from the City of Portland's new twelve million dollar facility. The company's bulk products are used extensively in city parks and commercial nursery production. Delivery is available if you're ordering as much as 7½ yards, or you can pick-up smaller quantities at the site.

North American Soils
5001 N. Columbia Blvd.
Portland, Oregon 97203
☎ *503/285-5125*

Hours Mon-Fri 7-5
Accessible Yes

Williams Fuel

44975 S.W. Seghers Road
Gaston, Oregon 97119
☎ *503/357-6730*

Hours *Mon-Sat 8-6, Sun 8-12*
(closed at 5 in winter)
Accessible *Yes*

Here you'll find potting soils in addition to topsoil, mushroom compost and bark dust sold in bulk. This neighborhood garden center also stocks paving materials, landscape rocks and crushed rock. Also see listing on page 373.

British Columbia

Coast Mountain Beauty Bark Ltd.

1010 Laurelwood Place
Squamish, British Columbia V0N 3G0
☎ *604/892-2023*

Hours *Daily 7-3 (May through Sept);*
Daily 8-4 (March & April
and Oct & Nov)
Accessible *No*
FAX *604/892-2024*

Coast Mountain's landscape bark products include nuggets (small, medium and large) for top-dressing, fine-textured grower's bark, and a bark mulch. These products are 100% Douglas fir bark with a low wood content. Customers can pick up bulk quantities at the facility or look for bags of the company's products in garden centres in the greater Vancouver area.

Haberlin Soil Supplies Ltd.

8700 Barnard
Vancouver, British Columbia V6P 5G5
☎ *604/263-6911*

Hours *Mon-Fri 8-4, Sat 9-1*
Accessible *Yes*
Catalog *Free*

This family-owned company offers a loam and manure mix for deep revitalization or creating new beds. They have specially prepared mixes for top dressing flower beds or lawns, plus a general landscape mix. In fertilizers they carry mixed manure and mushroom compost. All of Haberlin's products are sold in bulk.

VanDusen Botanical Garden

5251 Oak Street
Vancouver, British Columbia V6M 4H1
☎ *604/266-7194*

Accessible *Yes*

City gardeners eagerly await VanDusen's Annual Manure Sale, held in the parking lot on the third Saturday in April each year from 9 until 3. You can even pre-order this excellent, well-aged steer manure, which comes in 40-pound bags. In late October, there's the Tree-mendous Compost Sale when bags of light, feathery black mulch become available from the City of Vancouver's leaf collection program. Watch the newspapers or call for the exact date; there are no pre-sales for this one.

Pest Management

Those of us who came of age shortly after World War II were promised Nirvana by chemical companies. Soil could be kept forever fertile and pests would be eliminated. Now, proponents of organic gardening are ready to dispense with all synthesized chemicals. I'm not completely comfortable in either camp. Although I'm utterly opposed to hiring a "service" that sprays on a regular, whether-it-needs-it-or-not-basis, I'm not ready to advise my clients that they should never use chemical pesticides. This is a complex subject that demands utmost common sense. The benefits must be weighed against the risks.

The Integrated Pest Management philosophy represents the most recent and, in my opinion, most sensible approach to keeping pests at acceptable levels. It has been said that the worst plant pest may be the species *Homo sapiens*! Without question, we humans leave our plants more susceptible to disease and insect infestation when we fail to maintain healthy soil, prune improperly or inadequately water the garden. Good cultural practices are the basis of IPM.

Begin a pest management program by identifying what's "bugging" your garden – it may be a bug, but then again it may be one of a hundred plant diseases or stress due to climate or poor maintenance. County extension agents, local nurserymen and Master Gardeners all offer services and publications that help the gardener identify problems.

Determine the number of pests your plants can withstand and you can tolerate. Accept the fact that a certain amount of damage is normal, and then look for the least-toxic, most environmentally sound solution. Don't haul out big guns to attack little problems, or worse yet, "scattershoot."

The first line of defense should be mechanical control. These solutions include removing the offenders by hand, pruning out infested leaves or branches (taking care not to butcher the plant), drowning slugs in beer (they die happy), and setting out sticky paper or physical barriers such as netting and landscape fabrics.

Another promising avenue is biological control, which includes the release of predatory and parasitic insects. Keep in mind two problems with predators. One, they don't know where your property line is located and may flee. Two, natural enemies can only reduce the number of pests; if they eliminated all of them, the predators themselves would starve to death! There are also several biological agents that keep insects under control by causing disruption to the mating process.

Other pest control methods include spraying with oils (when the plants are dormant and the insects are most vulnerable) and the use of insecticidal soaps, which are effective for thinning populations of aphids, mealy bugs, mites, whiteflies and other soft-bodied insects. For soaps to work, you must wet the pest. You can make a somewhat effective insecticidal soap with three tablespoons of vegetable oil and three tablespoons of dish washing detergent in a gallon of water, but be sure to test it on a leaf or two before widespread spraying; some detergents damage plant foliage.

☞ **Money-saving tip: Seek advice on pest control from experts, such as Master Gardeners, who do not stand to gain by their recommendations.**

Monitor progress. Document both the treatment and the result. Use poisons only as a last resort, with the full knowledge that poisons also kill the good guys! Even naturally derived insecticides such as pyrethrum are lethal to beneficial insects. Use the right product for the particular pest or disease.

Chemical companies are becoming increasingly sensitive to ecological concerns, and their labeling is increasingly specific. Follow the instructions and cautions on the label to the letter. Use as little as possible. Don't dispose of unused chemicals in sewers; take them to a hazardous waste pick-up point. 🐾

Northwest Manufacturers

Ed Hume Seeds

P.O. Box 1450
Kent, Washington 98035

Mail Order
Catalog $1 (U.S.), $2 (Canada)

Ed Hume's catalog offers *Scareaway Bird Line*, a special plastic tape that creates an ultra sonic noise unpleasant to birds when it is stretched between poles. Not only is it useful for protecting seedlings and food crops, it is an effective way to stop birds from fouling decks, boats and buildings. Another environmentally sensitive product is *Slug deFence*, a polyethylene barrier that employs vacuum-grade table salt to repel the slimy mollusks. The catalog also lists *Yardtec* garden fabrics (a weed shield and a lightweight pest shield). You can get a free sample of these fabrics by sending a self-addressed stamped envelope to: Garden Fabrics, at the P.O. address listed.

Integrated Fertility Management

333 Ohme Gardens Road
Wenatchee, Washington 98801
☎ 800/332-3179

Hours Mon-Fri 8-5;
open Sat 8-12 (April-July)
Accessible No
Mail Order
Catalog Free
FAX 509/662-3179

Beneficial insects, diatomaceous earth, lures, traps, dormant oils and soaps of all sorts are the weapons offered in the first 31 pages of this company's catalog. Their whole business is structured to promote the use of organic materials. While the catalog is aimed toward the agricultural community, most of it's products are available in quantities small enough to serve the home gardener as well. Several of the beneficial predators are recommended for greenhouse use.

In business since 1981, Nature's Control offers beneficial insects and biological controls for garden pests, with special emphasis on greenhouse and indoor plant pests. They publish a brochure, "What's Eating My Plants?" which belongs in every gardener's library. The company's "living arsenal" includes ladybugs and predators that eat spider mites, white flies, aphids, thrips and mealy bugs. They have green lacewings, which the company describes as "walking garbage disposals," and praying mantis, which are "fun to have in the garden." They also sell diatomaceous earth and yellow sticky traps, plus jewelers 10x magnifiers to help you identify the little critters! The Tootsie-rolls they include with every order are not for the bugs, but to let customers know they're appreciated.

Nature's Control
P.O. Box 35
Medford, Oregon 97501
☎ *503/899-8318*

Hours *Mon-Fri 9-6:30*
Mail Order
Catalog *Free*
FAX 503/899-9121

Sterling makes Rescue™ products that lure and trap such pests as flies, yellowjackets and Japanese beetles. Another of their products attracts beneficial soldier bugs to your garden. The lure is a yellow plastic device that looks like a badminton birdie. Inside is a patented pheromone that simulates the odor a male soldier bug sends out to attract a mate. The company tells you not to expect miracles, but points out that, used in conjunction with mechanical controls, soldier bugs dine on such destructive species as gypsy moth caterpillars, cabbage loopers and birch leafminers. They're reputed to keep over a hundred different pests under control. Look for Sterling's traps in hardware stores and garden centers.

Sterling International, Inc.
P.O. Box 220
Liberty Lake, Washington 99019
☎ *1-800/666-6766*

Hours *Mon-Fri 8-4:30*

Watering Practices

Our climate is similar to that of the British Isles, right? Wrong! With our wet winters and dry summers, we have more in common with the Mediterranean region, Australia and South Africa. Yet, the notion prevails, especially among newcomers to the area, that there's no end to the rainy season in the Pacific Northwest. The fact is that Seattle typically receives less rainfall than San Diego during the summer. Seasonal distribution of rainfall is more critical to plant growth than total quantity.

Until recently, little attention has been paid to water-conservation, but water rationing in Seattle, Portland and other Northwest cities in the summer of '92 served as a wake-up call. Professionals in the "green industry" here are now researching drought-tolerant plants and looking at water-sensitive design. Homeowners should not get lulled back to a false sense of security by the rainy summer of '93. Autumn was drier than usual, and besides, water is likely to become more expensive, rain or shine.

Just as we have turned away from gas-guzzling cars, expect to abandon water-guzzling landscapes in the coming years. Demand for water is increasing dramatically as people flock to the Northwest. If we don't learn to conserve, we taxpayers are going to be asked to build dams and treatment plants, which do not come cheap. In some areas of the Northwest, sewer bills are already being tied to home water consumption. The more water you use, the higher your sewer bill, even though water used in the landscape does not go down the drain.

I first faced this illogical reality in Austin, Texas, where I practiced landscape architecture for several years. First, let me explain that Austin is a lush environment with lakes and hills and trees. It is in the same USDA Growing Zone as Seattle, and it has the same average annual rainfall. The difference is that Austin has "gully-washing, frog-choking" rains in spring, followed by long weeks of drought and intense heat. In summer, we Texans always watered lavishly. No problem. Water was cheap.

Then, Austin tripled in population during the '60s and '70s. Not wanting to build additional treatment facilities, the sewer department simply started raising the rates. Oh, did they raise the rates! By the early '80s, people were shocked by their utility bills – $250 a month to keep an average suburban lot green! About that time, the City of Austin instituted a Xeriscape™ program to promote low-water-use landscaping methods. We learned to cope.

Reduce the Need for Water

Landscape watering accounts for 50% of home water use in the summer. Lawns require about four times as much water as planting beds. Therefore, the single most effective way to reduce water use is to reduce the size of our lawns. Until the early nineteenth century, only the very wealthy could afford great swaths of lawn grass. Mowing had to be performed with a scythe, and watering was done by hand. As water costs go up, large lawns may once again become too expensive to maintain. People are beginning to question these relics of the English country estate into which we pour not only water, but also great quantities of fertilizers, herbicides and pesticides.

Grass can be replaced with decking, paved terraces, water features, ground covers and wildflowers. Now, I'm not suggesting that you need to plow under *all* of your grass. You may need a section of turf for children to play or for a grown-up game of croquet. You may simply love the texture of a soft green lawn. In the areas where you need grass, consider substituting one of the newer, more drought-tolerant varieties. Contact your county agent or a near-by botanical garden for recommendations on the grass best-suited for your area and soil-type. Keep turf areas well aerated to absorb maximum rainwater and free of weeds that compete for the available moisture.

The second strategy for creating a more drought-enduring garden is to group together plants with similar watering needs, even if that requires some transplanting. For example, Oregon grape, photinia and yews are less thirsty than azaleas and rhododendrons. If all of these species are mixed in the same bed, you end up over-watering the drought-tolerant plants to keep the others happy. It would be better to move the thirsty plants into a bed that's convenient to water, well-protected from afternoon sun and shielded from drying summer winds.

A third design strategy is to add more trees to your landscape. A plant growing in partial shade requires less water than the same plant grown in full sun. As the tree canopies spread, fewer sections of your garden will need frequent irrigation. If you're starting a new garden in a sunny, open environment, you would be wise to select your plants from a list of drought-tolerant species. (See Chapter 4.)

Good maintenance is another key component in conserving water. In the soil section of this chapter I discussed the importance of good soil. It bears repeating that well-aerated soil absorbs more water than hard, compacted earth. Organic matter mixed into the soil helps retain the moisture. Spread an organic mulch on top to help conserve water; it works both to inhibit weeds and reduce evaporation. Remove water-robbing weeds as soon as they appear.

Water Efficiently

The question most beginning gardeners ask is, "How often should I water," and the answer is, "Only when the plant needs it." Water requirements vary with the age of the plantings, soil conditions and the weather. The first few weeks after installation, plants need lots of moisture.

In Texas it is a common practice to build up a ring of soil around the outside of the rootball of each new plant. The ring acts as a reservoir, allowing you to provide extra water for the new plants without over watering an entire planting bed. I've not seen this simple step employed in the Northwest. It's a good trick if you're planting in hot, dry weather. However, the soil ring should be removed as soon as the autumn rains begin.

Once your garden is well-established, you should try to figure out precisely how much water it needs. One-inch of water per week is the old rule-of-thumb, but that may be too much or too little. Different areas of the garden will have different needs, depending upon sun or shade and slope of the land. Water only when the top four inches of the soil are dry (a bamboo chop-stick makes a dandy soil probe). Chrysanthemums are good "indicator plants" – when they wilt, you know the planting bed needs water. The mums bounce right back.

You can test the amount of water your sprinklers are putting out by placing cans in several areas (tuna cans, which are about a inch deep, work well). Run the water for thirty minutes and measure how much water accumulates in each can. Keep records. Pretty soon you'll be able to figure out how often and how long you should water to keep plants perky.

☞ **Money-saving tip: Learn to water without wasting a drop.**

The best time to water is very early in the morning. From mid-morning on, too much water is lost to evaporation. Watering at night encourages fungi and other pathogens. One long watering is generally better than several short ones. The idea is to encourage deep roots. However, long soakings may exceed the soil's infiltration rate, so keep a watchful eye and shut off the tap if you begin to see any standing water or run-off.

Most old irrigation systems put out more water than the soil can absorb, resulting in big losses to run-off and evaporation. Watering with hoses and portable lawn sprinklers may be even less efficient because the spread is generally uneven and the spray is thrown high in the air where it evaporates quickly in hot weather. Also, there's a chance of forgetting to turn the water off when you leave to run an errand. (It has happened to me. About the third time I returned to find water running down the street, I solved the problem with a $15 timer.)

The May, 1993 issue of *Consumer Reports*, which is available in most libraries, provides an extensive analysis of garden hoses, soaker hoses, sprinklers and such watering accessories as timers and couplers. It's worth reading before you invest in watering equipment. Not only does the seven-page article rate different brands for price and performance, but also it discusses how different kinds of sprinklers – impulse, rotary, oscillating and traveling – measure up in terms of evenness of coverage and speed of water output.

For my own small garden that has no lawn, I've switched over to a drip irrigation system because it delivers water to the plant's root system with minimal evaporation. Drip irrigation is not satisfactory for watering grass, but your trees, shrubs, flower beds and container plants can be handled with an easily installed system attached to outdoor faucets. The cost is quite low. I recently bought a 100-foot "sweating hose" at a local hardware store for $32. A Drip Mist™ system with emitters for 26 plants was priced at $32.99. More sophisticated drip systems can even be hooked up to an existing sprinkler system.

In the past decade, there has been a lot of improvement in automated sprinkler systems. Fabricated of new high-quality plastics and designed to throw as little water in the air as possible, today's irrigation systems cut down on evaporation. They feature computerized controls, which precisely regulate the amount of water that goes to each zone, and solenoid electric valves that adjust flow and prevent valves from getting stuck open.

If you're investing in a new irrigation system, insist on separate zones for lawn and planting beds, and be sure that the system can be adjusted for seasonal differences. Consider investing a few extra dollars for rain and moisture sensors, items that will save considerable water. Learn everything possible about the operation of the system. For future reference, keep an as-built drawing of your system that shows the layout of the lines and the location of each of the heads and valves.

If you have an old system, check its physical condition zone-by-zone at least once a year. Make sure the heads are not too low in the ground and not cockeyed, damaged or dirty. Shrub heads may need extenders if your plants have grown significantly. Look for mist over the sprinkler head, which indicates excessive water pressure.

Make sure all of the valves open and close properly and are not clogged with dirt. Check for line breaks caused by construction or freezes. Run a test of the controller to be sure each station actually runs the length of time for which it is set. Program the system for maximum efficiency. Consider retrofitting old systems with drip lines and "micro sprinkler" heads to cut the gallonage and avoid runoff. ✺

Grading and Drainage

For centuries farmers have used terracing to maximize rainwater. Rather than let water pour down a steep slope, you can construct a series of steppes or retaining walls that will not only hold the water on your site, but also will serve to prevent soil erosion. A layer of gravel beneath each terrace will prevent the soil from becoming waterlogged. If retaining walls are impractical, erosion control fabric is an excellent way to hold a steep slope. It's also good for covering newly-tilled soil on even a moderate slope. (See source listing on page 99.)

Another trick for conserving rainwater is to connect perforated pipe to the bottom of gutter downspouts to water the plants under the eaves of your house. A fan-shaped section of concrete or brick can also be used beneath a downspout to divert water evenly throughout a planting area. I've also collected rainwater in barrels under the down spouts for watering house plants when I've lived in cities where the tap water was excessively chlorinated.

Too much water is as harmful to plants as too little. If the surface drainage on your property is not sufficient to carry rainwater away from the house, you probably need professional help. Minor puddles that remain in lawn areas or planting beds for a few hours after a hard rain can be corrected by installing so-called French drains. The average homeowner can construct this simple subsurface drainage system. Dig a trench 12-inches deep and 12-inches wide, with the bottom of the trench sloping away from the problem area. Into the trench, place a four-inch perforated PVC pipe wrapped in filter fabric and backfill with coarse gravel.

Another solution may be the construction of a dry creek that leads excess water toward a slope or storm drain. When it isn't carrying run-off, a rock-lined creek bed may serve as an attractive landscape feature. Perhaps you'll want to run a flagstone walk beside it or design a bridge to cross it. For the creek bed to drain effectively, its slope should descend at least an inch per linear foot. 🌿

Sources for Drip Irrigation Equipment

Because I consider drip systems such an innovative and important addition to the Northwest gardener's repertoire, I'm going to break the first rule of this book and name a few products that are not made in Washington, Oregon, Idaho or British Columbia. (It should come as no surprise that drip irrigation equipment was developed in the arid Southwest.) The manufacturers listed below sell to homeowners through the hardware or garden sections of mass merchandisers in this region – **Builders Square, Costco, Eagle Hardware, Ernst, Fred Meyer, Home Base, Home Club, K-Mart,** etc. If you cannot find these products where you normally trade, call or write the manufacturer for the name of the nearest dealer. ✿

Aquapore Moisture Systems

610 South 80th Avenue
Phoenix, Arizona 85043
☎ *1-800/635-8379*

Aquapore's spongy-looking Moisture Master™ hoses are made of recycled tires. Buried or laid under ground covers and mulches, these flexible soaker hoses "weep" water evenly throughout your planting beds. They come in 25', 50' and 75' lengths, plus 250' lines that can be cut and fit to any length you need. The hoses can be combined with drip emitters and low-volume sprinkler heads to water your entire landscape. Look for display racks that offer accessories and parts, including compatible plastic piping that goes under walkways or other places where you don't want soaking action.

Hardie Irrigation

27631 La Paz Road
Laguna Neguel, California 92656
☎ *1-800/742-4335*

FAX 714/831-3212
Hours *Mon-Fri 8-5*

Lawn Genie™, RainJet™ and Drip Mist™ are members of the Hardie Irrigation family of do-it-yourself watering products. The company offers computer-designed irrigation layouts customized to your property. Send them a plot plan on their grid paper (which you can obtain through a dealer). You will be notified by mail when the plan and parts arrive at your local store. The Lawn Genie™ system, the company's premier line, is designed for curving landscapes and sloping ground. Their RainJet™ system works well for large, relatively flat lawns. The Drip Mist™ system is not part of the computer-designed package, but it is available in stores, and it comes with clearly written installation instructions. Call for a dealer in your area.

Pepco has taken its commercial irrigation products and put them in consumer-friendly packaging without changing the quality. The parts (fittings, couplers, tees, end plugs, elbows, etc.) are color-coded for simplicity of installation. They offer a free 28-page *Water Conservation Handbook* that illustrates how the different components work together to form a complete drip system. Technical help is available Monday through Friday, 8-5, on the company's 800 line.

Pepco Water Conservation Products, Inc.

4870 W. Jacquelyn Avenue
Fresno, California 93722
☎ *1-800/247-8138*

There's a Northwest connection here. Wade began in business in Oregon in 1865 as a farm implement company. Since the '30s they've been in agricultural irrigation. Their new drip and micro spray systems (made in California), allow you to install flexible tubing from a hose faucet and control the amount of water that comes out of each Acu-Drip™ pressure-compensating emitter. You can also convert the spray heads in the sections of your sprinkler system that water shrubs and trees to these water-saving drip emitters. The company publishes a Planning Guide that tells you how to install the system yourself, and a call to the 800 number will direct you to a nearby dealer.

Wade Manufacturing Co.

3081 E. Hamilton Avenue
Fresno, California 93721
☎ *1-800/695-7171*

Source for Erosion Control Products

Terra Enterprises manufactures a variety of land and water management materials. Because they are organic products, BonTerra Biologs™ and woven coconut fiber mats support natural re-vegetation and eventually biodegrade into natural humus. The company also makes tree shades and commercial-grade weed barriers. It maintains a staff to help solve problems with stream banks and difficult slopes. The products are distributed by Washington Culvert in Olympia (206/456/-1551), Oregon Culvert in Tualatin (530/692-0410) and in Western Canada by Wes Can (306/934-4549).

Terra Enterprises

P.O. Box 9485
Moscow, Idaho 83843
☎ *208/882-9489*

Hours Mon-Fri 9-5
Catalog Free

Pruning Practices

Pruning is both an art and a science. Unfortunately, few people know how to do it correctly. A drive through any neighborhood in the Northwest will yield examples of trees topped and shrubs sheared beyond recognition. Such pruning not only leaves the plants ugly, it makes them more prone to disease. The *Sunset Western Garden Book* has a four-page section that explains the basics of proper pruning. It's a good place to start learning the terminology and accepted techniques.

☞ **Money-saving tip: The least expensive pruning is no pruning at all.**

When designing a new landscape plan, I promise my clients they'll never have to do much pruning beyond occasional, judicious cuts to thin plants, remove unsafe or unattractive growth and repair damage. How can I make such a promise? By knowing the ultimate size of each plant and choosing the right variety for each situation!

For example, I use dwarf plants beneath windows, select small trees for small gardens, use low-growing plants at the front of a bed and graduate plant heights upward toward the back. I allow just enough space between the plants so that they'll ultimately grow together, but not crowd one another out. I never design clipped hedges. They're too labor-intensive for today's lifestyle, and besides, I prefer a loose, natural look.

Before redesigning the planting plan for an older garden, I decide which plants can be saved and which should be removed. Hopelessly overgrown shrubs cannot simply be cut in half. It's better to take them out and start over, choosing a plant that will not grow too large for the spot.

☞ **Money-saving Tip: Selective pruning can be used to tame a garden of unruly delinquents.**

Thin and head-back shrubs that lack structure, hang over pathways or obscure views. Some large shrubs, such as rhododendrons, camellias and Japanese privet, can be pruned into attractive small trees. If the plant has multiple stems, select a few heavy upright branches to serve as trunks and cut the rest to the ground. Then start at the bottom, exposing each trunk by carefully cutting off lower branches. Make the cuts close to the trunk, just outside the branch collar. Stand back and look, then continue "limbing-up" the lower branches until the overall shape is nice. To dress-up the landscape, plant a ground cover under the "new" tree.

"Renewal pruning" is another way to rejuvenate plants in an overgrown landscape. This method works well for shrubs that tend to put on all of their growth at the top. I've been known to cut leggy old specimens of abelia, nandina, mahonia and spiraea all the way to the ground, allowing the entire plant to regenerate from the roots. Thereafter, the homeowner removes a third of the growth each year, cutting out the oldest, woodiest canes. Such pruning forces plants to continually put out new growth from the bottom, keeping the plants fuller and more attractively shaped.

☞ **Money-saving tip: You can add years of life to your tree or shrub with good pruning practices.**

Timing is a critical factor in pruning. Some plants must be pruned during dormancy; others should not be pruned until after flowering. Some plants may be susceptible to fungus if they are pruned during the rainy season. Check with a professional arborist, qualified nurseryman or extension agent before beginning a pruning project if you are unsure.

Always prune with a purpose. Remove rubbing and crossing branches, suckers, weak branches and any broken or diseased limbs. In the latter case, always cut back to healthy wood and disinfect the tool with a solution of one cup of bleach in a gallon of water. Thinning a tree or large shrub is an acceptable practice if it is to provide good air circulation, let more light through the canopy or promote even branching patterns. Sometimes it becomes necessary to prune to avoid excess dampness around the house foundation or to improve the tree's chance of survival in a time of drought. Removing excess foliage reduces water consumption.

The best pruning removes branches back to the origin of growth. Make the cut almost flush with the branch from which it sprang, cutting just outside the branch collar (the ring that separates the branch from the trunk). If you're removing a large branch, three cuts are needed to ensure that the bark won't tear. The first cut should be from the bottom, just beyond the place where the final cut will be made. The second should be made from the top to remove the branch. The third and final cut is made to remove the stump just beyond the branch collar.

To head-back growth, make the pruning cut so that the outermost bud left on the branch is pointing in the direction you want the branch to grow. Always cut quickly and cleanly. It's better to perform small annual cuts than to wait until a plant is out of hand and take a chance on hopelessly ruining its shape.

☞ **Money-saving tip: Never top a tree. Topping permanently disfigures the tree, exposing the wood in each growth ring to decay and causing the tree to become hollow over time.**

Instead of topping, thin the tree to a network of even, regularly spaced branches. If you're trying to reduce the height of a tree, do it over a period of time.

☞ **Money-saving tip: Don't waste money on "pruning paint."**

Not only is it unnecessary to "dress" the wound, research now shows that this practice may slow the natural healing process.

☞ **Money-saving tip: Know when it's time to remove a tree.**

Dead or unhealthy trees are a liability. If the tree is leaning, if there's evidence of root rot and/or the trunk has hollows or deep open cracks, if there has been improper pruning in the past, storm damage or construction injury or if there are deep, open cracks at several of the crotches, it's probably time to call in a professional arborist. He or she is the person most qualified to determine if the tree can be saved. If the tree poses a danger to a house, power lines, cars or people, let it go and plant a replacement. 🌿

Sources of Information

Cedardale Orchards

P.O. Box 594
Conway, Washington 98238
☎ 206/445-5483

Mail Order
Catalog Free

In his 50-minute video, *Easy Steps to Fruit Tree Pruning,* Gary Moulton demonstrates how to prune fruit trees for maximum production. Mr. Moulton is a researcher at the Washington State Research and Experiment Unit at Mt. Vernon and a partner in a commercial orchard. The tape addresses tools and techniques, the differences between the pruning needs of various types of fruit trees and also covers espaliers and old trees. At $29.95 (plus tax and handling), it is an invaluable resource for anyone who needs a yearly "refresher course" before tackling this vital and complicated project.

Plant Amnesty

906 N.W. 87th Street
Seattle, Washington 98117
☎ 206/783-9813

Mail Order
Catalog Free with SASE

Cass Turnbull chose the name "Plant Amnesty" with tongue planted firmly-in-cheek. By using humor and controversy, she makes the point that trees and shrubs are tortured and killed by incorrect pruning practices. "It's getting worse every year," she says. She's quite tactful, of course, pointing out that you are "making common pruning errors," while the guy down the street is "committing savage butchery!" To learn how to do it right, send a legal-size stamped envelope to Plant Amnesty. You'll get back a free brochure that covers the basics of correct shrub and tree pruning and an updated list of pruning classes in the King County area, plus an order blank for literature and video tapes. She has also begun an Adopt-a-Plant service in King County, which finds homes for large shrubs and trees that would otherwise be cut down. The organization is opening a Portland branch, and the idea is catching on in other communities in the region.

Tools, Apparel & Landscape Supplies

Tools

A beginning gardener need invest in only a few basic tools. The five I use most are a medium-width pointed shovel, a spading fork, weeding hoe, garden rake and trowel. Over the years I've also acquired a flat shovel, leaf rake, edging tool and assorted other devices that promised to make gardening easier. For pruning, I have top-quality hand shears, loppers, pruning saw and a pole saw.

☞ **Money-saving tip: High-quality tools are the most economical long-term and the most satisfying to use.**

The more you use a tool, the better it should be. I look for tools that will last a lifetime. The difference between an English spading fork that sells for $60 and the Taiwanese fork you'll find at hardware stores and home centers for $15 is that the former is made in one piece of solid forged steel. Its tines will not rust or break, and it will penetrate clay soil with greater ease. For my money, it's worth the difference. You'll find the lowest prices on power tools and lawn mowers at the big hardware chains and home improvement centers. However, when you buy from an independent dealer, you're also buying service, so if you're not the "fix-it" type, don't base your decision on price alone. Because I have minimal storage space, I rent the large tools I use only occasionally. There are a number of companies that offer such items as aerators, chippers, sod cutters and tillers. Look in the yellow pages under *Rental*.

☞ **Money-saving tip: Split the cost of rental tools with a neighbor.**

The best little hand tools I've ever seen are made by Allen Simpson in Ontario, Canada. Their forks and trowels are made of a rust-free lightweight aluminum alloy, and they are guaranteed for life. Having gone through a trowel a year, I was attracted like a bear to honey when I saw them in the garden boutiques and nurseries I visited in British Columbia. The only place I've run into these tools in the U.S.A. was at my favorite gadget store, Brookstone, in Portland. (Call 1-800/926-7000 to receive the company's catalog, "Hard-to-Find Tools".)

You'll find a selection of excellent American, English and German tools at many of the region's specialty garden shops (see listings beginning on page 312) and large garden centers (Chapter 12). The Northwest Manufacturers listed in this chapter offer some very innovative items for the garden. The section at the end of this chapter, Professional Landscape Supplies, introduces home gardeners to sources where contractors shop for heavy-duty, back-saving garden tools and equipment you might not find in retail nurseries.

☞ **Money-saving tip: Take good care of your tools.**

Fine tools are expensive to replace, and sharp, clean tools make gardening easier. Clean off the soil and/or sap after each use and store your tools in a dry place. Periodically rub linseed oil on wooden handles and sharpen the blades of spades, hoes and pruning tools. ❀

Garden Apparel

Every well-dressed gardener wears a hat, gloves and garden boots. If you are really into making a fashion statement, you'll have elbow-high goatskin gloves and organically grown cotton shirts that say "Save the Earth." If, like me, you are given to gardening in ratty jeans and paint-spattered tee-shirts, you've probably noticed that your jeans are uncomfortable (not enough room to bend and squat), your cloth gloves have developed holes, you've ruined yet another pair of $60 athletic shoes and you've misplaced your hat.

This year, I've vowed to get some decent garden apparel. My husband gave me knee-high rubber boots for mucking around in bad weather. For warm weather gardening I'm planning to get plastic garden clogs. I'm also going to buy dungarees with kneepads from Kneezers (listed below) and a pair of goatskin gloves (they really are superior). I'm going to start the season with two new straw hats, a bottle of sunblock, shatterproof sunglasses and an apron that holds tools and seed packets! If next summer is as damp as the summer of '93, I think I'll check out a ski shop or sporting goods store for a lightweight nylon windbreaker jacket and shell pants, too. ❀

Northwest Manufacturers of Tools & Garden Apparel

"Technology for the cutting edge," is this company's tag line. They manufacture, import and export professional-grade agricultural and viticultural saws, pruners, loppers and shears. Under the Barnel label, you'll find bonsai scissors, Euro-style pruning shears and excellent pole saws. They distribute Hickok loppers, which are fabricated in Wenatchee, Washington, German horticultural knives and Japanese-made ARS pruning equipment. While the company does not sell directly to the public, they'll put you in touch with a dealer in your area.

Barnel International, Inc.

1075 N.W. Murray Road, Suite 256
Portland, Oregon 97229-5501
☎ *503/223-1533*

Hours *Mon-Fri 9-5*
FAX *503/248-0276*

Both Popular Mechanics and Organic Gardener have featured this company's Winged Weeder™. It's a dandy little hoe designed to speed-up weeding and cultivating and sod cutting, aerating, even scraping ice. The long-handled version accommodates the gardener's back, allowing you to stand upright while you work. They've a narrow-bladed weeder that makes it easy to get between plants and a hand-held variety, great for raised beds. These versatile tools are available in garden centers. If you can't find them nearby or want more information, call the company's 800 number.

Creative Enterprises, Inc.

P.O. Box 3452
Idaho Falls, Idaho 83403
☎ *1-800/388-4539*

Hours *Mon-Fri 8-5*
Mail Order
Catalog *Free*

Kneezers (a division of MN Productions) makes and distributes IronKneez™, which are pants with waterproof knee-pockets that hold replaceable foam pads. Designed to "insulate and protect the body part voted most likely to give out," the padded knees are attached to an Oshkosh dungaree, carpenter bibs or sweat pants. You're offered a choice of 100% cotton drill or denim dungarees. They've added children's sizes, and the products are available through mail-order or in select garden stores.

Kneezers, Inc.

P.O. Box 577
Freeland, Washington 98249
☎ *206/221-7995*

Mail Order
Catalog *Free*

Rainforest Gardens

13139 224th Street
Maple Ridge, British Columbia V2X 7E7
☎ 604/467-4218

Rainforest Gardens manufactures sturdy anodized aluminum plant labels, which are available by mail. See complete listing on page 191.

Seed Saver

P.O. Box 2726
Idaho Falls, Idaho 83403
☎ 208/522-2224

Mail Order
Catalog Free

Kristi Appelhans has invented a swell way to organize seeds you save over from one season to the next. Large enough to hold gloves and small tools, this sturdy 13 x 10 x 12-inch box (made of 50% recycled plastic) comes with fifteen airtight hanging bags and multi-colored index tabs. There's a larger size and a smaller one, too. The big one holds 25 bag/hangers and includes garden gloves and *The New Seed Starters Handbook*. The brochure also offers garden row markers, seed storage envelopes and other goodies.

Technic Tool Company

725 29th Street N.
Lewiston, Idaho 83501
☎ 1-800/243-9592

Hours Mon-Fri 8-5
Mailing address P.O. Box 1406
Lewiston, Idaho 83501

Tree pruning made easy! This company's power pruner is a new version of a telescoping tree-pruning saw. The small chain saw blade is operated by a gas-powered engine attached to the end of the pole. Call for the nearest distributor.

The Thom Manufacturing Company

P.O. Box 30004
Seattle, Washington 98103
☎ 206/783-4867

Hours By appointment only
Accessible No
Mail Order
Catalog Free

Roxie (a multiple-purpose, double-pointed shovel), Diggit (a long-handled framed screening tool for removing rocks from garden soil) and Pokey (an ingenious little hand-held weeding tool) serve the needs of people who want improve the quality of their soil and lighten their labor. On Sundays afternoons from late March through May the owner, Thom Graham, holds an "open garden" to demonstrate the tools and explain his in-the-garden composting method. He welcomes people to call for information. He will give you directions to his home in northeast Seattle or send you his flier.

This company's Foldit™ Utility Cart is a two-wheeled wheelbarrow that folds like an accordion. Opened, with the handle extended, the cart measures 30-inches wide, 55-inches long and 23-inches high. Made of rust-resistant aluminum and zinc-plated steel, it holds 330 pounds. Twenty-inch pneumatic tires make it easy to maneuver, even over rough terrain. If you have ample storage space and want a less expensive cart, the company also makes a non-folding model of the same cart, with a painted wooden floor.

Tipke Mfg. Co.

321 N. Helena Street
Spokane, Washington 99202
☎ *509/534-5336*

Hours *Mon-Fri 8-4:30*
Accessible *Yes*
Mail Order
Catalog *Free*

"So you like to dig in the dirt, or maybe you want to scoop, scrape, chisel or pry...," says the product literature for this folding hand shovel. The 6-oz. stainless steel U-Dig-It ™ can be opened and closed with one hand. It fits into a leather or cordura sheath that attaches to your belt. The product is sold through garden centers and catalogs. If you want it and can't find it, call for the name of a nearby retailer.

U-Dig-It Enterprises

3953 Brookside Lane
Boise, Idaho 83703
☎ *208/939-8656*

Sources for Professional Landscape Supplies

Note: These are the "supermarkets" where landscape professionals and serious home gardeners go for tools and building supplies.

Washington

"Everything from the Ground Up" is this company's tag line. They not only supply soils, mulches, decorative rocks, retaining wall materials and other building materials, but also basic tools, hoses, sprinklers and drip systems to maintain your garden. The company is also a large wholesale/retail garden center (with a sod farm and nursery behind the scene) that supplies plant materials. They'll ship products to out-of-town customers.

Circle S Landscape Supplies, Ltd.

3404 Old Lewis River Road
Woodland, Washington 98674
☎ *206/225-5845*

Hours *Mon-Sat 7:30-6, Sun 9-5*
Accessible *Yes*
Mail Order
Catalog *Free*
FAX *206/225-5845*

Gibson's Nursery and Landscape Supply

S. 1401 Pines Road
Spokane, Washington 99206
☎ 509/928-0973

Hours Mon-Sat 8-5:30
Accessible Yes
FAX 509/926-4352

Gibson's carries an unusually wide range of products for your landscaping needs. (Also see page 359). Much of the business is "to-the-trade," but the same products are available to retail customers, as well. They stock tools, sod, fertilizers and soil amendments. They are distributors for *Keystone* retaining wall systems and *Dewitt* geotextiles. They have topsoil and mulches, lighting products, pavers and a number of different edging materials.

Northwest Landscape Supply

12500 132nd Avenue N.E.
Kirkland, Washington 98034
☎ 206/820-9325

Hours Mon-Fri 7:30-5; open Sat 8-3 (March through October)
Accessible Yes
FAX 206/823-1937

Because this company deals mostly with contractors, Northwest Landscape Supply offers a selection of tools and other landscape items that retail garden centers don't normally carry. You'll find soils, a large selection of rocks and concrete paving stones (both slabs and interlocking pavers), plus lots of concrete planters and terra cotta pots. They carry Focus™ low voltage lighting, and such decorative items as sculpture, Japanese lanterns and fountains and pond materials, including water plants. Their PVC pond liners are available by mail-order.

West Sound Landscaping Supplies

6700 Bethel Road S.E.
Port Orchard, Washington 98366
☎ 206/876-8873

Hours Mon-Fri 8-6, Sat 9-4:30
Accessible Yes

"We are the only company in the area for landscape supplies and hard goods (i.e. railroad ties, landscape fabric, backpack sprayers, aggregates, bark and topsoil). We pride ourselves on high quality goods and services with rapid and prompt delivery," says Chuck Creiger. The company marks down its merchandise in late October and goes into the winter season with gifts for the gardener and Christmas trade. "We like our trade and want to help the homeowner accomplish the highest results possible." They freely offer advice on rock walls, irrigation and water gardening.

In addition to manufacturing and distributing topsoil mixes, mulches and the like, Pacific Topsoil carries construction-grade tools, railroad ties, paving stones, drainage pipe and fittings. See additional listing on page 86.

Pacific Topsoil, Inc.

14002 35th Avenue S.E.
Bothell, Washington 98012
☎ *206/337-2700*

Hours Mon-Fri 7-10, Sat 8-7, Sun 10-3;
close at 8 weekdays in winter
Accessible *Yes*
Catalog *Free*
FAX *206/337-3056*

Oregon

"Everything from the Ground Up" applies equally to this company's Troutdale location. See page 107.

Circle S Landscape Supplies, Ltd.

22420 N.E. Halsey
Troutdale, Oregon 97060
☎ *503/669-6820*

Hours Mon-Sat 7:30-6, Sun 9-5
Accessible *Yes*
Mail Order
Catalog *Free*
FAX *503/669-0852*

This company's 176-page catalog is a fabulous find for the home gardener! It offers top-notch professional pruning equipment, safety clothing of all descriptions, measuring tools, commercial-grade sprayers, spreaders and hand tools, and replacement parts for scores of name-brand tools. The 2,000-square-foot showroom in Eugene carries over 6,000 items.

International Reforestation Suppliers

2100 W. Broadway
Eugene, Oregon 97405
☎ *503/345-0597*
or 1-800/321-1037

Hours Mon-Fri 8-5
Accessible *Yes*
Mail Order
Catalog *Free*
Mailing address *P.O. Box 5547*
Eugene, Oregon 97405
FAX *1-800/933-4569*

Mallory Growers and Landscape Supply

1511 N.E. Highway 99
Eugene, Oregon 97402
☎ 503/689-7000

Hours Mon-Fri 8-6, Sat 10-5
Accessible Yes
Catalog Free
FAX 503/689-2533

You'll always find in-store specials on some of the thousands of items in stock at here. This outlet and its sister store, Rain or Shine, carries a large selection of hobby greenhouses, drip irrigation systems, professional-quality hand and power tools, composters, organic fertilizers and pest control products. You'll also discover everything needed for pond construction and maintenance, plus a wide range of weather instruments and garden ornaments.

Rain or Shine

13126 N.E. Airport Way
Portland, Oregon 97230
☎ 503/255-1981 or 1-800/248-1981

Hours Mon-Fri 8-6, Sat 10-5, Sun 12-5
Accessible Yes
Catalog Free
FAX 503/255-9201

Read above listing for Mallory Growers and Landscape Supply of Eugene. These companies are jointly owned.

British Columbia

Bricks 'N' Blocks

1371 McKeen Avenue
North Vancouver, British Columbia
V7P 3H9
☎ 604/984-3008

This company's name might imply that paving materials are the only products you'll find, but in fact Bricks 'N' Blocks supplies everything for the landscape except plants. They stock a large line of pots, statuary and fountains, garden tools, soils, mulches, filter fabrics, and just about everything else you could name. Various product lines go on sale at different times of the year, so be sure to inquire. They ship products into the U.S. See complete listing page 53.

An experienced staff is on hand here to advise do-it-yourself landscapers. "We are a complete and friendly supplier," say the owners. "If we don't have an item, we'll find out where it's available." It's a one-stop shopping spot for landscape contractors, but the company also welcomes retail clients. They have tools (hand and power), garden furnishings, ornaments, prefab gazebo kits, fence materials, Intermatic™ lighting, bulk soils, pavers and retaining wall systems and everything for water gardens. Selection is best early in the gardening season, but you'll find the best buys during the winter months.

Landscape Construction Centre, Inc.

5625 Regent Street
Burnaby, British Columbia V5B 4R6
☎ *604/291-0333*

Hours Mon-Fri 7-5:30, Sat 8-3 (Mar through Oct); Mon-Fri 8-5, Sat 8-3 (winter)
Accessible Yes
FAX 604/291-9717

"We are one of Vancouver Island's largest centres for lawn and gardening equipment," says David Skeed. Neiser's carries a large assortment of hand tools, plus mowers, tillers, brush cutters, chipper/shredders, sprayers and utility carts. "Our grounds-care experts personally evaluate the equipment needs of our customers. Our specialty is prompt, courteous service to the discriminating garden professional and to the residential market." The company hosts a pre-season sale (February and March) and post-season sale (October).

Neiser's Forest & Garden, Ltd.

134 Fourth Street
Duncan, British Columbia V9L 1S3
☎ *604/746-4232*

Hours Mon-Sat 8:30-5:30
Accessible Yes
FAX 604/746-1040

Northwest Landscape Supply offers a good selection of tools and a wide range of landscape construction materials – soils, rocks, landscape timbers, paving stones, retaining wall materials, etc. Asian pottery is a specialty here, and in the area of garden ornaments, the company carries planters, terra cotta pots, sculpture and Japanese lanterns. They distribute Focus™ low voltage lighting and offer water gardening materials, including water plants. Unlike the Seattle store, they also supply fence materials.

Northwest Landscape Supply

5883 Byrne Road
Burnaby, British Columbia V5J 3J1
☎ *604/434-4842*

Hours Mon-Sat 7:30-5
Accessible Yes
FAX 604/436-9443

Chapter Four
Ecologically Balanced Landscapes

"We have probed the earth, excavated it, burned it, ripped things from it, buried things in it... That does not fit my definition of a good tenant. If we were here on a month to-month basis, we would have been evicted long ago."

.....Rose Elizabeth Bird

Why We Should Look to Our Own Backyard

We are increasingly a city-dwelling population existing in man-made landscapes. Urban sprawl has paved over miles of natural vegetation. And, while we still have great tracts of heavily wooded land, our farms and tree plantations have supplanted much of the old-growth forest. Perhaps this is why voices calling for protection of natural habitats are especially strong in the coastal Northwest. Neither farms nor gardens are able to sustain the diversity of living organisms that once thrived in the Northwest's woodlands, wetlands and alpine regions and along its coastlines.

The continued loss of native plant species and the introduction of ornamental and commercial species are threatening the ecological balance of the Pacific Northwest. It's going to take unprecedented cooperation on the part of forest and farm managers, plant scientists, urban planners and even homeowners if we are to reincorporate the degree of genetic diversity necessary to ensure a sustainable landscape.

Just as environmental activists are working on regional issues, homeowners can influence new ways of development. With our pocketbooks we can vote for planned unit developments in which houses are clustered and large tracts of vegetation are left in place. And we can select more diverse landscape plants. As home gardeners, we've only recently recognized the need for planting in cooperation with our climate and terrain, rather than trying to fight it.

John and Carol Grant begin their book, *Trees and Shrubs for Pacific Northwest Gardens*, by noting that the Northwest has a climate all its own. They lead into Chapter Four saying, "The golden rule for selecting plant material for your garden is to start with those plants native to this region which are best suited to your particular set of cultural conditions; then combine them with plants which grow under similar climatic and cultural conditions in other parts of the world." So, we begin the plant materials section of this book with the subject of Northwest natives. 🌹

Northwest Natives

Arthur Kruckeberg's book, *Gardening with Native Plants of the Pacific Northwest*, introduces a wealth of wonderful plants that merit the attention of area gardeners. The attributes of plants native to any region include affinity for the local soils, adaptation to climate extremes and a natural resistance to insects and disease. Not only are plants more likely to thrive where they evolved, but also they appear to "belong." The ancient Greeks had a name for it, *genius loci*, a sense of place.

Dr. Kruckeberg points out the incredible diversity of Pacific Northwest climate zones and soil types. Simply calling a plant a Northwest native is to omit the key question: native to where? Each native plant evolved to fit a narrow range of site-specific variables. Obviously, a chain fern, which grows on shaded banks in dripping water around Puget Sound, would be a poor choice for a dry site east of the Cascades. Dr. Kruckeberg's book details the environment in which each of the Northwest natives grow, and he urges readers to match the plant with its normal niche.

A more difficult problem than knowing which natives belong where is finding a supplier for the natives you want. It is both unethical and illegal to collect plants from the wild. Fortunately, several regional growers are propagating natives from seeds and cuttings or legally digging plants that stand in the way of bulldozers. And, happily, more garden centers are making room for natives alongside their array of imported ornamentals.

Dale Shanks publishes a journal that lists the botanical and common names of 880 species of native plants keyed to 125 seed and plant sources. Some of these nurseries are in other parts of the country and some are "wholesale only," but, with its feature articles on native plants and extensive plant list, this up-to-date sourcebook belongs in the library of every ecologist and landscape designer in the region. To order, send a check for $9 to: *Hortus Northwest*, P.O. Box 955, Canby, Oregon 97013. 🦋

Sources for Native Plants

Keith and Lory Fitzgerald grow over a hundred species of Northwest native trees, shrubs and perennials. Most of their plants are container-grown from seeds and cuttings. Some bear tags that read, "I'm an Oregon native rescued by Boske Dell Natives from forests destined to be developed or logged." Among the natives they are actively propagating are tanbark oaks, trillium, twin flower, wild ginger and camas. They have ten varieties of penstemon and lots of ferns and bulbs. Some are available only in limited quantities; they offer an availability list. Having used these plants in their own garden, the Fitzgeralds are excited about the future for native species as more gardeners discover how carefree gardening with nature can be.

Boske Dell Natives
23311 S.W. Boske Dell
West Linn, Oregon 97068
☎ 503/638-5945

Hours By appointment only
Accessible Difficult
FAX 503/655-2692

Michael Dolan and his wife Carolyn are rapidly expanding into unusual ornamentals and Northwest natives. See complete listing on page 206.

Burnt Ridge Nursery & Orchards
432 Burnt Ridge Road
Onalaska, Washington 98570
☎ 206/985-2873

This wholesale nursery grows several species of natives and wetland plant materials. See complete listing on page 145.

Chehalem Mountain Nursery, Inc.
14375 S.W. Patricia Avenue
Hillsboro, Oregon 97123
☎ 503/628-0353

Cloud Mountain Farm & Nursery specializes in fruit trees, but it also grows a nice selection of native landscape plants. See page 207 for complete listing.

Cloud Mountain Farm & Nursery
6906 Goodwin Road
Everson, Washington 98247
☎ 206/966-5859

Collector's Nursery

16804 N.E. 102nd Avenue
Battle Ground, Washington 98064
☎ *206/574-3832*

Diana Reeck and Bill Janssen propagate some of our less-common native plants. They offer a wide selection of unusual perennials, vines, trees and shrubs, and Diana is developing a line of Pacific Coast iris. See complete listing on page 262.

Dragonfly Gardens

3575 S.E. Division Street
Portland, Oregon 97202
☎ *503/235-9150*

Hours *Mon-Sat 10-6, Sun 10-5*
(February through July);
off season by appointment only
Accessible *Yes*

While Dragonfly Gardens stocks a wide range of plants for both interior and exterior uses, Sarah Lizio calls her place a "specialty garden center" because the emphasis is on the best selections of native plants, vines, ferns, herbs, annuals, perennials and a few shrubs suitable for perennial borders. The staff is highly knowledgeable here. Sarah says, "Our main focus is on an environmentally sound garden environment." She grows lots of drought-tolerant perennials, and she says she especially likes bamboo for privacy and special effects. You'll also find bonsai and a wonderful selection of containers in all shapes and sizes. Don't miss the two "Midnight Madness" sales in late July and August.

Ferris Nursery

415 S.E. 98th Court
South Beach, Oregon 97366
☎ *503/265-5709*

Hours *By appointment only*
Accessible *Yes*
Catalog *Free*

Seventy-five percent of the species grown here are natives – such plants as coast red current, big leaf Oregon grape, coast strawberry, wild lilac, hairy manzanita, western azalea and Pacific wax myrtle. You'll also find certain non-native trees, broadleaf evergreens and ground covers, including ferns, selected for their ability to thrive on the coast. Located off Hwy. 101 between Newport and Waldport, this ten-acre nursery supplies retailers and landscape contractors. Individual homeowners looking for plants for such problem areas as seashores and erosion-prone banks need only make an appointment.

"We specialize in native and rare plants, growing over 300 species of plants native to the Pacific Northwest. These are listed in our catalog. However, at the nursery you'll find over 1,200 varieties of plants at any one time, making the choice hard for even the most experienced gardener," says Richard Fraser. He holds spring and fall kickoff sales in early March and late September. Call for information about the gardening seminars at this nursery, which is located on the northern tip of Saltsprings Island.

Fraser's Thimble Farms

RR #1, Site 26-A0 Arbutus Road
Ganges, British Columbia V0S 1E0
☎ 604/537-5788

Hours Daily 10-4:30
Accessible Yes
Mail Order
Catalog $1
FAX 604/537-5788

Robin Hansen's cyclamen nursery has recently branched into Northwest native shrubs and perennials. She grows the plants from seed, and many are not available in large quantities, but she's increasing the volume as people become more interested in the species of our region. She is just beginning production of marbled wild ginger and several of the native clematis, for example. See full listing on page 186.

Hansen Nursery

P.O. Box 446
Donald, Oregon 97020
☎ 503/678-5409

Dan Janzen's nursery is new on the scene and in the early stages of development. A recent graduate in horticulture, he's collecting plants to propagate from his own farm, where he has found rare native bulbs and wetland species. He's setting up a demonstration garden and actively growing vine maples, coast pines and red-twig dogwoods.

Janzen's Specimen & Native Nursery

20380 S.E. Webfoot Road
Dayton, Oregon 97114
☎ 503/868-7679

Hours By appointment only
Accessible Yes
Mail Order
Catalog Free

Located in Lewis County, about 25 miles southeast of Chehalis, Natives Northwest grows its trees, shrubs and ground covers in excellent clay loam soil. Several of the 38 species Chris Aldrich lists are available as seedlings for reforestation, and many more species are in production. He says, "Please contact us if you are interested in a plant not listed." His commitment to natives is strong.

Natives Northwest

190 Aldrich Road
Mossyrock, Washington 98564
☎ 206/983-3138

Hours By appointment only
Accessible Difficult
Mail Order
Catalog Free

Pacific Plant Company

616 Shore Road
Port Angeles, Washington 98362
☎ *206/457-1536*

Hours *By appointment only*
Accessible *Yes*
Mail Order
Catalog *Free*

Half of the plants on David Allen's 2½-page list are Washington natives. With his degree in botany, David has set up a practice as a consultant in restoration. He has begun his nursery on two and a half acres he describes as "classic wet side coniferous forest." He's also in the process of setting up gardens "to demonstrate the fantastic flora of the Olympic peninsula. Some of these primary succession plants, a mix of shade and sun-loving natives, have high ornamental value and should be used more often," he says.

Pheasant Valley Farms

16747 Leary Road N.E.
Woodburn, Oregon 97071
☎ *503/981-2353*

Hours *By appointment only*
Accessible *Yes*
Mail Order
Catalog *Free*

Douglas Chadwick's nursery deals exclusively in Northwest natives. His primary interest is the herbaceous plants – perennials, tubers and bulbs. He tells me that he's propagating (trial and error) many more species than you'll find on his list, and that many are destined for botanical gardens and arboretums. Doug wants people to understand the special needs of natives and offers instruction every step of the way. He ships roots, rhizomes and bulbs in the fall only.

Phil Parker

28293 S. Meridian Road
Aurora, Oregon 97002-9301
☎ *503/651-2100*

Hours *By appointment only*
Accessible *Difficult*

Cyclamen and ferns are specialties here along with other Northwest native perennials and bulbs. After working with Edgar Kline for ten years, Phil Parker bought this fifty-year-old business in 1987. His offerings include native anemones, columbine, wild ginger, lupines, checker mallow, star flowers, trillium, false Solomon's seal and such rare bulbs as Indian hyacinth and fawn lilies. Beginning in 1994, the nursery will be reconnecting with Russell Graham. Phil's mail-order business is being conducted through Graham's catalog. (See page 187.) Customers can arrange to pick up the Graham's plants at Phil's nursery in Aurora. You can also meet Phil Parker at The Weekend Garden Market on Saturdays (May through October) at Tri-Met's West Beaverton Park & Ride lot on the Tualatin Valley Highway.

"We offer over 100 varieties of container-grown trees, shrubs, ground covers and wildflowers native to the Pacific Northwest. While many are familiar and useful west of the Cascades, the plants are well-acclimated to the harsher climate of Eastern Washington. Our catalog contains a short description of everything we grow," says Kathy Hutton. "Go a little wild and plant native!" Selection is best March through May and September through November. The catalog also lists a Pacific Northwest Wildflower Mix and seeds for native, reclamation and turf grasses.

Plants of the Wild

P.O. Box 866
Tekoa (Willardfield), Washington 99033
☎ *509/284-2848*

Hours Mon-Fri 8-5
Accessible Yes
Mail Order
Catalog $1
FAX 509/284-6464

My assessment of the outstanding selection of plant materials at these garden centers was reinforced by highly-visible sections within the sales-yards labeled "Northwest Natives". See complete listings on page 367.

Portland Nursery

5050 S.E. Stark
Portland, Oregon 97215
☎ *503/231-5050*

9000 S.E. Division
Portland, Oregon 97266
☎ *503/788-9000*

Dick Cavender's friends call him "Red," and he grows native azaleas (*Rhododendron occidentale*); hence the name of this interesting little company. He describes his business as a "hobby that got out of hand," and his passion has led him into developing improved forms of this fragrant, attractive shrub. Other "hobbies" include tropical rhododendrons and pleione orchids; see page 246.

Red's Rhodies

15920 S.W. Oberst Lane
Sherwood, Oregon 97140
☎ *503/625-6331*

Yvonne and Russell Graham's catalog inventories a significant number of native woodland-dwelling species. See complete listing on page 187.

Russell Graham, Purveyor of Plants

4030 Eagle Crest Road N.W.
Salem, Oregon 97304
☎ *503/362-1135*

Sandy Nursery stocks native high mountain trees (mountain hemlocks, mountain pines and alpine firs) from Crater Lake. See complete listing on page 147.

Sandy Nursery

29804 S.E. Orient Drive
Gresham, Oregon 97080-8816
☎ *503/663-1795*

Soos Creek Gardens

12602 S.E. Petroritsky Road
Renton, Washington 98058
☎ *206/226-9308*

Helmut and Lourdes Brodka go in for native and natural landscaping. Their nursery carries a number of hard-to-find species, including bog plants. See complete listing on page 236.

Stanwood Nursery

9816 271st Street N.W.
Stanwood, Washington 98292
☎ *206/652-7226*

Hours Mon-Fri 9-6, Sat 9-5, Sun 11-4
(open April through October)
Accessible No
Mail Order
Catalog Free

Stanwood Nursery specializes in Northwest native ground covers, and the company has some unusual offerings, such as miner's lettuce, which is an edible, pink-flowering plant. They've a number of well-known species, such as kinnikinnik (three varieties), wild ginger, wild strawberry, creeping dogwood and creeping mahonia. Warm Beach Nursery is the wholesale division of this company, and all of the native shrubs and non-native ground covers it grows can be found or ordered through this retail outlet. The catalog includes quite a few drought-tolerant sedums and sempervivums, as well. On the back page is an invaluable spacing chart for planting common ground covers.

Trees Unlimited

21373 64th Avenue
Langley, British Columbia Canada V0X 1T0
☎ *604/534-8733*

The business of Trees Unlimited is large-caliper tree sales and relocation. They carry a number of species native to the Fraser Valley. See complete listing on page 149.

Trillium Gardens

P.O. Box 803
Pleasant Hill, Oregon 97455
☎ *503/937-3073*

Hours By appointment only
Accessible Difficult
Mail Order
Catalog Free
FAX 503/937-2261

Fifty-percent of the plants here are natives, including seven varieties of trillium, four varieties of shooting stars, three native irises and a good sampling of trees and shrubs. The selections are excellent. Owner Sheila Klest has put together an impressive list of other North American wildflowers that thrive in the Northwest, plus grasses, water plants, ferns and perennials. She's especially interested in plants that attract birds.

"Natives exist for nearly every garden need," says Wally Hansen. Observing that his own five-acre garden "would take a century to replicate," he relishes the great variety in plant form, flowers, foliage and fruit. His catalog lists seven firs and eight pines among the wide choices in evergreens and twenty deciduous species. Native trees in his catalog provide "the over-story framework," and the shrubs, ferns and ground covers he lists are mostly shade-loving plants that thrive in the understory. The publication is both descriptive and inspiring. It contains a map to guide you to Bower Court, a small country road that does not appear on most published maps. The nursery is about four miles east of Salem.

Wallace W. Hansen

2158 Bower Court S.E.
Salem, Oregon 97301
☎ *503/581-2638*

Hours *Sat 9-5; or by appointment on weekdays*
Accessible *Partially*
Mail Order
Catalog *Free*
FAX *503/581-9957*

Wood's Native Plants is a small father and son nursery located at 1,500-feet elevation in the Hood River Valley of northern Oregon. They container-grow hardy plants for shade and sun that are native to the inter mountain area, aiming to fill a niche in unusual ornamentals and wild lands re-vegetation. They market to both homeowners and specialist growers, offering a discount on sales over $100. Selection is best in August. In addition to such familiar plants as Oregon grape and elderberries, they are offering Dutchman's breeches, several varieties of penstemon and native lilies.

Wood's Native Plants

5740 Berry Dr.
Parkdale, Oregon 97041
☎ *503/352-7497*

Hours *By appointment only*
Accessible *No*
Mail Order
Catalog *$1*

Naturescaping the Urban Environment

In her wonderful book, *Restoring the Ecology of Our Own Back Yards*, Sara Stein observes, "We cannot in fairness rail against those who destroy the rain forest or threaten the spotted owl when we have made our own yards uninhabitable." She notes that our gardens are filled with introduced plant species that effect the larger landscape in two ways. First, they provide no food for indigenous birds, butterflies and other wildlife. Secondly, most require more water, fertilizer and pest controls than do the species that evolved within a region.

Ms. Stein lives in upstate New York, so the plants listed in her book are native to the Northeast and, therefore, unsuitable for Northwest gardens. But the book is well-worth reading for its message. Another well-known voice calling for change is Lady Bird Johnson, who in 1982 founded The National Wildflower Research Center in Austin, Texas, to encourage the propagation and use of "wild" plants in planned landscapes throughout the country.

It has been my privilege to interview Mrs. Johnson twice in the past decade. While she is identified in the public's mind with beautification, Mrs. Johnson views the commitment to wildflowers and native trees, shrubs and grasses as more than pure aesthetics. She believes that it is our "best hope" for ensuring continued habitation of this country, and of the planet. She speaks of living in a place "as the Lord made it," and says, "I think of beautification as making the world more beautiful within the context of what will grow."

Many of the native shrubs, ferns and herbaceous perennials found west of the Cascades evolved as shade-loving understory plants. Because dense tree canopies no longer exist in most residential neighborhoods, a total commitment to native plants is more difficult for urbanites than for people who live in rural settings. Selections from the native plant nurseries listed in the previous section must be more carefully evaluated, with a full understanding of the growth habit and environmental need of each species.

Our native conifers grow too large for small city lots, for example. Such desirable native deciduous trees as big leaf maples are difficult to garden under. Others, such as alders, are short lived (their purpose in the forest is to provide shade while the conifers germinate.) Madronas and native dogwoods often succumb to urban stresses. Bunchberry and salal, lovely as they are, tend to take over a tiny planting bed. However, in the right places, our native trees, shrubs and wildflowers can add texture to city gardens. Furthermore, our gardens can become more hospitable to the birds, butterflies, squirrels, reptiles and other creatures that once claimed the land we've usurped for human habitats. 🌿

Sources of Information & Products for Backyard Habitats

Note: You'll find additional sources for bird feeders and birdbaths in Chapter 11.

In 1991, Scott Lukens developed a hobby into a business that caters to backyard wildlife. "Birds are our primary focus," he says, "but we're really a nature shop." Begun in a cottage in Lake Oswego, the company has opened three other stores filled with shelters for bats, birds, squirrels, raccoons and other critters, all made by three dozen local artisans. You'll also find food and birdbaths and lots of books and information on wildlife and habitats. Scott publishes an educational newsletter, which goes to over 10,000 homes in the area. One of the contributors is landscape designer Judy Hutchinson, who works through the stores as a consultant to homeowners. Her special expertise is in the plants that provide food and shelter to migratory birds as well as those that live here year-round. While the company does not produce a catalog, they do ship products to customers. Call one of the stores to be included on the mailing list or for a schedule of classes and bird walks.

Backyard Bird Shop

352 B Avenue
Lake Oswego, Oregon 97034
☎ *503/635-2044*

3574 S.E. Hawthorne Boulevard
Portland, Oregon 97214
☎ *503/230-9557*

3893 S.W. Hall Boulevard
Beaverton, Oregon 97005
☎ *503/626-0949*

560 N.W. Eastman Parkway
Gresham, Oregon 97030
☎ *503/661-4944*

Hours Mon-Fri 10-6, Sat 10-5, Sun 12-5
Accessible Yes, except Lake Oswego
Mail Order

NWF's Backyard Wildlife Habitat information packet includes a program application, a booklet on planning and planting a habitat, and a paperback, *The Backyard Naturalist.* Send a check for $5.25 (includes postage and handling). Canadian citizens may also register their backyard habitat with the NWF.

National Wildlife Federation
Backyard Habitat Program

1400 Sixteenth Street N.W.
Washington, D.C. 20036-2266
☎ *1-800/432-6564*

The booklet, *Naturescaping: A Place for Wildlife*, contains excellent plant lists, site plans, and instructions for making feeders and nesting boxes for specific wildlife. Enclose a check for $11.50.

Oregon Department
of Fish and Wildlife

P.O. Box 59
Portland Oregon 97201

Wildflowers

Lady Bird Johnson's book, *Wildflowers Across America*, co-authored by distinguished horticulturist Carlton B. Lees, includes a section that correctly identifies the Pacific Northwest within the summer-dry climate zone. Pictured are such beautiful native wildflowers as storksbill, lupines, penstemon, phlox and Flett's violets. The authors make a convincing argument that these plants should be used not only for roadsides and parks, but also to make home gardens bloom and grow.

Wildflower meadows were called "flowery medes" in medieval times and were used for recreation before lawn grasses became available. Turf is considerably more practical for a game of touch football, but how just much grass do we need? As our water resources dwindle, fields of wildflowers may return to favor. Certainly the parking strips and other sunny, seldom-used areas of our lawns are good candidates for conversion to flowery medes.

There are some obstacles to overcome in gardening with wildflowers. For wildflowers to come back year after year, they must be allowed to dry out and set seed. They look rather "ratty" for a few weeks after the blooming period. Therefore, if you're growing wildflowers in highly visible areas, it's best to simply cut them down and replant seeds each year. Phil Fortunato, president of Briargreen in Kent, Washington (listed below) notes that wildflowers are tricky. "The primary mistakes people make are planting in the fall and mowing at the wrong time. We recommend mid-February for planting in the Northwest and believe that November is the best month to mow." ❧

Sources for Wildflowers

Briargreen, Inc.

P.O. Box 6639
Kent, Washington 98064
☎ 206/630-5024 or 1-800/635-TURF
(24-hour help line)

Hours Mon-Fri 8-5
Mail Order
Catalog Free
FAX 206/630-9124

"We researched wildflower mixes from a variety of seed sources for four years and planted wildflowers in irrigated and non-irrigated plots before offering blends to the public," says Phil Fortunato. He adds that his company works closely with homeowners to determine the best solution for the individual's site and desired results. He cautions against adding too much grass seed, saying that the ratio should be one-to-one, and he adds, ""We want people to be happy. People are often disappointed when they expect a lot of color in non-irrigated meadows." Briargreen offers four wildflower mixes for the coastal Northwest, as well as erosion control mixes.

Emerald offers two different mixes of wildflower seed, standard height and low-growing. They're also developing seeds for bird meadows. Donna Kluehe, the company's president, says that customer service is their forte. She is available as a consultant on soils, grasses, fertilizers and "all the information you'll need to grow wildflowers." She notes, "There's a lot to learn about the art and science."

Emerald Hydro-Turf, Inc.
9330 N.E. Halsey Street
Portland, Oregon 97220
☎ *503/254-8414 or*
1-800/826-8873

Hours *Mon 8-5*
Accessible *Yes*

Wildflower seeds are sold by the pound, quarter-pound, ounce or gram here. See complete listing on page 128.

Frosty Hollow, Consultants in Ecological Restoration
Box 53
Langley, Washington 98260
☎ *206/221-2332*

Fifteen year's experience with hydroseeding techniques carry over into planting wildflowers. Grass Master's mixes contain approximately sixteen varieties of perennials, annuals and biennials blended for the Northwest. The wildflower seeds are applied in the same way as the company's *Liquid Master Sod*, which contains seed, fertilizer, mulch fiber and a special high-organic component to quickly turn bare earth into a meadow. To receive a free flier or to reach a distributor, call: 206/867-1117 (Seattle), 206/565-8111 (Tacoma) and 206/687-2099 (Vancouver, Washington).

Grass Master Hydroseeding
21415 N.E. 60th Street
Redmond, Washington 98053
☎ *1-800/859-4727*

Hours *Mon-Fri 8-5*
FAX *206/883-2908*

JB International is a branch of JB Instant Lawn, and the companies work closely together to provide high-quality lawns for commercial and residential clients. JB International is a hydroseeding company and JB Instant Lawn has long been one of the premier sod farms in the Pacific Northwest. "We provide hydroseeding for both fine lawns and erosion control," says the company's spokesperson, "and we can hydroseed any mix of seed varieties wanted, from grasses to wildflowers. Our special mulch mix provides even coverage, reduces water run-off and preserves moisture. "

JB International
5289 Bluegrass Lane N.E.
Silverton, Oregon 97381
☎ *503/581-7823*

14020 N.E. 124th Street
Redmond, Washington 98052
☎ *206/821-0444*

Hours *Mon-Fri 8-5*
FAX *503/362-4739 (Oregon)*
or 206/821-0613 (Washington)

Natural Legacy Seeds & Rare Plants

R.R. #2, C-1 Laird
Armstrong, British Columbia V0E 1B0
☎ 604/546-9799

Both Canadian and U.S. gardeners can order seeds from this source for several perennials that grow as wildflowers in the Northwest. See listing on page 133.

Plants of the Wild

P.O. Box 866
Tekoa (Willardfield), Washington 99033
☎ 509/284-2848

This company offers a Pacific Northwest Wildflower Mix. See complete listing on page 119.

Seeds Trust/ High Altitude Gardens

4150B Black Oak Dr.
Hailey, Idaho 83333
☎ 208/788-4363

Seeds Trust deals in native grass seed and wildflower seeds from around the world. See complete listing on page 226.

Wildflower Carpet/ Lake Mountain Farms

9980 South State
Sandy, Utah 84070
☎ 1-800/795-3236

Wildflower Carpet™ is a patented sod mat with fifteen different varieties of sun-loving perennials that provide changing colors throughout the season. The five-foot-square mats are installed just like grass sod and meant to be mowed in the fall. The product is grown in Utah and distributed through: **Country Green Turf Company** in Olympia, Washington (206/456-10060); **Lower Valley Turf Company** in Terrebonne, Oregon (503/923-6422); **Willamette Wildflowers** in Aurora, Oregon (503/678-2597) and **The Turf Company** in Meridian, Idaho (208/888-3760).

Willamette Seed

P.O. Box 791
Albany , Oregon 97321
☎ 503/926-2728

Hours Mon-Fri 8-5
Accessible No
Mail Order
Catalog Free

Willamette Seed offers a Northern Region Mix, Low-grow Mix, Desert Mix, Shade Mix and an Annual Over-seed Mix. The company's Bloomcoat™ seeds have a brightly colored, non-toxic coating, which assists gardeners with even dispersal, and its Country Magic™ seeds are uncoated. Willamette Seed will ship any of its mixes or seeds for individual species, by the pound, to customers in the Northwest if there is no dealer nearby. You are welcome to call for a species list and additional information.

Forest & Wetland Restoration

Where natural areas have been disturbed, non-natives like Scotch broom, Eurasian blackberries and Russian thistle take over. Gorse, which is a popular hedge plant in England and Ireland, has become a flammable scourge on the Oregon coast. Teasel has ravaged our wetlands. Single-seed hawthorns are displacing native hawthorns in woodland areas. Because of the cattle industry, non-native grasses have spread like prairie fires. The list goes on and on. Whenever introduced plants compete more successfully than native species, the health of the ecosystem is threatened.

Please don't think I'm picking on the forest and agricultural industries. They are important to the economic health of the region, and they too can be negatively impacted by introduced species. My own father spent twenty years trying to eradicate mesquite trees on his farm in Central Texas. Mesquite is native to Mexico. It came into Texas with the cattle drives, as cows ate the beans and deposited them ever-northward in a perfect environment for germination – to put it delicately – warm, moist, fertile cow patties. Within a few decades mesquite had spread several hundred miles beyond its normal range and invaded prosperous farmland. The tree survives by sending out roots up to a mile in length searching for water; zap it in one place and it pops up somewhere else. Daddy did battle against these tenacious invaders with kerosene, dynamite and bulldozers. He didn't live to see mesquite chips as the darling of the backyard barbecue!

An example of a non-native species consciously (and stupidly) imported for agricultural use is the prickly pear cactus, which was introduced to Australia as cattle fodder. Cows wouldn't eat it, so the fields were plowed under and the cactus cut to sheds. Every piece regenerated, devastating thousands of acres of ranchland.

Homeowners need to be especially careful about the plants they bring in for stabilization of hillsides and for lining creek banks. Kudzu, "the vine that ate the South," was introduced into Georgia to provide erosion control. It quickly climbed telephone poles, twined its way along fence lines and smothered abandoned houses in its path. Last time I checked, it had almost worked its way to Texas! One more example is water hyacinth, which was brought in from Central America to clarify streams. It's now clogging major rivers throughout the southern states.

The moral to these horror stories: don't mess with Mother Nature! The nurseries I've listed in the following section sell plants specific to Northwest forest and wetland habitats. They are not only excellent plant sources, but also informed sources of information for anyone who owns property in a sensitive environment. 🌸

Sources for Forest & Wetland Plants

Balance Restoration Nursery

27995 Chambers Mill Road
Lorane, Oregon 97451
☎ 503/942-5530

Hours Mon-Fri 8-6
Accessible Yes
Mail Order
Catalog Free
FAX 503/942-5530

Balance Restoration Nursery offers a wide selection of native plants, particularly wetland and riparian species. Although the business is primarily wholesale, the company honors smaller orders at a retail price. Most of the stock is sold during the dormant season as bare root, tuber, rhizome, bulbs, etc. Occasionally merchandise is marked down in spring. The nursery offers contract growing, including container grown stock, and the owners provide consultation to help clients, architects and engineers accommodate native plants in their work. The company is located just off Territorial Road (the old Applegate Trail) about 3.5 miles south of Lorane.

Callahan Seeds

6045 Foley Lane
Central Point, Oregon 97502
☎ 503/855-1164

Mail Order
Catalog $1 (refundable)

"Since 1977, we have offered seeds of Western North American trees and shrubs," says Frank Callahan. "We also have Asiatic, European, South American, Australian and New Zealand sources." In total there are seeds for over 500 species, some quite rare. They are sold in 25-gram packets (slightly less than an ounce), and selection is best in fall and winter. The staff has made numerous trips to regions with similar climatic conditions, and they test suitability to Northwest landscapes before releasing plant seeds to the public.

Frosty Hollow, Consultants in Ecological Restoration

Box 53
Langley, Washington 98260
☎ 206/221-2332

Hours Daily 9-5 or by appointment
Accessible No
Mail Order
Catalog Free with SASE
FAX 206/321-6456

"We work mostly with agencies (U.S. Forest Service, Surface Water Management, etc.), providing seeds for restoration and consultation services in restoration project design and plant salvage before construction projects," reports Marianne Edain. The company's tree, shrub, wildflower, grass and perennial seeds are sold by the pound, quarter-pound, ounce or gram. The company is very conscientious. "We collect pre-ordered seed only. Orders should come to us in spring; we deliver in late fall and winter," she notes.

Growth Unlimited specializes in reforestation stock, including several firs, cedar, Monterey cypress and hybrid poplars. The company is also committed to controllable clumping varieties of ornamental grass. They grow four varieties of New Zealand flax, six different *Miscanthus*, bear grass and Japanese blood grass. Their giant reed grass is especially nice for waterside plantings and the pampas grass is valuable as a windbreak. The nursery is located ten miles south of Bandon on a private gravel road off Highway 101.

Growth Unlimited Nursery, Inc.

Sydnam Road
Bandon, Oregon 97411
☎ *503/347-4114*

Hours Mon-Sat 7-5:30
Accessible *Yes*
Mail Order
Catalog *Free*
Mailing address *P.O. Box 291*
Langlois, Oregon 97450

This conifer seedling nursery grows Douglas fir, Western cedar and Western hemlock. Lewis River Reforestation also offers consultation on preparation of the site and planting methods. Its trees are shipped as two-year-old transplants, with a minimum order of 100. Selection is best from June through October.

Lewis River Reforestation, Inc.

1203 N.W. Hayes Road
Woodland, Washington 98674
☎ *206/225-6357*

Hours Mon-Fri 8-2 (June through Nov);
Mon-Fri 7-5 (Dec through May)
Accessible *No*
Mail Order

Ron Vanbianchi's nursery specializes in native freshwater wetland plants for habitat restoration or creation. He offers such plants as Pacific willow, ninebark, red elderberry, slough sedge and water parsley, plus a number of more "eso-teric" species. All are propagated and grown at the nursery. "No wetlands are disturbed to provide the plants," he emphasizes, noting that his company also provides nest boxes for wood ducks, song birds, flying squirrels and bats. This company is important to know if you're gardening on property with standing water, bog areas or a pond.

Pacific Wetlands Nursery

7035 Crawford Dr.
Kingston, Washington 98346
☎ *206/297-7575*

Hours By appointment only
Accessible *Yes*
Mail Order
Catalog *Free*

Qualitree Inc.

11110 Harlan Road
Eddyville, Oregon 97343
☎ 503/875-4192

Hours Daily 8-4
Accessible No
Mail Order
Catalog Free

Qualitree specializes in reforestation and Christmas tree stock. The company will grow almost any tree seedling species on contract. It offers several ornamental species, including dawn redwood, Port Orford cedar, atlas cedar, deodar cedar and Engelmann spruce. Varieties vary from year-to-year. Selection is best from November through March, and the minimum order is $30. Qualitree's promotional seedlings have met with enthusiastic response from schools and organizations celebrating Arbor Day, Earth Day and other special events.

Watershed Garden Works

2039 44th Avenue
Longview, Washington 98632
☎ 206/423-6456

Hours By appointment only
Accessible Yes
Mail Order
Catalog Free

Watershed grows native plants on contract for environmental restoration and propagates woody plants from seeds and cuttings for site-specific projects. Filling a special niche in the marketplace, this company provides plants to private landowners for the purpose of restoring damaged ecosystems. Many of the plants are useful for erosion control and adapted to harsh, dry environments. "Clients seem to be attracted to us because we are a small business. If we don't have a particular plant, we will try to find it for you," offer Scott and Dixie Edwards.

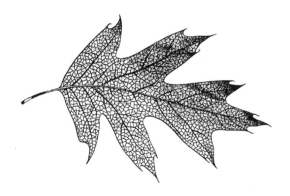

Coping with "Dry Spells"

Replace landscapes with cactus and gravel? Learn to love brown lawns? Pray for rain? Seattle landscape designer Dan Borroff thinks there are better ways to deal with summer droughts. A convert to low-water-use landscapes, he maintains that many of the plants Northwesterners prefer are incompatible with our climate. "Apply a different aesthetic," he says. "Don't imitate someone else's standard of beauty."

Our eagerness to copy English or Japanese gardens has led us to plant species that, if left alone, would not adapt to our climate. England rarely experiences long summer droughts, and Japan receives about five-inches of rain per month throughout the year. I'm reminded of a country and western song. We've been "lookin' for love in all the wrong places..."

The choices in drought-tolerant plants for the Northwest are wider than you might imagine. For example, the *Sunset Western Garden Book* lists over a hundred drought-tolerant trees, shrubs, vines, perennials, bulbs and annuals suitable for areas west of the Cascades. Yes, yucca is on the list, but so are a number of lush-looking plants. Consider goldenrain trees, rock roses, germander, escallonia, wisteria, coreopsis, and bearded or Pacific iris.

County extension services, water districts and such organizations as the Northwest Perennial Alliance are also busily researching plants that thrive with little supplementary watering. Expect to hear a lot more about the subject in the coming months. The King County Cooperative Extension Service (206/296-3986) offers a free booklet, "Low Water Use Plants" by George Pinyuh.

Most plants that "make the list" are native to dry-summer climates. Some evolved in sunny sites in the Pacific Northwest and some in the southwestern United States. Researchers are looking closely at plants from South Africa, Australia, the Mediterranean region and other places in the world where climatic conditions have favor adaptation to periods of drought.

Nature has devised numerous ways for plants to cope with long periods of drought, including a felt-like coat of hair or varnish-like substance on the leaf surface. Silvery leaves reflect rather than absorb sunlight, and small leaves lessen the area of evaporation (pine needles are the ultimate example). A visit to many of the region's botanical gardens will introduce you to a wealth of plants that thrive in our dry-summer climate. You'll find handsome succulents that store moisture in thick stems or leaves ('Autumn Joy' sedum, for example) and a number of plants that have deep tap roots like daylilies or fleshy roots like tall bearded iris.

Another ploy for survival is to simply go dormant in hot, dry weather, which is why many of the Northwest lawn grasses look better in winter than in summer. A number of deciduous shrubs, like snowberry, exhibit the same technique. Surprisingly, many familiar bog plants are drought-tolerant because bogs often dry-up in summer. Researchers are also discovering that native rhododendrons are more adapted than those that evolved in evenly moist climates, probably for the same reason.

It won't work to simply drop prairie or desert plants into coastal Northwestern gardens. Our winter rains rot the roots of many drought-tolerant plants that evolved elsewhere. Other excellent plants fail to flower here because our summers are short and not accompanied by prolonged periods of sizzling heat. The drought-tolerant plants that do thrive in the Northwest generally require good drainage. In choosing plants adapted to seasonal drought, also consider their appearance. Rhododendrons look natural in the coastal Northwest; cacti and palms don't. 🥀

Sources for Drought-tolerant Plants

American Ornamental Perennials

29977 S.E. Weitz Lane
Eagle Creek, Oregon 97022
☎ 503/637-3095

Hours Special weekends only
Accessible Difficult
FAX 503/637-3096

This wholesale nursery is well-known in the trade as a source of unique and useful plants including ornamental grasses, sedges, rushes, native grasses and perennial flowers. Says owner Steve Schmidt, "We offer quality plants, great service, and a written guarantee that all plants will be true to name and grow the first season. Our commitment to tough and hardy plants is demonstrated in the fact all our field-grown grasses have not been irrigated for the last four years. Seeing is believing!" Retail sales are held in May and October. Call for dates and directions to the nursery. The company also offers consulting services and public speaking/slide shows by request.

Colvos Creek Farm

P.O. Box 1512
Vashon, Washington 98070
☎ 206/441-1509

The Colvos Creek catalog offers a wide range of uncommon plants, with an emphasis on natives and drought-hardy material. See complete listing on page 262.

Good Shepherd Gardens and Nursery

7016 Jones Avenue N.W.
Seattle, Washington 98117
☎ 206/783-8262

Hours By appointment only
Accessible Yes

Gil Schieber's garden is a horticultural marvel. Diverse and distinctive, it offers clients a perspective on over 1000 varieties of plants, including fifty different grasses, xeriphytic plants, edible fruiting varieties and plants for attracting wildlife. He travels a lot and is always trying new things from seeds and cuttings. He'll "contract grow" plants other gardeners want to try. He teaches classes through the Seattle Tilth Association and holds two sales each year, on the second Sunday in June and second Sunday in October.

Grahame Ware's mail-order nursery supplies Canadian and U.S. enthusiasts with seeds for native plants and adapted species that thrive in interior climates. The pamphlet/catalog lists 30 ornamental grasses, several rare perennials (including 20 varieties of penstemon) and an excellent selection of western alpines. All orders include a valuable and descriptive propagation and cultural guide. A consultant and designer, Mr. Ware is planning a display garden and retail nursery in the near future; he holds sales on Victoria Day and Labor Day weekends (call for information) and participates in the British Columbia Alpine Garden Club's Sale at the VanDusen Gardens. He also teaches "a most eclectic" class on rock gardening at Okanagan University in Vernon.

Natural Legacy Seeds & Rare Plants

R.R. #2, C-1 Laird
Armstrong, British Columbia V0E 1B0
☎ *604/546-9799*

Hours *By appointment only*
Mail Order
Catalog *$1 (U.S.)*

Owners Chris and Joe Schugmann suggest sturdy walking shoes when you visit their nursery. "Primitive conditions, wonderful plants," they say, adding that customers are welcome to have picnics by the waterfall. "Our nursery specializes in compact hardy flowering perennials and subshrubs for the small garden, rock garden, woodland, and the understory of a mixed border. We also grow a small selection of choice dwarf species rhododendron and dwarf conifers on their own roots. We create our own special potting mixes according to the needs of the plant." All plants are container grown and started in a cold frame. Among the company's many drought tolerant species are crimson bishop's hat, dwarf Siberian wallflower, blazing star, foxglove, encrusted saxifrage and several penstemons.

Schugmann's Nursery

4300 Mosquito Lake Road
Deming, Washington 98244
☎ *206/592-2989*

Hours *By appointment only*
Accessible *No*
Mail Order
Catalog *$1*

Squaw Mountain Nursery grows drought-patient sedums and sempervivums. See complete listing on page 232.

Squaw Mountain Gardens

36212 S.E. Squaw Mountain Road
Estacada, Oregon 97023
☎ *503/630-5458*

Summary of Water-wise Gardening Practices

1. Develop a Good Design Plan
Appreciate a less manicured, more natural aesthetic.
Add more trees.
Create wind barriers.
Group plants with similar water needs.
Replace lawns with ground covers and wildflower meadows.
Deck or pave-over a portion of the lawn.
Use mulch as a design feature for color and textural contrast.
Control the rainwater falling on the site by carefully grading the slopes.

2. Amend the Soil
Add organic matter to maximize its water-holding capacity.
Cultivate to improve penetration and aeration.
Add polymer wetting agents to the soil in container plantings.

3. Pick the Right Plants
Consider slope, exposure and soil type in your choice of plant materials.
Prefer drought-tolerant species over more thirsty plants.

4. Plant Correctly
Plant in early spring or mid-fall to take advantage of the rainy seasons.
Make a soil ring around newly-planted trees and shrubs during the dry months.

5. Mulch, Mulch, Mulch

6. Water Efficiently
Use a soil probe; water only when the top four inches are dry.
Establish watering priorities.
Irrigate with the lowest possible volume to minimize run-off.
Water in early morning to minimize evaporation.
Collect water for container plants in rain barrels connected to down spouts.

7. Maintain the Garden
Raise the height of the lawn mower.
Prune judiciously to reduce transpiration through leaf surface.
Fertilize only to keep plants healthy, not to force rapid growth.
Remove weeds as soon as they appear to minimize competition.

Chapter Five
The Garden's Green Foundation

*"Man must go back to nature
for information."*

.....*Thomas Paine*

Beginning with the Basics

If you've recently acquired a home (old or new), take a year to become acquainted with the property before making any big decisions. Walk around each day; observe the light patterns at different times of the year. After every rain, watch for standing water or rapid runoff. Keep a notebook for jotting down ideas. Window shop at area nurseries. Envision.

If you find a plant you simply can't live without or friends give you cuttings from their gardens, store these plants in your own "nursery," an area somewhere out-of-sight on your property, until you've had time to plan your garden as a whole. This experimental area of your garden will later provide a place to grow-out small plants and continue to serve as a holding area for transplants.

Existing Trees

Your first priority should be trees. If the property has large trees, count yourself blessed and make sure they are healthy. When I bought a home on a quarter-acre lot in Austin, Texas, I called in an arborist to evaluate the 27 trees on the property. Much to my surprise, he found encircling roots that were threatening to choke-out the large sycamore I was depending upon to shade my house from the afternoon sun. Had the problem not been found and corrected, I would have lost the tree. He also found symptoms of iron deficiency in several oaks and recommended thinning out some of the smaller trees to allow the best to grow more fully.

☞ **Money-saving tip: Hire a qualified arborist to evaluate and treat your existing trees or to remove a tree, if necessary.**

A professional arborist may not only prolong the life of your trees, but also save you from a stay in the hospital. Most people don't have the proper tools and ladders to safely prune large trees. If a tree must be removed, the International Society of Arboriculture recommends that you negotiate a written contract that specifies how the tree is to be removed, where the wood will be taken and who is liable in case of damage.

Making the decision to remove a tree is difficult. Even when you know that a tree is ugly or diseased, it is tempting to wait for an act of God. But if it has brittle limbs that may fall onto your roof, messy fruits that make your walkways hazardous, or roots that clog your sewer line (weeping willows are infamous), you might as well admit the truth and take it out. If a tree can be saved by pruning and feeding, spend the money. Consider planting a young tree to provide shade and sustenance for the future.

The Garden's Shrubbery

Shrubs should be your next priority. Remove overgrown "foundation plantings," especially those that have been pruned into tight little boxes and balls in a vain attempt to keep them from covering over the windows. Shrubs lined up like soldiers across the front of a house are out-of-date. They also tend to make the house look smaller. If you have a boring pair of junipers flanking the corners of your house, dispense with them too!

Plant annuals or veggies until you've had time to make a new plan. Consider redrawing the line of the planting beds to make them deeper or more interesting in shape. Plan a varied and richly-textured combination of ground covers, shrubs and small trees to set off the lines of the house. Look at dwarf varieties of shrubs and trees that will never again cover the windows or overgrow the beds. By starting afresh, you can allow your plants to retain their soft, natural forms. ❧

Choosing Ornamental Trees & Shrubs

Trees and shrubs represent big investments. There's a wealth of plant material available, and the choices become more difficult each year. Gardeners today have developed sophisticated taste from travel and exposure to books and magazines that show well-designed gardens from all over the world. Nurseries have kept pace by offering an ever-widening variety of plants and numerous new hybrids of the old familiar shrubs and trees.

☞ **Money-saving tip: Pick the right plant for the right place.**

In choosing a new tree, consider its ultimate size, mature form and suitability for your garden. Obviously, small trees are more appropriate for small yards. But, there are other important questions to ask. Is the tree low or high branching? How fast will it grow? Does it need lots of open space? Will its roots allow other plants to grow beneath its canopy? Is the wood strong enough to withstand wind?

The trees you pick to surround outdoor living areas are especially critical. Do they offer flowers or foliage color in the season you'll use the space? Is the bark attractive in winter? Will they drop fruit or large seeds on people, pavement and cars?

☞ **Money-saving Tip: Plant trees to reduce the cost of heating in winter and provide cooling effects in summer.**

Pay attention to the specifics of your site – patterns of sun and shade, the micro climate created by adjacent buildings and fences, and the slopes and soil conditions. You'll want deciduous shade trees on the south and west sides of the house to mitigate summer sun. You may need evergreens to serve as windbreaks in winter or to provide privacy.

Choose your conifers very cautiously. While there are numerous evergreens that are appropriate for small gardens, including dwarf varieties of pine, yew, arborvitae, cypress and Korean fir, most are too big for urban lots. If you're thinking of buying a "living Christmas tree" as part of your garden's green foundation, let me tell you about the deodar cedar that took over my in-laws' yard in Seattle.

Assured (by someone who I hope is no longer in the nursery business) that it would never grow taller than twelve feet, the Greens planted the tree in front of their house when my husband was a boy. Fifty years later, this cedar's trunk is over four feet in diameter. It poses a threat to their house, the neighbor's house, the power lines and every bus that goes by. Of course, nothing will grow under it. They've had the monster topped three times (it's truly ugly), but the price for removing it is astronomical. So, use that Christmas tree as a container plant, donate it to a park department, or plant it and cut it for Christmas next year!

Evergreen shrubs should be used to provide the garden's year-around good looks, but don't overlook deciduous shrubs. They can add a lot of seasonal color. I like flowering deciduous shrubs planted against a backdrop of evergreens so that when the deciduous plants are bare in winter they do not create a conspicuous hole in the landscape. And since many of the wonderful old flowering shrubs tend to become "leggy," I generally plant perennials and ground covers at their base. I'm enthusiastic about the new, more compact varieties, such as miniature forsythia and dwarf hydrangeas.

Design Tips

We plant-lovers have to resist the temptation to buy one of everything. Too many different species make a fidgety-looking landscape. A garden should be like a symphony, with recurring themes. Choose fewer varieties and mass shrubs of the same variety in groups of three or five for a bigger effect. Always buy an uneven number of the same species unless you are using a pair for plants to flank a doorway or mark the entrance to some part of the landscape. (Don't ask me why planting in uneven numbers is more visually pleasing, just trust me on this one. It works!)

Select shrubbery that will complement the color of your house. If a client has a red brick house, for example, I would never plant magenta-pink azaleas anywhere on the property. Likewise, pink brick and red rhodies are generally incompatible. I've often suggested painting a house some shade of gray, tan or white simply because landscape plantings play best against a neutral background.

I encourage my clients to choose an overall color scheme and stick with it throughout the garden. I have never hesitated to remove or transplant existing shrubs that exhibit color clashes. One of my clients bought a home that had one of every imaginable color of rhododendron. We removed all the reds and oranges and grouped the remaining pink and purple varieties by color, using white rhodies as "separators." To add color through the seasons, we interspersed other flowering species. The result is far more pleasing.

Avoid concentrating all your color in one season. One of my gardening friends described spring in the Northwest as "a painted harlot!" Everything blooms at once. Then in summer, Northwest landscapes, which are typically filled with rhododendrons, azaleas, dogwoods and spring bulbs, become rather dull. It always surprised me to visit Seattle in July and find the city more drab than Austin, Texas, which is ablaze with blooming crepe myrtle and tough, drought-tolerant annuals and perennials in the heat of the summer. With such a wealth of summer-blooming plants to choose from here, it's a pity to include only those that bloom in spring.

Flower color, which is relatively short-lived, is just one aspect of the plant you choose. Consider the texture of its leaves. You can use this old Japanese trick to make a small garden seem larger: plant coarse-textured shrubs up close to the living areas, medium textures in the middle ground and fine-textured plantings at the rear. (The plants will appear to recede, creating an illusion of depth.) Consider also that sheen often attracts the eye as much as color.

Try for variety in the shades of green, and add an occasional red or purple-leafed plant to create more interest in the planting scheme. You can use variegated plants to create subtle color harmonies. White or gray hues serve as peacemakers in the garden. The Northwest is blessed with gradual frosts in autumn that produce yellows, oranges and reds, so be sure to include some plants for fall color, too. For winter interest, look for shrubs and trees with attractive bark, sculptural forms and/or berries.

In landscape design, you are painting a picture in three dimensions. Consider the mature form of each plant and its ultimate size. You'll rarely need to prune if you choose plants that will not overgrow the spots for which they are intended. Never plant large shrubs and trees under eaves or power lines, and make sure that plants are spaced at proper distances from each other.

When mature, the shrubs should slightly overlap one another, without crowding others out. Correct spacing is one of the most difficult aspects of planting design. You need to base your decision on each plant's ultimate, unpruned width. For example, if I'm massing a certain variety of rhododendron that normally spreads to five-feet, I space the plants about two and a half feet apart. There are a number of books that specify the height and width of common landscape shrubs. Often the plant tag will provide this information.

☞ **Money-saving tip: If you cannot afford large, mature shrubs, don't be tempted to crowd a lot of little plants together.**

Leave enough space between young plants for them to attain their full width. Fill-in with annuals for the first few years if the bed looks skimpy. Eventually they will grow together, and the shrub mass will shade out most weeds. Your ultimate goal should be to re-create a forest canopy. Group shade-loving plants beneath the trees and encourage communities of self-sustaining plants.

☞ Money-saving tip: Consider Ease of Maintenance

The plants you'll find in the nurseries are not all equally easy to grow. Before you choose the exact species for a specific place, you should know that certain varieties are more resistant to pests and disease than others. Unfortunately, some of the Northwest's most beloved plants – rhododendrons, azaleas, dogwoods, spruces and roses – are the very ones most often brought into the Master Gardener's clinics with problems!

Root weevils and nematodes are the rhododendron's biggest enemies. In most cases, good sanitation and maintenance will prevent insects from becoming a life-threatening problem. Most nurseries can direct you to the varieties of rhododendrons that are more resistant to pest and disease problems. Dogwoods are susceptible to anthracnose, so if you want a dogwood, you'll be wise to choose a kousa, which outperforms the native or Florida dogwood in terms of fending-off the fungus. You would be wise to avoid spruces, which are very susceptible to pests, and choose instead from the hundreds of other conifers that perform well in Northwest gardens. As for roses, knowing the best varieties and applying proper cultural practices makes all the difference between poor and good performance.

Talk to a nurseryman about the plants you are considering for your landscape. If the salesperson at a nursery doesn't seem knowledgeable, ask to speak to the owner or manager. Inquire about the plant's characteristics and maintenance needs. Be sure to ask about guarantees!

☞ Money-saving tip: Learn how to select a healthy plant.

Look for supple branches and plump buds that would indicate a young, vigorous tree. Conifers should show evidence of recent increase in size. Pull a plant out into the aisle to inspect it. If a container-grown tree has a stake in it, ask the salesperson to untie it. If the tree bends, the trunk is too weak. Look for healthy leaves and a full branching pattern. A gnarled, misshapen tree that nobody else wants might work as a picturesque focal point, but generally you will want a plant with a consistent shape and evenly spaced branches.

You'll find trees and shrubs offered in three different forms: bare-root (which must be planted while they are dormant), balled-and-burlapped (usually field-grown plants that have been dug during the cool months) and container-grown plants (typically more expensive, may be root-bound, but can be planted at any time). One is not inherently better than the other; there are advantages and disadvantages to each.

☞ Money-saving tip: "Bargain plants" are usually no bargain.

Poor root development and unbalanced or dried-out roots are the most difficult defects to detect when you walk through a nursery, yet the roots are key to the plant's survival. Reject plants that have roots growing out of the container or roots that encircle the trunk. Don't be afraid to ask the salesperson to remove a shrub or tree from its container so that you can inspect for encircling roots. (Once you get the plant home, if you find that it has tightly wound roots, take a spray nozzle, wash the roots and spread them out by hand. Otherwise, they'll continue to grow in circles and the plant will never develop properly.)

☞ **Money-saving tip: Learn proper planting techniques.**

The major cause of plant loss is due to improper planting. Remove tags, wires and everything else that is not biodegradable. Cut the string from around burlap. Remove the top six-inches of the fabric after the plant is in the hole. If it becomes obvious that the balled and burlapped plant has been grown in heavy clay soil, remove the burlap completely and wash away some of the soil with a spray nozzle as you're backfilling the hole. I've been called to clients' homes to inspect a dead tree as long as two years after it was planted. In digging it up, we discovered that the roots were still growing in the shape of the container or that the burlap was intact, with no roots penetrating the surrounding soil.

Avoid planting too deep. There's an old saying, "Never plant a $50 tree in a $5 hole." The maxim is true, but you don't need to dig to China. Calculate the depth and width of the soil in the container. Make the hole one-inch less deep than the container's soil depth, but twice its width. The shallow depth is critical because the plant will die from lack of oxygen if it is planted too deeply. The extra width is important because all of the feeding roots are in the top six-inches, and they need room to spread quickly.

Mix garden soil and composted organic matter (half and half) and fill in around the sides of the plant, gently tamping in the backfill and moistening the soil as you go. Water thoroughly. If the soil settles, add more backfill around the edges. Do not pile soil on top of the rootball. Apply a two-inch layer of mulch over the top, but don't place mulch up against the trunk of the plant. Be sure the dark ring or stain that's usually found just above the root ball remains above the finished ground surface. Never use synthesized nitrogen fertilizer on a newly planted tree or shrub. It will burn the roots.

Stake young trees if they're in a location subject to high wind or if the rootball is small in proportion to the height and branching pattern. Three evenly placed stakes work best. Use a soft strapping material or guy wires covered with a piece of rubber hose to avoid damaging the trunk. Remove the stakes after the first year. Keep the soil moist but not waterlogged. If you plant a tree or large shrub during the dry months, build a low mound around the outer rim of the rootball to act as a water-retaining basin. Be sure to remove the ring of soil before the rainy season begins.

☞ **Money-saving tip: Protect your investment with proper maintenance techniques.**

Keep a watchful eye for pests, disease and dieback. Reduction in new shoots and a scarcity of new leaves are reliable clues that the tree or shrub is needing attention. Mulch trees and shrubs to cut down on climatic stress. (Mulch also prevents damage by lawn mower or string weeder.) Read all about proper pruning techniques in Chapter 3.

☞ **Money-saving tip: Shop around.**

Mail-order nurseries and growers offer consumers savings by eliminating the middle man. Large nurseries buy in volume, often passing the savings on to customers. Do what the professionals do. Mail or fax a plant list to several suppliers to check availability and prices.

Most people buy their shrubs and trees at the large garden centers near their own homes, and in Chapter 12 you'll find some of the best in the region. This section lists other sources you may not know. Some nurseries and garden centers specialize in large trees of various species, and others concentrate on the best varieties of a single species. Some are primarily "to-the-trade," but will sell to retail customers under certain circumstances. ✽

Sources for Specimen Trees & Shrubs
Washington

Four acres that look like a park make a fine setting for a large selection of trees, shrubs, ground covers and unusual grafted conifers. Alpine Nursery has an additional five acres where the trees are field-grown. The nursery features living topiaries and unusual varieties of Japanese maples, and it's strong in fruit trees and berries, too. In spring, the company also offers bedding plants and perennials. Sales occur in August and September. The conifer selection is best in the fall.

Alpine Nursery, Inc.
16023 S.E. 144th Street
Renton, Washington 98059
☎ *206/255-1598*

Hours Daily 9-5:30
Accessible No

You'll find weekly specials on the flowering trees, shrubs, weeping conifers and native plants at this twenty-acre nursery in the Nooksack River Valley. See complete listing on page 207.

Cloud Mountain Farm & Nursery
6906 Goodwin Road
Everson, Washington 98247
☎ *206/966-5859*

Landscape architect Michael Lee grows a wide range of unusual conifers and broadleaf evergreen trees and shrubs. See complete listing on page 262.

Colvos Creek Farm

P.O. Box 1512
Vashon, Washington 98070
☎ *206/441-1509*

New in '93 and coming on strong is Boyd Shirley's small nursery that focuses on unusual trees and shrubs, but also offers interesting perennials. The plants are attractively displayed. "I started the nursery because I couldn't find the plants I wanted," he says, as he points out stewartias, fragrant snowball, snake bark maples, staghorn sumacs, evergreen holly oak and Seybold magnolias as examples. He plans to stick to a selection of better hybrids in the woody ornamentals and the "big and bold" perennials he especially likes.

Cottage Grove Nursery

4815 Guide Meridian Road
Bellingham, Washington 98226
☎ *206/398-1231*

Hours Mon-Sat 9-6, Sun 10-5
(mid-Feb through October);
closed in winter
Accessible Difficult on gravel

Furney's Nursery

21215 Pacific Highway S.
Des Moines, Washington 98198
☎ *206/878-8761*

13427 N.E. 16th
Bellevue, Washington 98005
☎ *206/747-8282*

5261 State Highway 303 N.E.
Bremerton, Washington 98310
☎ *206/373-8812*

Furney's three large garden centers offer an amazing scope of choices in landscape plant material. Sizes range from seedlings and rooted cuttings to 35-foot-tall specimen trees. See complete listings on pages 337, 340 and 348.

Heronswood Nursery

7530 288th N.E.
Kingston, Washington 98346
☎ *206/297-4172*

Excellent alternatives are available by mail from Heronswood Nursery, which specializes in uncommon trees and shrubs. See complete listing in Collector's Plants, page 265.

Hollyvale Farm

P.O. Box 69
Humptulips, Washington 98552
☎ *206/987-2218*

Hours *By appointment only*
Accessible *Limited*
Mail Order
Catalog *Free with SASE*

Hollyvale's fifty-four registered varieties of holly were developed by John Weiman, and some are to be found nowhere else in the world. "We sell the best holly in the U.S.A.," says owner Bonnie L. Heintz. "We plant to order – you order ten plants in spring, and we'll have them in the fall (or vice versa)." Bonnie and her partner have 26 years of combined experience, and they are advised by holly experts throughout the world. "We give advice over the phone. All the time!" Their hollies can be found in Kew Gardens in London, the National Arboretum in Washington D.C. and in the royal gardens in Holland and Denmark.

Olympic Nursery

16507 140th Place N.E.
Woodinville, Washington 98072
☎ *206/483-9254*

Hours *Mon-Fri 9-5, Sat 10-4*
Accessible *Partially*

Specializing in large field-grown balled & burlapped trees, Olympic Nursery stocks both conifers and decidu-ous varieties. Among its twenty or so deciduous species are several choice maples, zelkova, aspen, Mt. Fuji cherries and other flowering fruit trees. Most are in the range of two to six inches in caliper. They've several kinds of ever-greens, in heights from five to twenty feet, suitable for use as screening mate-rial. The company will deliver and install the plants it sells.

Horticulturist Herb Senft grows uncommon trees and shrubs for fellow "plantaholics." See complete listing on page 180. "How can you tell if you're addicted?" he poses. "Do you look at the foliage when watching James Bond? Have you asked your garden center to open a drive-through window?"

See complete listing on page 180.

Skyline Nursery

4772 Sequim-Dungeness Way
Sequim, Washington 98382
☎ *206/683-2294*

"We have five growing nurseries with a very extensive list of landscape plants, including 500 varieties of rhododendron, 100 varieties of azaleas, weeping evergreens, weeping birch and unusual grafted maples," says owner Fred Palmer. "We also grow many ground covers and dwarf varieties of conifers and shrubs." He particularly recommends three summer-flowering trees, tall stewartia (*Stewartia monadelphia*), Japanese snowdrop (*Styrax japonica*) and kousa dogwoods, all of which the company grows in quantity. "Our plants are dug and transplanted each year, thus making very fibrous root systems that can be successfully transplanted any time of the year. They are grown in full sun with no protection, so they are very hardy. We provide finished trees up to ten feet tall, offer planting services, and have a good staff to assist you with plant use and microclimate needs."

Star Nursery and Landscaping

13916 42nd Avenue S.
Seattle, Washington 98168
☎ *206/241-2115*

Hours *Mon-Sat 8-4:30*
Accessible *Yes*

Celebrated in the trade for its extensive selection of trees and shrubs, Wells Nursery grows everything it sells. Many of the dwarf conifer varieties the company offers were developed here. The nursery maintains an impressive inventory of large deciduous and evergreen species, too, and the staff will recommend qualified contractors to plant "investment trees" on your property. Among the fine flowering trees and shrubs in stock are kousa dogwoods, hydrangeas, lilacs and rhodies. Wells also offers several select ground covers.

Wells Nursery

424 E. Section Street
Mt. Vernon, Washington 98273
☎ *206/336-6544*

Hours *Mon-Sat 8:30-5*
Accessible *Yes*

Wells Medina Nursery

8300 N.E. 24th Street
Bellevue, Washington 98004
☎ *206/454-1853*

In search of unusually fine trees, landscape architects often take their clients to Wells Medina. See complete listing on page 339.

West Coast Wholesale Nursery

18720 State Route 203
Monroe, Washington 98272
☎ *206/794-5457*

Hours *Daily 8-5*
Accessible *Yes*

West Coast is one of the few big wholesale nurseries in the Northwest open to the general public. The 35-acre Monroe facility includes a clean, paved sales yard that's well-stocked year-around. Japanese maples are the specialty. This large supplier, which has served nurseries on both the West Coast and the East Coast for the last 15 years, has over 25,000 trees in production at its two locations. Prices are reasonable, quantity discounts are available and advice is free for the asking. The nursery is located three and a half miles south of Monroe on the Monroe-Duvall Highway.

Whitney Gardens & Nursery

Highway 101
Brinnon, Washington 98320
☎ *206/796-4411*

In addition to rhododendrons, for which Whitney Gardens is famous, this fabulous nursery stocks a large number of unusual specimen trees. See complete listing on page 155.

Oregon

Big Trees Today of Oregon, Inc.

7365 S.W. Trinity Place
Cornelius, Oregon 97113
☎ *503/224-6190*

Hours *By appointment only*
Accessible *No*
Catalog *Free*
FAX *503/640-2877*

Big Trees Today lives up to its name with selected species available up to 14 inches in caliper. A specialized nursery and planting service, the company offers field-grown, commercial-landscape-quality trees. "Our trees are not thin, spindly container-grown plants," says Terry Hickman. The location is four miles south of Hillsboro, Oregon, off the Johnson School Road.

Located in the foothills of Chehalem Mountain in Scholls, this wholesale nursery grows a wide variety of ornamental shrubs, trees and ground covers. They list several species of native plants, wetland plant material and ornamental grasses, as well. While they cannot ship to retail customers, serious gardeners are welcome to shop here.

Chehalem Mountain Nursery, Inc.
14375 S.W. Patricia Avenue
Hillsboro, Oregon 97123
☎ *503/628-0353*

Hours *Mon-Fri 9-3*
Accessible *No*
FAX *503/628-0606*

Several years ago, Flora Lan Nursery was mistakenly listed in a magazine as a mail-order source for trees and shrubs. It's actually a wholesale nursery that was unprepared to ship plants. Not wanting to disappoint anyone, they set up Five Star Gardens to handle the orders, and it's a tremendous success. The company grows 1,400 varieties of several hundred species, including heathers, rhododendrons, kalmias, camellias, magnolias, azaleas, hydrangeas, conifers and maples. The catalog is strictly a plant list with no descriptive material, but it provides an exceptional variety of trees and shrubs. All plants are one-gallon size.

Five Star Gardens
Route 2, Box 252B
Forest Grove, Oregon 97116
☎ *503/357-8386*

Mail Order
Catalog *Free*

This mail-order nursery is a nationally known source for conifers, shrubs and flowering trees. See complete listing in Collector's Plants, page 263.

Forestfarm
990 Tetherow
Williams, Oregon 97544
☎ *503/846-6963*

Marjory and Roger Gossler's rare plant nursery carries an excellent selection of deciduous flowering trees and shrubs, including magnolias, hydrangeas and stewartias. They claim the largest selection of witch hazels (*Hamamelis*) anywhere. See complete listing on page 264.

Gossler Farm's Nursery
1200 Weaver Road
Springfield, Oregon 97478
☎ *503/746-3922*

Hazel Dell Gardens

23230 S. Highway 99E
Canby, Oregon 97013
☎ *503/266-4071*

Hours *Mon-Sat 8-4:30*
Accessible *No*
FAX *503/266-6996*

Primarily a wholesale nursery, Hazel Dell Gardens sells its trees, shrubs and ground covers to retail customers. Come prepared to go into the fields and accept the fact that not everything is tagged. There are sixty-five acres of plant materials here! The company grows an unusually wide selection of deciduous magnolias (some patented varieties), evergreen azaleas and dwarf conifers, plus excellent selections in many other popular ornamentals. The owners recommend their scarlet oaks as exceptional shade trees and mention that the Hogans red cedar is especially good as a drought-tolerant windbreak for large properties.

Kasch Nursery

2860 N.E. Kelly Place
Gresham, Oregon 97030-2793
☎ *503/661-0357*

Hours *By appointment only*
Accessible *Yes*
Mail Order
Catalog *Free*

The clientele for this dwarf conifer nursery has developed mostly by word-of-mouth, so if you were unfamiliar with the company, the secret is out! Tim and Lorry Kasch sell unusual conifers and grafted ornamentals by mail and also by appointment at their retail location. 'Horstmanns Silberlock' Korean fir, 'Idaho Gem' Douglas fir and 'Blaue Hexe' noble fir are just a few of the collector's conifers grown here. You'll find directions to the nursery printed on the catalog.

Loucks Nursery

14200 Campground Road
Cloverdale, Oregon 97112
☎ *503/392-3166*

Hours *By appointment only*
Accessible *No*
Mail Order
Catalog *$1 (refundable)*
Mailing address *P.O. Box 102*
Cloverdale, Oregon 97112

"As far as we know, we have the biggest selection of named varieties of Japanese maples in Oregon. Many are good for container growing and bonsai," say Mert and Marjorie Loucks. Their plants are grown for the wholesale trade, and all are one-year grafts and larger. Cloverdale is not on every Oregon map. It's south of Tillamook, just five miles inland from the coast. Be sure to ask for directions to the nursery when you make an appointment.

Elizabeth Hollingsworth says, "If you have ideas and money and holes in the ground, we have plants to make your life more pleasurable. Pick your own from ten acres of growing grounds filled with fresh, clean, crisp, healthy containerized landscape plants. There's even a play area for the kids." You'll find good buys at the "Twofer" sales in June, July and October, and there's usually a bargain area. The nursery is situated five and one quarter miles east of Clackamas. Conifers, shrubs, ferns, ornamental grasses and ground covers are the focus at this mostly wholesale nursery.

The Plantsmen
19127 S.E. Highway 212
Clackamas, Oregon 97015
☎ *503/658-3720*

Hours *Daily 8-5*
Accessible *No*
FAX *503/658-3269*

"We grow row crops," explains owner Monte R. Cooke. The company keeps a large inventory of shade and flowering trees, as well as evergreen shrubs and living Christmas trees. You'll find lots of mugho pines, assorted junipers and large selections of arborvitae, rhodies and azaleas. Planting and maintenance tips are always available. "This is a working man's nursery in a nice setting with park-like trails. We offer growers' prices to the retail trade. Once you find us, you will be back." Mark downs occur in July and August.

Sandy Nursery
29804 S.E. Orient Drive
Gresham, Oregon 97080-8816
☎ *503/663-1795*

Hours *Daily 8-7 (spring & summer);*
9-5 (fall & winter)
Accessible *Yes, with exceptions*

An outlet for one of the largest wholesale growers in the region, Valley View stocks over a thousand varieties of trees, shrubs and herbaceous garden plants. See complete listing on page 378.

Valley View Nursery
1675 N. Valley View Road
Ashland, Oregon 97520
☎ *503/488-2450*

From December through mid-April, Westwinds ships hybrid poplars up to eight-feet in height via UPS. Call for ordering information. See nursery listing on page 381.

Westwinds Nursery, Turf and Landscape
Rt. 1, Box 1920
Hermiston, Oregon 97838
☎ *503/567-7235*

Idaho

Franz Witte Landscape Company

9770 W. State Street
Boise, Idaho 83703
☎ 208/853-0808

Hours Daily 8-6
(mid-March through November)
Accessible Difficult on gravel
FAX 208/853-4503

Green goods of all kinds are the focus here, with an emphasis on "finished stock." You'll find two to six-inch caliper shade trees, eight-foot-tall conifers, and shrubs worthy of a mature landscape. Even the perennials Mr. Witte carries are specimen-size plants. He describes himself as a "gleaner," one who looks for the best material from small growers in the region. The nursery maintains a huge selection of hostas, twenty-five varieties of specialty conifers and unusual varieties of Japanese maples ranging in price from $39 to $1,500. The owner's sense of playfulness is evidenced by a flock of plastic flamingos and the funny signs that greet customers. Children will enjoy digging in the sandbox or watching the fish and ducks.

Mountain Springs Nursery

2075 Upland Drive
Sandpoint, Idaho 83864
☎ 208/263-5214

Hours Sat 9-5 (March through Nov)
or by appointment
Accessible Yes

"The majority of our business is in large-caliper trees (blue spruce, sub-alpine fir, aspen and other deciduous species) appropriate for the heavily forested areas of Northern Idaho," says Denny Shellhorn. This family-run wholesale/retail nursery relocates trees relocation with a 44" Vermeer Treespade. You'll also find good selections in perennials and both evergreen and deciduous shrubs. They stock a variety of spiraeas, cotoneaster and viburnums, plus a number of cold-hardy rhododendrons. Merchandise is marked down in the fall.

Pocatello Sod & Trees

1524 Sod Farm Road
Pocatello, Idaho 83204
☎ 208/232-8987

Hours Mon-Fri 8-5, Sat 8-2
(April through Nov)
Accessible Yes

The sod in this company's name is Kentucky blue grass, which it sells by the square foot. The trees are Colorado blue spruce, Austrian, Scotch and ponderosa pine, Douglas fir and quaking aspen. The nursery offers choose-and-cut Christmas trees in November and December.

Webb Nursery grows trees and shrubs suitable for dry, cold climates above 6,000 feet. The company offers quaking Aspen trees in all sizes and a wide range of other hardy plants. Also see listing on page 386.

Webb Nursery

162 Glendale Road
Bellevue, Idaho 83313

891 Washington Avenue
Ketchum, Idaho 83340
☎ *208/726-4927 (both stores)*

Hours *Daily 8-5:30 (April through Sept);*
Mon-Fri 8-4:30 (Oct through March);
Daily 8-5:30 (holidays)
Accessible *Yes*
Mail Order
Catalog *Free to public within state;*
$4 outside Idaho
Mailing address *P.O. Box 744*
Ketchum, Idaho 83340
FAX *208/788-2633*

British Columbia

These garden centres are supplied by Cannor's wholesale division, which grows over 400 species of trees and shrubs on 400 acres in the Fraser Valley! While fruit trees are the specialty, they are but a small part of the whole. Gardeners drive miles for the quality and selection offered by this major supplier. Also see listings on pages 392, 393 and 396.

Cannor Nurseries

34261 Marshall Road
Abbotsford, British Columbia V2S 1L8
☎ *604/854-1616*

48291 Chilliwack Central Road
Chilliwack, British Columbia V2P 6H3
☎ *604/795-5914*

4660 Elk Lake Road
Victoria, British Columbia V8Z 5M1
☎ *604/658-5415*

"We specialize in large-caliper tree sales and relocation," says Judy Hauser. "With our equipment and professional staff, we are capable of packaging and moving trees up to 12" caliper. We also buy, sell and offer storage service for our customers." The company is noted for good selections in fruit and nut trees, as well.

Trees Unlimited

21373 64th Avenue
Langley, British Columbia V0X 1T0
☎ *604/534-8733*

Hours *Mon-Fri 8-4:30,*
Sat by appointment
Accessible *No*
FAX *604/534-1824*

Rhododendrons & Friends

Members of the *Ericaceae* family are particularly well suited to the region west of the Cascades. They are so well suited, in fact, that a large number of nurseries specialize in ericaceous plants. This large, showy tribe includes such familiar genus names as *Andromeda, Arbutus, Arctostaphylos, Calluna, Enkianthus, Erica, Gaultheria, Kalmia, Leucothoe, Oxydendrum, Pernettya, Pieris, Rhododendron* and *Vaccinium.*

You'll find a number of desirable natives within the family, from Pacific madrone trees to shrubs like salal and evergreen huckleberry. Kinnikinnik and bog rosemary are especially fine native ground covers. Our Pacific rhododendron (*R. macrophyllum*) and deciduous Western azaleas (*R. occidentale*) never look out of place in a Northwest garden.

Many of the native ericaceous species cannot compete for "splash" with species found in other parts of the world or the multitude of hybridized varieties bred for color and form. Native kalmias pale beside the Eastern mountain laurel, for example, and the three Western "alpine heathers" are not as dependable in garden situations as European heaths and heathers. Therefore, most of the local specialists grow non-native species and the thousands of colorful cultivars thereof. Certainly no group of shrubs can match rhododendrons and friends for beauty and length of blooming season.

Members of this family (native or imported) are happy dwelling together in the garden. All want acid soil; most need ample water and good drainage. They generally prefer afternoon shade. The larger the leaf, the less sun tolerant the plant will be. This is especially true of rhododendrons. Growers can tell you which varieties will do best in the location you have in mind. ❧

Sources for Ericaceous Plants
Washington

A&R Propagating is a small family-run nursery producing mostly azaleas, rhododendrons and other ericaceous plants including blueberries and huckleberries. "We have the largest assortment of rhododendrons on the Olympic Peninsula after Whitney Gardens, says Frank Skerbeck, who notes that his nursery helps support a rhododendron show garden. Selection is best during the February to July bloom period. They hold a sale in October when plants are thinned-out in the propagating beds.

A&R Propagating

3225 E. Masters Road
Port Angeles, Washington 98362
☎ 206/457-9177

Hours Mon-Sat 8-6, Sun 12-6
Accessible Partially
Catalog Free

The primary West Coast retail grower of the genus *Kalmia*, Barbara Brown offers twenty varieties. Mountain laurel (*Kalmia latifolia*), an east coast native, enjoys the same growing conditions as rhodies. The species is remarkably drought tolerant, hardy to minus 20 degrees, slow-growing, and hard-to-find as mature plants. Brown's has a stock of seven-year-olds about three feet in height. The dwarf varieties are also quite popular, especially as bonsai subjects. The nursery ships small-size kalmias of every variety. In addition to mountain laurels, they grow lots of azaleas and rhodies, and they've recently branched into a full-scale garden center.

Brown's Kalmia & Azalea Nursery

5100 Lincoln Road
Blaine, Washington 98230
☎ 206/371-2489

Hours Mon-Sat 9-5, Sun 1-4
(except in winter)
Accessible Yes
Mail Order
Catalog Kalmia list with SASE
Mailing address 8527 Semiahmoo Dr.
Blaine, Washington 98230
FAX 206/371-5551

Fawn Farms Nursery

607 State Highway 409
Cathlamet, Washington 98612-9730
☎ 206/849-4769

Hours Mon-Fri 9-7, Sat 9-4 (summer);
Mon-Sat 9-4 (fall through spring); by
appointment on Sunday
Accessible Yes

Fawn Farms stocks a wide variety of azaleas, plus many yaks and small-leaf varieties of rhododendrons. You'll also find several varieties of unusual grafted Japanese maples, deciduous conifers, and uncommon deciduous shade and flowering trees. The owners grow a lot of nice perennials, as well. Dolly Hartzell writes, "Come and enjoy the beauty and peace of our island. The geese fly overhead, and the Colombian Whitetail deer browse in the field as you shop in the tranquillity of our little family-owned nursery." From Oregon, take the ferry from Westport to Puget Island. From Washington, take SR-4 to Cathlamet, Main Street south to SR-409 and cross the bridge to the island.

Hammond's Acres of Rhodys

25911 70th Avenue N.E.
Arlington, Washington 98223
☎ 206/435-9206

Hours Daily 10-dark
Accessible No
Mail Order
Catalog $2

Hammond's collection of rhododendrons from around the world spans a range of heights from one inch to 26 feet. Because they spread up to three-feet in width, the tiny ones make a terrific ground cover. There are two fields and twelve greenhouses full of container-grown rhodies and azaleas here! The nursery carries a large selection of drought-tolerant rhodies and also stocks kalmias, fruit trees and blueberry bushes. The owners advise customers on a one-to-one basis and provide pamphlets on the care and feeding of the plants they sell.

Hazelwood Gardens Rhododendron Nursery

11230 S.E. 80th Street
Renton, Washington 98056
☎ 206/255-3318

Hours Daily 9-6 (Feb through July); by
appointment (Aug through Jan)
Accessible No

"We specialize in rhododendrons, kalmias, azaleas and lilacs," say partners Duane Johnson and Bonnie Bodin. "You'll find a few rhododendron varieties here that other growers may not have, such as 'Tropicana' and 'Frank Gallsworthy'. We keep our eyes open to new hybrids, try to educate our customers in the care of rhododendrons and help people with pest control and other problems. If we don't know the answer to their questions, we find out."

"We have the largest selection of heaths and heathers in North America – nearly 400 different cultivars," say Bob and Alice Knight. "We've been growing heathers commercially for more than 30 years and have mail-order customers in all 50 states plus most Canadian Provinces. Selection is best from June through-November; but plants are available throughout the year in containers." They supply instruction sheets with their plants, and the staff is well-trained to answer questions and offer advice.

Heather Acres, Inc.
1199 Monte-Elma Road
Elma, Washington 98541
☎ *206/482-3258*

Hours Mon-Fri 8-4:30; by appointment during winter months
Accessible *Yes*
Mail Order
Catalog *Free with SASE*
Mailing address *P.O.Box 850*
Elma, Washington 98541

Sallie D. Allen is a noted authority on ericaceous plants, and her own garden is a forty-year collection of rare trees, shrubs, ground covers and natives. She is willing to sell plants out of her garden, but since she's in a quiet neighborhood, it is vital that you make an appointment. She appreciates help with the digging, so bring a shovel. Ask about her hands-on propagation classes and study groups. She is a gold mine of information and her landscape is interesting in every season.

Heathwood Cottage Nursery
18540 26th Avenue N.E.
Lake Forest Park, Washington 98155
☎ *206/363-3189*

Hours By appointment only
Accessible *Partially*

"We've been described as a small Butchart garden," writes Eloise James. "Our plants are in the ground and the nursery is meant to look like a park – a place to walk, look and smell, to ooh and aah. I love people and plants and like what I am doing, so consequently I enjoy talking about my subject. I want people to know and appreciate rhodies. I'm also totally sold on the deciduous azaleas for their beauty and hardiness." Ms. James offers tours as well as garden advice. Her place is located north of Eatonville between Highway 7 and Highway 161.

James Rhododendron Nursery
37114 Eatonville Cutoff Road E.
Eatonville, Washington 98328
☎ *206/832-6187*

Hours Mon-Fri 9-7, Sun 1-5
Accessible *Yes*

Kattenhorn Gardens

13711 48th Drive S.E.
Snohomish, Washington 98290
☎ *206/337-9253*

Hours *Sat 10-5, Sun 12-5 (April & May);*
by appointment throughout the year
Accessible *No*

From one-gallon plants to field-grown landscape-size specimens, the two hundred varieties of rhododendrons you will find here have been carefully selected and tended by owners Bob and Charlene Templeton. From I-5: take exit 186 east to Seattle Road (approximately three miles) and turn right. Take a left on 136th, which becomes 48th Drive or Kattenhorn Road. Look for the sign.

☆DESTINATION
Rhododendron Species Botanical Garden

2525 S. 336th Street
Federal Way, Washington 98063
☎ *206/661-9377*
(gift shop & general information);
838-4646 (from Seattle),
927-6960 (from Tacoma)

Hours *Daily (except Thurs) 10-4 (March through May), Sat-Wed 11-4 (June through Feb)*
Accessible *Yes*
Catalog *Free with membership*
Mailing address *P.O. Box 3798*
Federal Way, Washington 98063-3798
FAX *206/838-4686*

This non-profit botanical garden displays 500 different species rhododendrons (as opposed to hybrid rhododendrons). Its twenty-four acres are open to the public year-around, but of course the ideal rhody-viewing time is in April and May. The garden also features a fern collection and heather collection, as well as significant collections of maples and alpines. The gift shop sells plants, garden books, tools and gifts. The garden is located on the grounds of the Weyerhaeuser Headquarters, although it is not affiliated with the company, and the Pacific Rim Bonsai Collection is adjacent to the garden. The Rhododendron Species Foundation's education program offers classes, demonstrations and field trips. With a membership, you'll be kept well-informed and given discounts on plants.

Silver Sun Nursery

4506 147th Avenue N.E.
Lake Stevens, Washington 98258
☎ *206/335-0414*

Hours *Sat & Sun 9-5*
(mid-April through May);
by appointment throughout the year
Accessible *No*

Silver Sun is a small nursery specializing in field-grown dwarf and semi-dwarf rhododendrons. The company's 100-plus varieties are especially ideal for small gardens, including a good selection of dense, compact yak hybrids (*R. yakushimanum*), which are very cold-tolerant, late-blooming plants with unusual foliage. From Highway 9, travel east on Highway 92 for three miles, turn left on 44th and continue one mile, turn left on 147th Avenue N.E.

A wholesale nursery, The Sweetbriar opens its doors to the public only four weekends each year (the last weekend in April, the first weekend in May and in mid-July and mid-September) What a special treat these events afford the home gardener! You'll find a wide selection of interesting, high-quality plant material and a very knowledgeable staff. They propagate over 100 varieties of rhodies (both field-grown and containerized), including a large selection of the easy-to-grow, difficult-to-propagate yak hybrids. They've an ever-expanding collection of perennials as well.

The Sweetbriar

13825 132nd Avenue N.E.
Kirkland, Washington 98034
☎ *206/821-2222*

Hours *Special weekends only*
Accessible *Yes*
Mailing address *P.O. Box 25*
Woodinville, Washington 98072
FAX *206/821-2986*

Now here's a gorgeous place! Whitney Garden's seven acres exhibit 2500 varieties of rhododendrons, plus large stocks of specimen azaleas, mountain laurels, maples, magnolias and camellias. In business since 1955, this "destination" nursery estimates that some of the plant material is 50 years old, and 20-foot-tall rhododendrons can still be found among the stock. The color show begins in February and extends into July. Peak blooming season occurs around Mother's Day. Autumn color is also spectacular in the large oaks, maples, magnolias and katsuras. Whitney's colorful catalog includes planting and cultural recommendations, a two-page schedule of blooming times for rhodies and a map of the nursery. The grounds are open for viewing from 9:00 in the morning until dusk. You'll see a box requesting a $1 donation for walking the grounds (a bargain), and they offer guided tours for groups. They'll ship anytime (September through April is best) and will take orders on certain plants. The nursery is located on Hood Canal, halfway between Port Townsend and Shelton.

DESTINATION ☆
Whitney Gardens & Nursery

Highway 101
Brinnon, Washington 98320
☎ *206/796-4411*

Hours *Daily 10-5:30*
Accessible *Partially*
Mail Order
Catalog *$4 (refundable with purchase of more than $50)*
Mailing address *P.O. Box F*
Brinnon, Washington 98320
FAX *206/ 796-4999*

Oregon

✩DESTINATION
The Bovees Nursery

*1737 S.W. Coronado Street
Portland, Oregon 97219*
☎ *503/244-9341*

Hours *Wed-Sat 9-6, Sun 1-6
(closed in Aug and Jan except
by appointment)*
Accessible *Yes, most areas*
Mail Order
Catalog *$2*

To serious rhododendron collectors, The Bovees Nursery is a national treasure. This elegant landscaped garden was originally planted in 1952 by Bob and Gertrude Bovee. Over a thousand species rhododendrons, hybrids and azaleas grow under the canopy of stately magnolias, paper bark maples, Persian parrotia, Chinese witch hazel and Japanese snowdrop trees. The species are displayed in their series, as they would be growing naturally in China, Japan, Korea, India, etc. In addition, Bovees' has a collection of over 300 different varieties of tropical rhododendrons, *Vireyas*, which make wonderful container plants outdoors in the summer.

Dover Nursery

*42125 S.E. Kleinsmith
Sandy, Oregon 97055*
☎ *503/668-7565*

Hours *By appointment only*
Accessible *Yes*

Although the 500 rhododendron varieties they grow cover a full range of sizes, Dover Nursery specializes in dwarf and semi dwarf varieties. "We are always evaluating new varieties, looking for those that are exceptional in the landscape – plants that have nice form and foliage throughout the year and won't overgrow their space, plants that are cold and/or sun tolerant and more disease resistant," says owner Mike Stewart. "A lot of varieties that come out aren't the best landscape plants." Primarily a wholesale resource, the company is always happy to sell to people looking for exceptional quality. They are not set up for mail order, but you can obtain a plant list at the nursery.

Greer Gardens
*1280 Goodpasture Island Road
Eugene, Oregon 97401-1794*
☎ *503/686-8266*

Greer Gardens is best-known for its rhododendrons and azaleas. You'll find this very special nursery listed in Collector's Plants on page 264.

"We have rhododendrons that at maturity are four-inches tall and plants that grow into trees. We offer over 1000 varieties of rhododendron hybrids and over 400 species rhododendrons in every color of flower except black and green," says Jan Kelley, speaking proudly for this small family-run nursery. She notes that the firm, which does most of its business mail-order, was formerly known as Hall Rhododendrons. "We specialize in new Northwest varieties, but grow rhodies suitable for every climate in the country and offer telephone assistance that covers all aspects of plant culture." Week-long sales are held in May and September.

Kelleygreen Rhododendron Nursery

6924 Highway 38
Drain, Oregon 97435
☎ *503/836-2290 or 1-800/477-5676*

Hours *By appointment only*
Accessible *No*
Mail Order
Catalog *Free*

Hardy evergreen azaleas are the specialty here. "We grow over 400 varieties," says Art Stubbs. "I believe we are the only nursery west of the Mississippi that sells the 'Williamsburg' variety." Because he and his wife Eleanor live on the property, they are generally available for retail sales, but appreciate a phone call before customers arrive. They also ship plants (see details in the catalog). The azaleas bloom from March to July, the selection is best in August and September.

Stubbs Shrubs

23225 S.W. Bosky Dell Lane
West Linn, Oregon 97068
☎ *503/638-5048*

Hours *By appointment only*
Accessible *Very difficult*
Mail Order
Catalog *$2 (refundable)*

Located just three miles inland from the Oregon coast, this ten-acre nursery displays over a thousand species and hybrid rhododendrons in a hilly, heavily wooded setting. Although their business is primarily wholesale, the owners welcome retail customers to their big beautiful garden and freely dispense garden advice.

Willard Thompson Nursery

2874 Alsea Highway
Waldport, Oregon 97394
☎ *503/563-3570*

Hours *By appointment only*
Accessible *Yes, but hilly*

British Columbia

C&T Azalea Nursery

16651 20th Avenue
Surrey, British Columbia V4B 5A8
☎ *604/536-7283*

Hours *Daily 9-8 (Feb through July);*
9-5 (Aug through Jan)
Accessible *Yes*
Mail Order *(to British Columbia only)*
Catalog *Free*

Carved from second-growth mixed forest, this nursery exists in a park-like setting under a canopy of huge trees. Here you'll discover three acres of hardy rhododendrons and azaleas from two to twenty-five years old. All are field grown; most have been root-pruned and transplanted annually. Many of C&T's varieties are exclusive. "As specialists, we offer expertise to clients and occasionally speak to garden clubs and write for newspapers and magazines," says Hart Wellmeier. "We also have the most exclusive collection of locally grown bonsai in Canada." Call for information about their seasonal sale in October.

Roses

The roses I cherished in Texas came from a supplier of old roses who started cuttings from abandoned homesteads and fence rows. One of his offerings, 'Caldwell Pink,' grew at my great-grandmother's house, which had been standing empty for years. Any plant that can tolerate both neglect and the Texas climate is worth its weight in gold. I never include hybrid roses in a Texas landscape unless the owner specifically asks for them. Few of my clients have time for the expert

pruning, the regular feeding and the spraying for black spot, powdery mildew and a variety of insects that most hybrid varieties require.

I'm seeing renewed interest in the older, more hardy varieties of roses throughout North America. Old roses are wonderful as shrubs in a mixed border. They flourish with very little pruning and almost no "doctoring." The downside to old roses is that most have a short period of bloom. The flowers are less showy than hybrid varieties. However, French Meidiland roses and David Austin's English Roses, which are derived from crossing modern and old types, may offer gardeners the best of both worlds. They combine shrubby forms with modern colors, and they have long periods of bloom and wonderful fragrances.

The Northwest is replete with sources for roses, old and new. Now that I live in rose country, I've made room in my garden for some of the fabulous hybrids pictured in the catalogs listed below. I love climbing roses draped over fences, tree roses in pots, and miniature roses used as ground covers and in hanging baskets.

Because properly pruned hybrid rose bushes look ratty several months of the year and because they prefer a bed all to themselves, I prefer an out-of-the-way spot for my cutting garden. This allows me to plant varieties that would not complement the landscape's overall color scheme. I have neither the time nor the inclination to spray every week, so I look for the most disease-resistant varieties. I exclude varieties such as 'Mr. Lincoln' or 'Tropicana' or 'Sterling Silver', even though they are gorgeous.

If you want to ensure the best success with the least effort, choose a location that provides full morning sun and good air circulation to lessen the possibility of fungal diseases. Water with a drip irrigation system and prune-out infected parts on a regular basis. I believe it is possible to keep hybrids happy with little more than good soil and a clean growing environment.

Kenneth Moppins of Everett, Washington, a chemist-by-training and proponent of organic gardening practices, shared with me his hints for growing roses without an arsenal of chemicals. Use three teaspoons of baking soda and one teaspoon of vegetable oil in a gallon of water for powdery mildew. For black spot, he recommends sulfur dust (use only when the temperature is below 80-degrees). He also provided me with a recipe for an inexpensive rose food: mix two pounds of alfalfa meal or pellets and a cup of sea-weed concentrate in five gallons of water. Let the substance sit overnight and apply about two cups per bush. "The formula is good for any shrub," he says, "but it really helps roses take off and grow."

Rose Societies in every city and hamlet in the Northwest offer classes and demonstrations on the care and feeding of roses. Different categories of roses have different pruning requirements. Because all roses bloom on new growth, you'll want to master pruning techniques that promote strong plant development. The severe pruning practices your grandmother may have taught you have fallen out of favor. Even experienced rosarians say they still have lots to learn about every aspect of growing this very special plant. 🌺

☞ **Money-saving tip: If you're investing some of your money in roses, invest some of your time in education.**

Catalog Sources for Roses

Carlton Rose Nurseries, Inc.

P.O. Box 366
Carlton, Oregon 97111
☎ 503/852-7135

Hours Mon-Fri 8-5
Mail Order
Catalog Free
FAX 503/852-7511

"If you enjoy roses, you can grow our exclusive patented florist varieties," says Jerry Strahle. Having served commercial growers for 54 years, the company is now offering the same bushes used by suppliers of fresh-cut roses. Call about their Open House in May, which is the only time the research gardens are open to the public.

Edmunds' Roses

6235 S.W. Kahle Road
Wilsonville, Oregon 97070
☎ 503/682-1476

Hours Mon-Fri 8-5
Mail Order
Catalog Free
FAX 503/682-1275

Exhibition and European varieties are the specialty of the house. All are budded on a multiflora rootstock and field-grown for two years before harvesting. What attracts the Edmunds' clientele is an outstanding service policy. "We work with our customers to deliver the plants at the optimum time," says Kathy Edmunds. An experienced staff gives advice year-round. They do not have a garden center, but the fields are open to the public in September with over 100,000 roses in bloom. Call to verify the dates. Plants are shipped from mid-November to late May. Products available in the catalog include Swiss pruning shears, rose gardener's gloves and *Leaky Pipe* soaker hoses.

Six-hundred varieties of old roses, two display gardens, and a couple infected with rampant rose passion have put the little town of St. Paul on the horticultural map. The Heirloom catalog now goes to several countries in the world, and gardeners throughout Rosedom are sending John and Louise Clements cuttings so the couple can return old favorites to commerce. They grow only own-root roses and ship in special six-inch pots designed for tree seedlings to ensure strong root systems. From 'Abbotsford' to 'Zephirine Drouhin', the catalog lists climbers, shrub roses, moss roses, musk roses, rambling roses, English roses, gallicas and more.

Heirloom Old Garden Roses

24062 N.E. Riverside Drive
St. Paul, Oregon 97137
☎ 503/538-1576

Hours Mon-Fri 8-4, Sat & Sun 10-4
Accessible Difficult on gravel
Mail Order
Catalog $5

Jill Ingraham propagates antique and classic roses from the '30s, '40s and '50s. Among her offerings that few other growers in the area have are the coffee-colored 'Julia's Rose' and 'Talisman', a hybrid tea introduced in 1939. Jill's display garden features over 200 varieties. Just over 100 are listed in the catalog. She explains that she collects cuttings from all over, and then "tries everything out to see how it performs before listing it."

Ingraham Cottage Garden

370 C Street
Scotts Mills, Oregon
☎ 503/873-8610

Hours By appointment only
Accessible Yes
Mail Order
Catalog $1
Mailing address P.O. Box 126
Scotts Mills, Oregon 97375

Every gardener in North America knows that Jackson & Perkins means roses. After all, it has been in business since 1872. If you get the tempting catalogs, you know that J&P now means perennials, bulbs, drought tolerant ground covers, furniture and containers, arbors and gazebos, tools, lawn care products, organic gardening supplies, fruit and vegetable seed, flowering shrubs and vines, too! If you don't get the catalog, you should. Call or write to get on the list. When you order roses, J&P includes the helpful pamphlet, *Home Gardener's Guide to Roses,* and it supplies instructions with every plant

Jackson & Perkins

P.O. Box 1028
Medford, Oregon 97501
☎ 800/292 GROW
for placing orders

Mail Order
Catalog Free
FAX 800/242-0329

continued on next page--

Jackson & Perkins

-continued

the company sells. Customer service representatives are available from 6 a.m. 'til 6 p.m. Pacific time, Monday through Saturday to answer questions. The company grows it's roses in California, but if you're in the Medford area during the blooming season, stop by the Display Garden in front of the shipping headquarters at **2518 S. Pacific Highway**. Here you can stroll among all-time favorites and vote for your picks within the test garden. Each of the 36 beds contain several yet-unnamed varieties. Ballots and catalogs are in the Visitor Center. Continue down the road a half-mile to Harry & David's Country Store, where you'll find J&P roses for sale. (See page 316.)

Justice Miniature Roses

5947 S.W. Kahle Road
Wilsonville, Oregon 97070
☎ 503/682-2370

Hours Mon-Sat 9-3
Accessible No
Mail Order
Catalog Free

You'll find over 250 varieties of miniatures in this company's catalog. Some of its miniature roses are exclusive introductions from the hybridizing efforts of Sean McCann in Dublin, Ireland and Sam McGready IV of Auckland, New Zealand. Others are the Justice family's own hybridized varieties and the latest introductions from major hybridizers in the U.S. "Folks who are looking for the older varieties will generally find them in our inventory as well," says Jerry Justice. "For our drop-in customers we feature an excellent selection of hanging baskets and miniature trees. Their bulk makes shipping impractical."

Oregon Miniature Roses

8285 S.W. 185th Avenue
Beaverton, Oregon 97007
☎ 503/649-4482

Hours Daily 9-5
Accessible Yes
Mail Order
Catalog Free
FAX 503/649-3528

Roses as ground cover? Why not! They're colorful, vigorous and fun to grow. These days miniature roses can be found cascading from hanging baskets and appearing in all the best perennial borders. Bountiful bloomers all, this company's offerings include hundreds of varieties from moss mini-roses to fabulous patio trees, including miniature climbers. With mouth-watering names like "Peaches 'n Cream" and "Strawberry Swirl," how can you resist? You'll also find several shrub roses and rose care products.

Bamboo & Other Grasses

There's a lot to love about bamboo. This giant grass is relatively drought tolerant and not as difficult to control as it's reported to be, as long as you plan for containing the plant *before* putting it in. Bamboo spreads by underground rhizomes that strike out from the mother plant. The secret is in defining the space you want the planting to occupy and constructing a two-foot-deep soil barrier around the root zone. There are clumping varieties and running varieties; the former are easier to contain, and they possess a more fountain-like form.

Bamboo's texture adds a graceful touch in a water garden or an Oriental landscape. It comes in an amazing number of forms, textures and leaf patterns and in heights from six inches to 60 feet. The tall varieties provide full privacy in one to three years. Tall varieties are also striking as vertical accent plants or as screening material. Dwarf varieties are excellent for erosion control on hillsides. These low plants form a weed-free, low-maintenance ground cover within two years. Bamboos are also nice in containers. Some varieties require shade, others thrive in the hottest sun.

Ornamental grasses of all kinds (the category includes true grasses, sedges, reeds and some members of the lily family) are getting a lot of play in the gardening press. The good news is that their textures and forms make a nice addition to a mixed border. Several species with colorful spiky leaves and plume-like flowers make gorgeous accent plants in containers. Ornamental grasses are also wonderful in flower arrangements. One of my favorites is purple fountain grass, which is not winter hardy. It can be treated as an annual in the garden or stored in a pot in the greenhouse.

Most ornamental grasses are tough and drought resistant, and therein lies the bad news. I have a real question about the advisability of introducing plants that evolved on the prairie into woodland areas of the Pacific Northwest. Although a number of wholesale nurseries are testing a variety of grasses for our region, the jury is still out on their potential for invasiveness. All I can tell you is that Johnson grass, which was introduced to Texas farms for cattle feed, now grows wild in every urban alley and vacant lot. When its seeds blow into your garden, you've got a serious problem.

Clumping varieties that don't set seed are the *only* grasses I would allow in my garden. Among the best are varieties of *Ophiopogon, Liriope* and *Luzula*. I also like some of the blue fescues, which work well as ground covers, and a few of the tall, fountain-shaped clumping varieties.

Eric Nelson, well-known lecturer and grass enthusiast, recommends golden variegated hakonechloa ("a really swell plant that likes our climate"), the 'Hameln' cultivar of fountain grass and dwarf pampas grass. He says that *Miscanthus sinensis* 'Strictus' is excellent because "it blooms early and stands up straight, which are the two traits you want in a grass for our area." He also notes, "Anytime a grass looks bad, cut it down. It will come back."

Don't even think about planting prairie cord grass, which has already become a naturalized pest in Northwest tidelands, and beware of bronze sedge, fox-red curly sedge and cotton grass. In short, ask lots of questions before you take home some cute little four-inch pot of grass – it may turn into a beast. ✿

Sources for Bamboo

☆DESTINATION
Bamboo Gardens of Washington

196th Avenue N.E.
at Redmond-Fall City Road (SR 202)
Redmond, Washington 98053
☎ *206/868-5166*

Hours *Daily 9-5 (spring through fall);*
9-4 (winter)
Accessible *Yes*
Mail Order
Catalog *$4*
Mailing address *5016 192nd Place N.E.*
Redmond, Washington 98053

The folks at Bamboo Gardens not only explain strategies for keeping bamboo under control, but also extol its virtues. Highly drought-tolerant once established, living bamboo is useful for evergreen screening and erosion control, and it's elegant in containers. Harvested, bamboo is a very decorative garden material. The company sells bamboo fences both in kits and as custom-ordered designs. "Our poles are high-quality and inexpensive – we import from an old company in Southern China. We make and sell the best bamboo deer scares and water pipes in the U.S., and to complement these lovely garden features, we sell handsome hand-carved stone sculpture," says Daphne Lewis. "Our catalog has more information on how to grow bamboo than any book you can buy." The company offers instructional seminars throughout the year, the most popular of which is the Japanese fence-building workshop. "When we take down a booth or show, we sell at 10% off. We have seminars most Sundays from March through October." Ask to be placed on the mailing list. Bamboo selection is best in late summer. You'll also discover water plants here, plus fountains, garden ornaments, house plants and decorative rocks.

Judy and Don Jensen invite you to come out and enjoy their peaceful gardens and koi pond. Don has a passion for bamboo, and he offers more than twenty varieties. He strongly believes that bamboo is an under-used evergreen landscape plant. Judy is the "herb lady," but herbs are only some of the vast array of plants the couple grow. They've fountains and water plants, ornamental grasses, perennials, roses, shrubs, trees and vines. Their cozy little gift shop carries herbal and general gardening books, plus a variety of culinary, fragrant and ornamental gifts and garden accessories. They host a Holiday Open House the first two weeks in November. He offers classes in using bamboo in the landscape, and she teaches herbal crafts. Call for a schedule.

Fairlight Gardens

30904 164th S.E.
Auburn, Washington 98002
☎ *206/631-8932*

Hours Wed-Sat 10-6
(April through second week in Sept)
Accessible No

Owner Rick Valley offers four-dozen varieties of bamboo, chosen for their utility in the Northwest climate. Included in his catalog are non-running Chinese Mountain bamboos, which he notes are excellent companion plants for rhodies. He ships small potted plants from late June onward into the year and can ship bare-root from September through April. He doesn't maintain a retail location.

Northern Groves

P.O. Box 86291
Portland, Oregon 97286
☎ *503/774-6353*

Hours By appointment only
Accessible No
Mail Order
Catalog $1

Sources for Ornamental Grasses

A wholesale nursery, this is a well-known trade source for ornamental grasses, sedges, rushes and native grasses. Retail sales are held in May and October. See listing on page 132.

American Ornamental Perennials

29977 S.E. Weitz Lane
Eagle Creek, Oregon 97022
☎ *503/637-3095*

Chehalem Mountain Nursery, Inc.

14375 S.W. Patricia Avenue
Hillsboro, Oregon 97123
☎ *503/628-0353*

You'll discover several species of ornamental grass at this wholesale nursery. See complete listing page 145.

Forestfarm

990 Tetherow
Williams, Oregon 97544-9599
☎ *503/846-6963*

See complete Listing in Collector's Nurseries, page 263.

Gossler Farm's Nursery

1200 Weaver Road
Springfield, Oregon 97478
☎ *503/746-3922*

See complete Listing in Collector's Nurseries, page 264.

Greer Gardens

1280 Goodpasture Island Road
Eugene, Oregon 97401-1794
☎ *503/686-8266*

See complete Listing in Collector's Nurseries, page 264.

Growth Unlimited Nursery, Inc.

Sydnam Road
Bandon, Oregon 97411
☎ *503/347-4114*

Growth Unlimited keeps several varieties of controllable, clumping ornamental grass in inventory. See listing on page 129.

Natural Legacy Seeds & Rare Plants

R.R. #2, C-1 Laird
Armstrong, British Columbia V0E 1B0
☎ *604/546-9799*

Grahame Ware's mail-order business supplies Canadian and U.S. enthusiasts with seeds for thirty ornamental grasses. See listing on page 133.

Rainforest Gardens

13139 224th Street
Maple Ridge, British Columbia V2X 7E7
☎ *604/467-4218*

Canadian and U.S. gardeners can order from three pages of grasses (most cold-hardy to Zone 5). See complete listing on page 191.

Siskiyou Rare Plant Nursery

2825 Cummings Road
Medford, Oregon 97501
☎ *503/772-6846*

See complete Listing in Collector's Nurseries, page 265.

Ferns

Ferns are such an integral part of the woodlands in the Pacific Northwest that it's difficult to imagine a garden without ferns as part of the green foundation. The very names of our native ferns suggest not only grace and elegance, but also diversity. Holly fern, lace fern, lady fern, licorice fern, parsley fern, maidenhair, deer fern, shield fern, sword fern, chain fern, woodsia, oak fern, beech fern, rock break, spleenwort... Delicate or distinctive in their foliage patterns, some are very drought-tolerant, others are moisture-loving woodland dwellers.

There are so many unusual native and introduced ferns that its a shame to only grow the common ones. Most Northwest gardeners prefer evergreen ferns, but I also love the deciduous ones, especially in combination with spring-flowering bulbs. The trick is to cut down deciduous ferns after the first frost or in late November (whichever comes first), allowing the bulbs to send up foliage. The fern fronds then come up in late spring to cover-over the bulb foliage as it turns brown and withers. 🌸

Sources for Hardy Ferns

No other nursery in the United States propagates and sells hardy ferns in the quantity or the selection that is offered at Barfod's. Torben Barfod and Judith Jones propagate evergreen and deciduous varieties from every continent except Antarctica. Judith got into ferns as an interested gardener who began reading everything written about the subject, and she now lectures internationally. Torben, a Dane, came to this country in 1948 and established his credentials as a nurseryman. The two teamed up in the early eighties. They offer lectures and nursery tours by advance booking. Barfod's waterfall pond and display garden are inspirational, and its displays at the Northwest Flower and Garden Show garner rave reviews. At any one time you'll find at least seventy-five different varieties in the company's several greenhouses. Selection is best from March through October.

DESTINATION ☆
Barfod's Hardy Ferns

23622 Bothell Way S.E.
Bothell, Washington 98021
☎ *206/483-0205*

Hours *Mon-Sat 9-5, Sun 12:30-5*
(March through Oct);
by appointment only
(Nov through Feb)
Accessible *Yes*

Fancy Fronds

1911 4th Avenue W.
Seattle, Washington 98119
☎ *206/284-5332*

Hours *By appointment only*
Accessible *No*
Mail Order
Catalog *$1 (refundable)*

Fancy Fronds, which is run by Judith Jones, is the mail-order division of Barfod's. (See previous page.) The minimum order is $10 and shipping is via UPS. Judith's garden is open by appointment, and to meet her is to become enthusiastic about ferns!

Foliage Gardens

2003 128th Avenue S.E.
Bellevue, Washington 98005
☎ *206/747-2998*

Hours *By appointment only*
Accessible *Yes*
Mail Order
Catalog *$2*

"We offer spore-grown (no collected plants) native, hardy and exotic ferns, plus a few tender varieties. Some are marked 'one per customer' and selection is best in April and May. Our list changes as new crops mature," says Sue Olsen. She has made a video, *Foliage Gardens presents a Short Course on Ferns,* and she lectures on request. "My husband, a retired Boeing engineer is now propagating Japanese maple cultures, particularly the lower growing varieties, which we are now offering to the public, as well."

Chapter Six
The Flower Garden

"Don't hurry, don't worry. You're only here for a short visit. So be sure to stop and smell the flowers."

.....Walter C. Hagen

Color in the Landscape

Fashion can be as heartless to flowers as to skirt lengths — "out" before they're "in." Now that seed companies have come up with blossoms as big as basketballs and glow-in-the-dark colors, the old-fashioned look is fashionable again. The most sought-after characteristics in the garden today are soft hues, sweet fragrance and resistance to pests and drought.

To me, a flower garden is most appealing when its colors are carefully orchestrated. It's hard to surpass the color schemes devised by Gertrude Jekyll almost a hundred years ago. Her secret was in the way she painted year-long successions of living pictures, setting-off intense colors with soothing drifts of white and gray and green.

The textures of the English cottage gardens have also inspired generations of gardeners. Beds are deep and layered, with plants arranged in graduated heights from the lacy border plants in front to stately spikes and confident clumps of efflorescence at the rear. Often the perennials are mixed with old roses and other deciduous shrubs and played against an old brick wall or a profuse screen of evergreens. These are the flower gardens of my dreams.

☞ **Money-saving tip: Avoid impulse buying. Stick to your Master Plan.**

It is so easy to fall in love with a beautiful little plant sitting on a table waiting to go home from the nursery. I, too, have to resist the urge to buy plants that don't really fit into my planting scheme. Sometimes we plantaholics just can't overcome temptation... Luckily for me, I can indulge my passion for perennials in my clients' gardens. There, I've been able to grow some of the species too big or too brightly colored for my own small garden.

Design Tips

I keep a notebook that lists the annuals, perennials and bulbs I love, with columns for height, color and season of bloom and sun/shade requirements. Being a "lazy gardener," I put a big star by the varieties that require the least water, fertilizer and tender loving care. When I need a two-foot-tall, pale-pink, summer-blooming sun-lover, I have a ready resource book that offers me several choices to fit the need.

I plan the planting bed on ¼-inch grid paper, first drawing big overlapping oval shapes. See an example of this, taken from an old garden book on page 202. I then assign one plant per square, which allows me to estimate the number of plants I will need. I never plant fewer than five of a variety, usually nine or eleven. I lay out the bed on the ground with stakes and string to make a one-foot grid that makes it simple to translate the plan-on-paper to the actual garden plot. I always make a few changes as I do the planting; it's difficult to work out every detail in a two-dimensional plan. You go with what is most pleasing to the eye in the actual three-dimensional space.

Because I'm especially fond of flower gardens that offer a wide variety of textures and a limited range of colors, the garden of a dahlia collector or a chrysanthemum fancier is seldom appealing to me. But gardens are made to please the gardener, and if you want to "specialize" in a particular plant, it's still possible to create an attractive display using the same design principles and carefully orchestrating the plants by color and height. ❀

Annuals & Perennials

Perennial gardening has never been more popular. But "perennial" is not a synonym for "permanent." Many gardeners abandoned annuals thinking perennials would be easier, and they returned to annuals for the same reason! A perennial garden requires faithful care. Different perennials have different needs. Some, such as delphinium, require staking. Most need to be deadheaded during the blooming season, cut down in fall, mulched and periodically divided. Few perennials have the sustained bloom period of annuals, so gardeners who want a big summer show may tuck-in a few annuals, especially near the front of the bed.

The possibilities for beautiful combinations are unlimited. For example, one of my favorites for a dry sunny spot combines purple coneflowers, white obedient plants, yellow yarrow and blue delphinium at the rear and Shasta daisies, yellow daylilies, purple salvia, artemisia and burgundy chrysanthemums in the middle ground. As border plants in front, lamb's ears, yellow 'Zagreb' coreopsis, creeping baby's breath and pink dianthus would complement the other plants in the grouping.

I almost always include chrysanthemums in a perennial bed, not only because I enjoy the late fall show, but also because they serve as a moisture meter! When chrysanthemums begin to wilt, you know it's time to water. They bounce back quickly. The new 'Pacificum' chrysanthemum makes a wonderful ground cover at the front of the bed. Its flower isn't showy, but the variegated foliage is beautiful throughout the growing season. (Don't count on it as an indicator of dry soil, however. One of its best characteristics is drought-tolerance.)

Perennials are usually sold in four-inch pots or one-gallon cans. If I'm planting in the fall, I always purchase one-gallon plants so that the root systems are sufficiently developed to get the plant through the winter. Inspect the rootball for matted or encircling roots. If you find a problem, you can cut halfway up the root ball and gently spread the roots. Plant in a hole up to twice the size of the diameter of the root ball. Amend the garden soil if it is low in organic matter and backfill the planting hole with good soil. Water thoroughly. After the first freeze, I normally cut perennials to the ground and mulch over the roots for winter protection.

Once the plants are established, you'll need to start dividing to keep the more vigorous growers from taking over. Division rejuvenates old plants; most perennials produce inferior blooms when crowded. In general, you'll divide spring and summer bloomers in late fall, and fall bloomers in spring. There are exceptions to every rule, of course. For example, peonies and bleeding heart don't like to be disturbed at any time of the year. As you become an experienced perennial gardener, you'll get to know the individual needs of each species.

☞ **Money-saving tip: Trade "divisions" with a friend.**

A few days before digging the clumps, water the perennial garden thoroughly. If the center of the plant has died out, break off and replant clumps of the outer roots. If the roots are hopelessly tangled, insert two spading forks, back-to-back, into the center of the clump and press the handles together for leverage.

Be willing to correct your mistakes. No matter how much planning has gone into a perennial garden, there are always a few surprises. One drift of plants grows taller than the species behind it, the color combination isn't just right, or "somebody" begins to out-compete his companions in the garden. Perennials are easily moved, and that's part of the fun. Don't get discouraged if it takes three or four years to get everything just right.

Bedding Plants

According to the Professional Plant Growers Association, the most popular annual bedding plants are impatiens, geraniums, petunias, begonias, pansies, lobelia, marigolds and sweet alyssum. But, nurseries are also reporting new interest in such old-fashioned favorites as cosmos and sweet peas (especially the new bush types). Such biennials as foxgloves and hollyhocks are also back in demand as gardeners restore old homesteads or create "period" gardens. Families are again passing down seeds from generation to generation like treasured heirlooms.

Annuals are wonderful, of course, in containers and hanging baskets (see Container Gardening in Chapter 8). Annuals have lots of landscape uses, as well. They make excellent "fillers" in new planting beds and in perennial borders to add touches of color in mid-summer when few perennials and bulbs are at their peak. They can even be used as quick sun-screens. I remember my mother growing castor beans and candlebush and training morning glories up on strings in front of west-facing windows as protection against the hot Texas sun.

There's new interest in annuals that can take summer heat, such as cleome and carpet varieties of petunias that don't get leggy. Some of the drought-tolerant annuals that are favorites in southern gardens – Madagascar periwinkle, Peruvian verbena and annual salvia – are now becoming available in the Northwest. And, gardeners are coloring the winter landscape with flowering kale, pansies and snapdragons.

☞ **Money-saving tip: Annuals can be grown easily and inexpensively from seed.**

Beginner's mistakes with seeding annuals include failing to thin the plants, planting tall varieties in front of the shorter ones, and sowing every tint in the botanist's palette. But the best thing about planting annuals is that next year you can make a fresh start! The only seed source for annuals listed in this section is Butchart Gardens, page 191. You'll find other flower-seed sources beginning on page 223. 🌺

Sources for Perennials & Bedding Plants

Washington

Seattle Metropolitan Area

Cottage Creek Nursery

13232 Avondale Road
Woodinville, Washington 98072
☎ *206/883-8252*

Hours *Daily 10-5*
(call for extended hours
in spring and summer)
Accessible *No*
Catalog *Free rose list*

Betty Thomas grows a large selection of perennials, including a number of unusual and rare varieties. She has a lot of hardy geraniums, for example, but to single them out is to ignore all the other wonderful choices. She's almost as well-known for roses as for the perennials. You'll find 650 varieties, including old roses and 50 to 60 different David Austin English Roses. Cottage Creek also functions as a friendly neighborhood garden center, with an array of annuals, shrubs and trees, as well as ornaments and books.

"We are primarily growers, with 30,000 square feet under glass," says Jon Ackermann. "We specialize in four-inch and gallon-size annuals, perennials, specialty bulbs and ground covers, which we sell both retail and wholesale." The company also grows herbs and such specialty vegetables as European lettuces. All its edibles are grown from seed and tailored for coastal N.W. climatic conditions. Located on five acres on the south slope between Union Hill and Novelty Hill in Redmond, the facility is difficult to find on first try, but memorable once you have discovered it. What an array of choices! Hillcroft is a regular stop for many of Seattle's best landscape designers and contractors.

Hillcroft Nursery, Inc.

9430 195th N.E.
Redmond, Washington 98053
☎ 206/885-9520

Hours Mon-Fri 8-5, Sat 10-5, Sun 12-4
(March through Sept);
Mon-Fri 8-4 (fall & winter)
Accessible Yes
Catalog Free

This is a "backyard" nursery with a twist – many of Ann Bucher's plants are grown on top of her garage and house (and reached by ladder). "I specialize in hellabores and astrantia, a popular cut flower in England that likes partial shade and heavy soils. I'm increasing my native plant offerings as I can," she says, noting that she's now growing wild ginger, trilliums and vancouveria. "I tend to grow shade plants and plants that don't need a lot of moisture. Most of the plants offered are on display in the garden so people can see what they look like as mature plants. They are available here for longer periods than in the larger nurseries, which may only stock plants during their prime time. Like everyone else, I try to grow unusual varieties, but also to select and stock the best of the old standards. I am glad to spend time and make suggestions to individual customers."

Madrona Nursery

815 38th Avenue
Seattle, Washington 98122
☎ 206/323-8325

Hours By appointment only
Accessible No
Catalog Free with SASE

☆DESTINATION
Pat's Perennials

7531 224th Street S.E.
Woodinville , Washington 98072
☎ *206/483-6634*

Hours *Wed-Sat 10-5 (mid-March through mid-July and mid-Aug to mid-Sept)*
Accessible *No*

Pat's is a favored destination for garden groups and devoted gardeners. Strolling paths meander through two acres of gardens, alongside both shady and sun-drenched borders. Eight-hundred varieties of perennials are grown in the planting beds and seven greenhouses on the property. Among the specialties are 40 varieties of astilbe, 35 different hostas and 35 daylilies. A plant list is available at the nursery. It's a place to be savored. From Highway 522, take a right at the first stop (Paradise Lake Road), then right on Bostain Road. Follow the signs another mile and a half.

The Sweetbriar

13825 132nd Avenue N.E.
Kirkland, Washington 98034
☎ *206/821-2222*

Although The Sweetbriar opens its doors to the public only four weekends each year, gardeners seeking a fine collection of perennials and ground covers would be well-advised to put this wholesale nursery's public weekends on the calendar. See complete listing on page 155.

Islands in the Sound

Agate Nursery

16675 Mariner Avenue N.E.
Bainbridge Island, Washington 98110
☎ *206/842-4108*

Hours *By appointment only*
Accessible *Yes*

"I grow things I fancy," says Anne Holt. A trip to Santa Fe recently inspired new interest in drought tolerant plants. Among the fascinating bulbs and perennials you'll find at her place are kaffir lilies in three colors, matilija poppies, California fuchsias (*Zauschneria*) and gunnera. She also grows viburnums, dwarf fruit trees, Japanese maples and dwarf conifers.

The Country Store grows all its perennials in fields rather than greenhouses, so you know the plants are hardy. The company packages its own specialty perennial seed and ships both plants and seeds. "While we offer a plant list, one should call ahead to be sure we have the plant you want. They come and go with the season," says Vy Biel. The early-1900s building that houses The Country Store has been photographed by all the Metro newspapers. It's located mid-island on the main highway, about seven and a half miles from any ferry. Also see page 341.

DESTINATION ☆
The Country Store and Farm

20211 Vashon Highway S.W.
Vashon Island, Washington 98070
☎ *206/463-3655*

Hours *Mon-Sat 9-6, Sun 12-5*
Accessible *Yes*
Mail Order
Catalog *$1*

Here, an educational-based home nursery with display gardens surrounds a simple Victorian-style farm house. Hedges enclose the nursery area and an espaliered apple walk leads into the growing area. Most of the unusual varieties that are sold in the nursery can be observed through the seasons in the display garden. Owner Mary Fisher's plant list is comprehensive; it includes lots of antique dianthus, specialty herbs and lavender, and much, much more. She also sells hand-made pots. Watch for the end-of-the-season sale. To get to the nursery, take the Mukiteo ferry to Whidbey Island. Go up Highway 525 about a mile. Make a sharp left onto Cultus Bay Road. Proceed four miles to the nursery entrance. Follow a half-mile private drive to nursery.

Cultus Bay Nursery

4000 E. Bailey Road
Clinton (Whidbey Island),
Washington 98236
☎ *206/221-2329*

Hours *Fri, Sat & Mon 9-5, Sun 12-5*
(April through Sept); or by appointment
Accessible *Difficult*
Catalog *$2*

Pete Ray's wholesale nursery is well-known and well-respected in the "green industry." He supplies unusual perennials, including several drought-tolerant species and a nice mix of trees, shrubs and ground covers to specialty nurseries throughout the region. Puget Garden Resources is open to the public two weekends each year, spring and fall. Send Pete a note to add your name to the mailing list!

Puget Garden Resources

10322 S.W. 165th
Vashon Island, Washington 98070
☎ *206/567-4542*

Hours *Two weekends a year*
Accessible *Yes*

Northwest Washington

✩DESTINATION
A&D Peony and Perennial Nursery

6808 180th S.E.
Snohomish, Washington 98290
☎ *206/668-9690,*
485-2487 (from Seattle)

Hours *Daily 9-6 (spring);*
Wed-Sun 9-6 (summer and fall);
closed Dec through February
Accessible *Partially*
Mail Order
Catalog *$1.50 (refundable)*

An uncommon nursery in an uncommon setting, A&D features over a thousand varieties of peonies, tree peonies, daylilies, hostas and assorted perennials for the woodland garden. Included are many of the most recent peony introductions as well as many rare and scarce varieties from the past. While peonies are part of the company's name, the owners are sold on hostas for their remarkable ability to tolerate wet conditions in winter and drought in summer. From mid-April through June, A&D shimmers with color, and when the weather turns warm, the green Hosta Walk offers a cooling respite. The owners invite you to stroll along their stream bed, past the duck pond up to Emma's Garden. Every year the walk gets better. And their catalog is equally appealing! From I-5: take exit #183. Go east on 164th, then turn right (south) on the Bothell-Everett Highway Turn left (east) on 180th.

Cora's Nursery and Greenhouse

902 24th
Anacortes, Washington 98221-2810
☎ *206/293-5478*

Hours *Daily during daylight*
Accessible *Yes*

Cora specializes in rare, scarce and old-fashioned perennials, ones not carried by all the nurseries. You'll find a half-dozen varieties of fall asters, the candelabra, auricula and denticulata primulas, twinspur and some unusual lavenders. This one-woman operation offers a few select shrubs and such vines as akebia, clematis, climbing nasturtium and trumpet creeper. "Most all plants for sale can be seen in my garden," she says, "and my advice is from personal experience."

Cricklewood offers a selection of hard-to-find and unusual plants for both "plantaholics" and ordinary gardeners. Evie Douglas says she grows plants she likes or thinks should be more available. Her selection changes yearly, but it includes bulbs, ornamental grasses, ground covers, herbs, roses, shrubs, deciduous trees, vines and water plants as well as perennials. Her homey cottage-style garden allows customers to see mature plants. There's ample room for picnics or garden meetings. "Its not always tidy, but there is usually something in bloom," she adds, noting that her husband is an arborist who does tree disease diagnosis and damage evaluations. She provides a good plant list and sometimes gives slide shows for garden clubs and plant organizations. Advice? "You bet!" From Snohomish turn south on Lincoln, go 2 miles, right on Treosti Road, left on Shorts School, left on Nevers Road. From Highway 522, take the Monroe exit, turn left and go 4.5 miles to Treosti. Take a left, then proceed as above.

DESTINATION ☆
Cricklewood

11907 Nevers Road
Snohomish, Washington 98290
☎ *206/568-2829*

Hours *Fri-Sat 10-5 (mid-April through June); by appointment all year*
Accessible *Yes*
Mail Order
Catalog *$1*

Tony and Judy Tilley grow meritorious garden plants, including uncommon varieties of hosta, spring and summer bulbs, dwarf daylilies and other perennials. Good garden performance and lasting ability as cut flowers are two of the criteria they consider. You'll find lots of delicious little woodland and rockery plants – variegated liriope, double primulas, variegated Solomon's seal and double bloodroot. Sun-tolerant selections include *Geranium renardii* (and 29 other varieties of hardy geraniums), crocosmias, and two variegated yuccas. The Tilleys offer guests a shady picnic table and friendly advice. You'll find Judy at the Bellingham Farmer's Market on Saturdays from April through October. From I-5 (northbound), take North Lake Samish exit. Take a left on Samish Way for approximately 4.5 miles, then a left on Galbraith Lane. From I-5 (southbound), take Samish Way exit.

Galbraith Gardens
1650 Galbraith Lane
Bellingham, Washington 98226
☎ *206/671-0704*

Hours *By appointment only*
Accessible *Partially*
Catalog *Free*

✩DESTINATION
The Gathering Garden

32716 68th Avenue N.W.
Stanwood, Washington 98292
☎ *206/629-2706*

Hours *Daily 9-5 (March through Oct)*
Accessible *Difficult*
Catalog *Free*

Together, Isobel Johnson and Daniel Sawyer have thirty years of experience growing "unusual, under-used and non-intimidating" perennials and herbs. With over 250 genera to choose from, some of their favorites are alliums, eryngiums (sea holly), primula, scabiosa, salvia and penstemon. You'll find over a thousand varieties of perennials and a number of annuals to cut and dry, including a three-foot-tall ageratum. This year you'll also find several thymes, ornamental oreganos, hardy geraniums, Michaelmas daisies and a lot of new hellebores they're growing from stock plants and seeds she found in England in 1992. Most of the stock is grown in four-inch pots, but you'll also find some specimen plants in quarts and gallons. From I-5: take exit #218 (Star Bird Road). Go west on Milltown Road and take a left on Silver Nail Road. Turn right on 332nd Street N.W. and left onto 68th Avenue N.W.

Thompson's Greenhouse

637 Highway 9
Sedro Woolley, Washington 98284
☎ *206/856-2147*

Hours *Mon-Sat 9-5, Sun 12-5*
(April through June);
Mon-Fri 9-4:30 (July through March)
Accessible *Yes*

Stephen and Brenda Thompson specialize in annuals and perennials; of the latter they grow over 200 varieties – campanulas, thymes and delphiniums, to mention but three. They've lots of colorful bedding plants, sedums and patio plants. They feature both custom-designed and pre-made container gardens. The inventory is exclusively outdoor plant materials, and it includes fruit trees and berries, ornamental flowering trees, shade trees, conifers, flowering shrubs, roses, and ground covers. Merchandise is marked down from August into the fall. They serve both wholesale and retail customers from all points in Skagit county.

Set in the scenic Stillaguamish River Valley on what was once a dairy farm, Waverly Gardens is the kind of place that makes a city-dweller weep with envy. Carl and Waverly Jaegel have transformed the grounds below their farmhouse into a large garden with herbs and perennials. A profusion of old European roses and wisteria, clematis and honeysuckle cover the arbors. An old hay rake and a weathered barn that houses miniature ponies, angora goats, chickens, a tame steer and a goose complete the picture. Sympathetic to the needs of both plants and wildlife, they've built aviaries and a small duck pond. "We use no herbicides or chemical fertilizers, and all plants on the premises are organically grown." The garden offers a wide selection of usual and unusual perennials to please both novice and collector. The shop carries handmade wreaths, potpourri and pottery by local artisans, antique garden accessories, garden books and more. Carl designs arbors, bridges and treillage and makes garden furniture. From I-5, take Exit # 208 and head west through Silvana on Highway 530. Turn left at Larson Road and keep going straight. (Larson becomes Silvana Terrace.)

DESTINATION ★
Waverly Gardens

4321 Silvana Terrace Road
Stanwood, Washington 98292
☎ *206/652-0300*

Hours *Daily 10:30-5 (April through August); by appointment all year*
Accessible *Yes*

Old-favorite perennials and new varieties from Europe are featured here, as well as bog plants, dwarf conifers and flowering shrubs for the perennial border. The owners are even experimenting with carnivorous plants for natural insect control. "We try to offer something of interest to experienced as well as novice gardeners and information for those who want it. The "how to" is as important as the plant," declare Allan and Karen Oudean. Unannounced sales are posted when the owners phase out a plant. "We can answer most questions on pruning and growing healthy plants and what to plant in locations with difficult light and soil conditions or drainage problems."

Willow Creek Farm & Nursery

7521 137th Avenue S.E.
Snohomish, Washington 98290
☎ *206/568-6024*

Hours *Thurs-Sun 10-6 (summer); Thurs-Sun 10-dusk (spring and fall); closed Dec 20 through January*
Accessible *Yes*

Olympic Peninsula

B&D Lilies

330 P Street
Port Townsend, Washington 98368
☎ 206/385-1738

Bob and Dianna Gibson offer ever-green daylilies and astilbe as companions to their large selection of lilies. See complete listing on page 199.

Heronswood Nursery

7530 288th N.E.
Kingston, Washington 98346
☎ 206/297-4172

Heronswood Nursery offers a number of perennials that are not normally encountered in the trade. See the complete listing for this mail-order source in Collector's Plants on page 265.

Skyline Nursery

4772 Sequim-Dungeness Way
Sequim, Washington 98382
☎ 206/683-2294

Hours Mon-Sat 8-5
Accessible Yes
Catalog $1

In his catalog Herb Senft writes, "What I wish most to communicate is that gardening is the sharing of experiences: of adventures and successes, balanced by mistakes and losses." And what he wrote to me began, "I love what I'm doing; every day brings new discoveries as well as challenges. I love to talk about plants and the environment. Sometimes it can be detrimental: 'Nurseryman Labels Community Aesthetically Handicapped' is not a headline a business normally desires." (He enclosed a copy of an editorial.) "What I have is a very loyal and wonderful group of friends that I can share plants with. I do not advertise aside from involvement with flower shows." The alpines, bonsai, bulbs, conifers, fruits and berries, ornamental grasses, ground covers, herbs, native plants, perennials, species roses, shrubs, rare and unusual deciduous trees, vines and wildflowers he grows speak volumes too.

South Sound

"Gardening has brought much joy to my life. When you find pleasure in an activity, you want to share it with others," explains Judy Tauscher. "Anyone can have a satisfying gardening experience growing hardy perennials. They will soon have year-around color and foliage variations with minimal effort. All my 250 varieties of perennials are grown outdoors, some field-grown. I use organic methods and farmyard fertilizer. And I talk to my plants." The perennials she sells are mostly two or three year old plants. The nursery also carries ferns, ground covers, ornamental grasses, herbs and native plants. Judy offers planting parties to which she brings a truck full of plants to the host's home and gives a 45-minute lecture. Guests may buy off the truck. Call about the Open House in May and October Sale. From the Narrows Bridge, take the Prudy exit. Cross Purdy Bridge, follow Penrose State Park signs. Look for the Aziel Gardens sign near the Park, 20 miles south of Purdy in Pierce County.

Aziel Propagation and Perennial Gardens

14916 38th Street
Lakebay, Washington 98349
☎ 206/884-9980

Hours Wed 10-4
Accessible Yes

Eastern Washington

Bill and Wendy MacKay grow over 450 different varieties of daylilies. Backwoods Specialties, which was formerly known as "Donna's Lilies of the Valley," plans to expand into other specialized ornamentals in the future. It's a family owned and operated business. "Our growth," they say, "will come from learning our customers' desires and filling their needs. The MacKays ship their plants in fall and spring. If you're in the area in the summertime, call for directions."

Backwoods Specialties

2554 Onion Creek Road
Northport, Washington 99157-1003
☎ 509/732-4275

Hours By appointment only
Accessible Yes
Mail Order
Catalog Free
Mailing address P.O. Box 1003
Northport, Washington 99157-1003
FAX 509/732-4275

Blossoms & Bloomers

E. 11415 Krueger Lane
Spokane, Washington 99207
☎ *509/922-1344*

Hours *Fri-Sun 10-4 (May & June)*
or by appointment
Accessible *Yes*
Mail Order *(roses)*
Catalog *$1*

Drought-tolerant perennials, old roses grown as shrubs and plants that attract birds are the specialties here. Geraldine Krueger combined these plants with a gazebo, arbors, barnwood benches and old farm equipment to create a charming two-acre country garden. Noting that harsh winters led to her "discovery" of old garden roses, she built-up a collection of approximately 300 plants, including a fragrant pink climber her grandfather nurtured on his homestead in the Rocky Mountains of Idaho. She offers private group tours and hosts a special gala on Mother's Day. The roses are available by mail, and the little catalog also lists four varieties of honeysuckle and several shrubs beloved by birds. A shop on the premises offers books and garden accessories not available in the catalog.

Lamb Nurseries

101 East Sharp Avenue
Spokane, Washington 99202
☎ *509/328-7956*

Hours *Fri-Sat 9-5 (spring);*
Mon-Sat 9-4 (summer);
by appointment all year
Accessible *Yes*
Mail Order
Catalog *$1*

Gardeners all across the country know Lamb Nurseries. "We specialize in hardy perennials and rock garden plants," says owner Nicola Luttropp, "and some of the varieties we offer, such as hardy violas, are not available anywhere else in the U.S." Lamb's 75-page catalog is filled with excellent cultural descriptions of the perennials and flowering shrubs and vines the nursery supplies. Members of the staff provide gardening and design advice to local customers.

Perennials are coming on strong at this large garden center. See complete listing on page 360.

Stanek's
E. 2929 27th
Spokane, Washington 99223
☎ 509/535-2939

Central Washington

"We carry a huge selection of perennials," says Cindy Mahre. (Eastern Washington's largest wholesale grower confirms the fact that she carries everything their company grows.) A staff of "enthusiastic gardeners" conducts small classes on perennials for shade, sun and drought conditions. "We are always excited to share our knowledge of plants that do well in the inland Northwest," she adds, noting that she also inventories a wonderful selection of ornaments, books and gifts for gardeners, as well as bulbs, ferns, herbs, roses and a few small shrubs. The perennial selection is best in April and early May, and the annuals come on strong in May.

Loo Wit Gardens
3806 Summitview
Yakima, Washington 98902
☎ 509/966-7010

Hours Daily 9:30-6 (Feb through July 4 and Sept through Dec 20)
Accessible Yes, except restrooms
FAX 509/965-2529

Southwest Washington

Diana Reeck and Bill Janssen hybridize hostas and propagate a wide selection of unusual perennials. See complete listing on page 262.

Collector's Nursery
16804 N.E. 102nd Avenue
Battle Ground, Washington 98064
☎ 206/574-3832

Perennials grow amid the azaleas and rhododendrons featured here. The offerings include hardy orchids and ornamental grasses. See complete listing on page 152.

Fawn Farms Nursery
607 State Highway 409
Cathlamet, Washington 98612-9730
☎ 206/849-4769

Robyn's Nest Nursery

7802 N.E. 63rd Street
Vancouver, Washington 98662
☎ *206/256-7399*

Hours *Thurs & Fri 10:30-5:30,*
Sat 10:30-2 (mid-March through June
and Sept & Oct);
by appointment all year
Accessible *Partially*
Mail Order
Catalog *$1*

Rows and rows of perennials and ornamental grasses bloom and grow at this country nursery. There are lots of hostas, too, from familiar landscape varieties to the latest, most elite. Also available is an abundance of information on culture and growth habits – yours for the asking. Robyn Duback's garden, which is open during nursery hours, is filled with specimen plants (most of them labeled) that demonstrate companion planting. "The landscape is in a continual state of uprooting, redesigning and replanting, which makes it exciting to visit and revisit," notes Robyn.

Oregon

Portland Metropolitan Area

☆DESTINATION
Caprice Farm Nursery

15425 S.W. Pleasant Hill Road
Sherwood, Oregon 97140
☎ *503/625-7241*

Hours *Mon-Sat 10-4; Daily 10-4 in May*
Accessible *Yes*
Mail Order
Catalog *$2 (refundable)*
FAX *503/625-5588*

"We are a small family run business specializing in peonies, tree peonies, daylilies, Japanese and Siberian Iris and hostas, says Dot Rogers. "We offer a large selection of the newer, modern varieties while retaining many of the older favorites as well. We guarantee our plants – customer satisfaction is the number one priority here at Caprice." The nursery publishes an attractive color catalog. Staff members not only answer garden questions at the nursery, but also by phone or mail.

This mail-order-only nursery specializes in old-fashioned perennials and cottage garden plants. It's a family-owned organization, located 1000-feet above sea level in USDA Zone 7. Owner JoAnn Wiltrakis notes that the catalog contains her own favorite performers, including some very hard-to-find varieties. She writes, "I have tried to describe my experience with the plants, both positive and negative. We take pride in growing healthy plants. We would like to know how the plants adapt to your climate and growing conditions. If you are looking for a particular variety, please let us know. There are many plants we have in quantities too small to list in the catalog."

Daisy Fields
12635 S.W. Brighton Lane
Hillsboro, Oregon 97123
☎ *503/628-0315*

Mail Order
Catalog *$1*

The focus at Dragonfly Gardens is on perennials, "especially those we deem of garden merit, like the drought-tolerant Matilija poppy (*Romneya coulteri*) or cupid's dart (*Catananche caerulea*)," says owner Sarah Lizio. See complete listing on page 116.

Dragonfly Gardens
3575 S.E. Division Street
Portland, Oregon 97202
☎ *503/235-9150*

Willamette Valley

Egan Gardens, which is well-known for annuals and container plants, is branching heavily into perennials. See complete listing on page 254.

Egan Gardens
9805 River Road N.E.
Salem, Oregon 97303
☎ *503/393-2131*

Here's another little specialty nursery started by a devoted gardener. Deann Hudgins' home garden is mother to the plants she sells. Welcoming all visitors who would like to come by for inspiration and advice, she grows perennials (including 24 varieties of buddleia), ground covers, water plants and deciduous shrubs, and she stocks containers and garden ornaments. From Silverton, take Highway 213 toward Molalla. About five miles from Silverton, take a right at the yellow blinking light. Go a mile and a half, then turn left at Hazelnut Ridge Road.

Garden Grotto Nursery
6704 Indian Springs Road N.E.
Scotts Mills, Oregon 97375
☎ *503/873-8235*

Hours *By appointment only*
Accessible *Partially*

Hansen Nursery

P.O. Box 446
Donald, Oregon 97020
☎ *503/678-5409*

Hours *By appointment (Wed only)*
Accessible *Yes*
Mail Order *(cyclamen only)*
Catalog *Free with SASE*

Hansen Nursery specializes in hardy, rare cyclamen and native perennials, many of which are uncommon in the trade and unfamiliar to most gardeners. Robin Hansen says, "Cyclamen are native to the Mediterranean, so they do extremely well here in the Pacific Northwest with its cooler, but similar climate. I prefer working with plants adapted to our dry summers and wet winters, able to tolerate our conditions with a minimum of fuss. I welcome visitors to the nursery, but ask that you call ahead. I will ship cyclamen on request; the native plants are available only at the nursery at this time." You can also find her plants at the sales sponsored by The Hardy Plant Society of Oregon, Leach Botanical Garden and Berry Botanic Garden. Ask for directions when you make an appointment to visit the nursery.

Incahoots of McMinnville

905 N. Baker
McMinnville, Oregon 97128
☎ *503/472-4923*

Hours *Mon-Fri 9-6, Sat 9-5*
Accessible *Partially*

"A hot cup of coffee, the aroma of potpourri, and some of the most beautiful music in the world make Incahoots a memorable shopping experience," say Janet and Brian Bailey. "Our distinctive blend of merchandise is a combination of the classic, the new, the novel, the natural. So, whether it's a reward for yourself or a gift for someone special, Incahoots has what you need." They've perennials by the hundreds, house plants, bulbs and seeds, ferns, ground covers and herbs, containers, irrigation systems and organic supplies, vegetable starts and roses, too. Watch for sales through the seasons.

Yvonne and Russell Graham offer uncommon hardy herbaceous perennials with an emphasis on American natives and unique companion species. The catalog is replete with bulbs, ferns, ornamental grasses, ground covers, perennials and wildflowers. While Northwest natives are by no means the focus of the collection, the catalog does flag a significant number of our region's woodland-dwelling species. Visitors are welcome to visit the nursery by appointment to get ideas. The owners suggest you be ready for uneven ground, tilled paths and mud in season!

Russell Graham, Purveyor of Plants

4030 Eagle Crest Road N.W.
Salem, Oregon 97304
☎ *503/362-1135*

Hours *By appointment only*
Accessible *No*
Mail Order
Catalog *$2 (refundable)*

North Oregon Coast

"A lot of my customers tell me, 'we've never seen this many perennials and herbs in one nursery.' So, before you select plants through mail order, come shop at Wisteria Herbs and Flowers," suggests owner Linda Montgomery-Dean. She carries a large and varied selection of scented geraniums and other out-of-the-ordinary annuals, too. With over 600 varieties to choose from, this nursery is a lot bigger than it appears from the highway! Look for the sign a mile and a half south of Newport across the Yaquina Bay Bridge.

Wisteria Herbs and Flowers

5273 S. Coast Highway
South Beach, Oregon 97366
☎ *503/867-3846*

Hours *Daily 9-4 (spring through fall)*
Accessible *No*

Eugene Area & South Oregon Coast

The Gossler's catalog includes a fine selection of perennials, bulbs and grasses. See complete listing in Collector's Plants on page 264.

Gossler Farm's Nursery

1200 Weaver Road
Springfield, Oregon 97478
☎ *503/746-3922*

Lorane Hills Farm & Nursery

Easy Acres Drive
Eugene, Oregon 97405
☎ *503/344-8943*

Hours *By appointment only*
Accessible *Difficult on soft surfaces*
Mail Order
Catalog *Free*
Mailing address *P.O. Box 5464*
Eugene, Oregon 97405

Evelyn Hess says, "We specialize in those exuberant perennials remembered and loved from Grandmother or Great Aunt Nel's garden. They are strong, hardy, outdoor-grown plants which take-off quickly and thrive in Northwest landscapes. Visitors enjoy the country drive to our nursery nestled in wooded hills seventeen miles southwest of Eugene. Here they can stroll among shade-loving perennials beneath the fir trees or walk the sunny borders to see how plants combine and perform in the ground. Since we add little or no water to our sunny borders, visitors also can observe the relative drought tolerance of plants. We grow an assortment of plants in pots for customer convenience, but will also dig from the field or border if the weather and plant size cooperate. Garden advice is freely and happily given to all potential customers (or anyone else who asks). We also have a consultation service and give occasional classes and talks." Take Lorane Highway to Territorial Highway and travel south a half-mile to Easy Acres Drive. Go another half-mile and look for the sign on the left side of the road.

Southern Oregon

Forestfarm

990 Tetherow
Williams, Oregon 97544
☎ *503/846-6963*

Forestfarm, a mail-order source for rare and unusual plants, offers a wide array of ornamental grasses, ground covers and perennials. See complete listing in Collector's Plants, page 263.

This splendid mail-order nursery specializes in perennials for everlasting arrangements and fragrant plants that attract hummingbirds and butterflies to the garden. The plant list includes a number of native American herbs. Owners Jim and Dotti Becker have written an 85-page book, "A Concise Guide to Growing Everlastings," which, along with other books on related subjects, you'll find in the back of their catalog. All Goodwin Creek plants are grown organically. They are shipped in well-rooted 2¾-inch pots or as seeds. Orders may also be picked up at their retail shop, Secret Garden, in Ashland. See listing on page 317.)

Goodwin Creek Gardens

P.O. Box 83
Williams, Oregon 97544
☎ *503/846-7357*

Mail Order
Catalog $1

Siskiyou offers bulbs, ornamental grasses and lots of lovely little plants for the perennial garden. See complete listing in Collector's Plants, page 265.

Siskiyou Rare Plant Nursery

2825 Cummings Road
Medford, Oregon 97501
☎ *503/772-6846*

Central Oregon

As a specialist in plants that do well on the dry side, Joyce Macdonald grows herbs of all kinds and perennials that like good drainage. Noting that her nursery is in Zone 4 and that the alkaline soil there contains lots of pumice, she reports great success with such prairie plants as purple coneflowers, coreopsis, gaillardias, liatris, daylilies, sedums, creeping thyme and tarragon.

Joyce's Garden

64640 Old Bend-Redmond Highway
Bend, Oregon 97701
☎ *503/388-6884*

Hours Mon-Sat 9-4
(call for off-season hours)
Accessible Yes
Mail Order
Catalog $2

Idaho

Michael and Joan Mount pack a lot of plant material into their small store. See complete listing on page 385.

Green Things

13910 Highway 12
Orofino, Idaho 83544
☎ *208/476-3022*

Edward's Greenhouse

4106 Sandcreek Street
Boise, Idaho 83703
☎ 208/342-7548

Hours Mon-Fri 8-7, Sat 8-5, Sun 10-5
(April through June); Mon-Sat 8-5
throughout the year

Accessible Partially
Catalog Free perennials list

Edward's Greenhouse supplies Idaho gardeners with colorful drought-tolerant perennials in a wide range of heights and textures. Owners Garnette and Mike Monnie seek out unusual species, such as sea holly (*Eryngium amethystinum*), uncommon varieties of such common perennials as columbine, asters, daylilies, dianthus, lilies and iris. They carry quite a few native wildflowers, and they've a good selection of water-wise ground covers, as well. See other listings on pages 221 and 255.

Mountain Springs Nursery

2075 Upland Drive
Sandpoint, Idaho 83864
☎ 208/263-5214

Mountain Springs Nursery offers an excellent selection of cold-hardy perennials. See complete listing on page 201.

British Columbia

Fraser Valley

Ferncliff Gardens

8394 McTaggart Street
Mission, British Columbia V2V 6S6
☎ 604/826-2447

Dahlias are the specialty here, but David Jack's daylilies and peonies also add joy to the perennial garden. See complete listing on page 201.

Elke and Ken Knechtel publish an excellent catalog of herbaceous perennials, especially plants for shady gardens. They've a large selection of North American natives, including ferns, grasses and iris. For gardeners in the Fraser River Valley who frequent the nursery, the catalog lists a calendar of monthly events that includes plant displays and lectures. They ship plants to gardeners throughout Canada and into the U.S. "We grow over 70% of the perennials we sell. Among our specialties are hardy geraniums. This year we're introducing *Geranium X oxonianum* 'Anmore' and 'Phoebe Noble'. Both are now receiving good comments in England. We also carry a good selection of perennials from Bressingham Gardens of England. We search the world over for garden-worthy plants that not only delight the serious gardener, but also can be grown by the novice." The company also manufactures sturdy anodized aluminum plant labels.

Rainforest Gardens
13139 224th Street
Maple Ridge, British Columbia V2X 7E7
☎ *604/467-4218*

Hours Sat 10-3 (March through Nov)
or by appointment

Accessible Yes
Mail Order
Catalog $2 (refundable)
FAX 604/467-3181

Vancouver Island

If you have visited The Butchart Garden's famous floral display, then you'll eagerly await the arrival of their seed catalog. In its pages, you'll find all the familiar annuals from ageratum to zinnias, plus a number of biennials, perennials and rock garden plants. There are some enticing mixtures as well – wildflowers, a hanging basket selection, a children's collection and a cut flower mixture. The seeds are featured in The Butchart Gardens' Gift Shop. This emporium is an excellent source for garden gifts, books and tools, too!

DESTINATION☆

The Butchart Gardens Ltd.
Box 4010
Victoria, British Columbia V8X 3X4
☎ *604/652-4422*

Hours Open daily at 9;
closing times vary month-to-month

Accessible Yes
Mail Order
Catalog $1 (refundable)
FAX 604/652-3883

Bulbs

For the sake of simplicity, I'm calling any plant that stores its life-cycle underground a bulb. Actually, the group includes corms (gladiolus, crocus and freesia), rhizomes (agapanthus and most iris), tubers (anemone, cyclamen, ranunculus), tuberous roots (alstroemeria, tuberous begonias and dahlias) and true bulbs (tulips, hyacinths, lilies, daffodils, amaryllis, etc.).

No landscape is complete without bulbs – from the first crocus in late winter through the cheerful spring displays of tulips, daffodils and iris and into the summer and fall with lilies, glads and dahlias. Bulbs lend elegance to the garden. They are more effective en masse and most natural-looking when planted in soft, flowing drifts. They combine beautifully with annuals, perennials and shrubs.

It's tempting to order one of every variety. To make a big impact, however, I prefer to buy at least two dozen of the same variety. I plant "minor" bulbs in groups of four dozen or more, lest they be lost in the landscape. Like all the garden's permanent plantings, bulbs should be orchestrated by color. Consult a bloom-sequence chart to spread out the joy and to ensure pleasing color combinations of the varieties that bloom at the same time.

Success begins with good-quality bulbs. All are easy to grow, but most prefer sun and well-drained soil. In wet-winter climates with clay soils, plant bulbs over a sand or grit base. Since spring blooming bulbs begin showing color while the weather is still cool and rainy, I like to plant them where the display can be enjoyed from a window in the house. However, the best site for bulbs is where *they* will be happiest.

One problem for the garden designer is that the foliage should never be cut down until it is completely brown. The bulb rejuvenates itself by drawing down nutrients from the foliage. To hide the bulb foliage as it withers and browns, spring-flowering bulbs can be interplanted with deciduous ferns in a naturalized setting or within a ground cover such as sweet woodruff or forget-me-nots in a perennial border.

I like iris and lilies and callas in big clumps as accent plants. I like to tuck some of the little-known native bulbs in woodland settings and use Pacific iris in rock gardens. I scatter species tulips and let them naturalize on a grassy bank and plant miniature daffodils in containers on my deck. The Pacific Northwest is "bulb heaven." One more reason I'm delighted to live here! 🌼

Catalog Sources for Bulbs Through the Seasons

For Early Spring, the Crocus, Daffodils and Tulips

Corbett, Oregon is daffodil country! Here's the first of three daffodil farms in this one town that are spin-offs from the hybridizing efforts of the late Murray Evans. Jeanie and Frank Driver specialize in intermediate and miniature daffodils, and their catalog provides a source for diversifying and expanding your medley of spring blooms! In the fall, you can meet all of the growers and buy their bulbs at the Oregon Daffodil Society Bulb Sale in Albany, Oregon. (See page 281).

Bonnie Brae Gardens

1105 S.E. Christensen Road
Corbett, Oregon 97019
☎ *503/695-5190*

Hours *By appointment only*
Accessible *No*
Mail Order
Catalog *Free with #10 SASE*

Four generations of the Evans family have been in the daffodil business. Having succumbed to "Yellow Fever," Ronald and Sandy Evans carry on the family tradition. "This is an intimate farm compared to the days when the family raised daffodils by the acres and tons," says Ronald. "Thirty-five years ago Uncle Murray Evans elected to scale down and specialize, starting his own program of hybridizing. Over his lifetime 'Unk' gave us over 200 new varieties (many named for his favorite Oregon locations), in beautiful pinks, the whitest whites and deepest yellows."

Columbia Gorge Daffodil & Tree Farm

3413 S.E. Mannthey Road
Corbett, Oregon 97019
☎ *503/695-2763*

Hours *Weekends by appointment*
Accessible *No*
Mail Order
Catalog *Free*
Mailing address *P.O. Box 205*
Corbett, Oregon 97019

Grant Mitsch Novelty Daffodils

6247 S. Sconce
Hubbard, Oregon 97032
☎ *503/651-2742*

Accessible *Yes*
Mail Order
Catalog *$3 refundable with first order*
Mailing address *P.O. Box 218*
Hubbard, Oregon 97032

Elise and Dick Havens carry on a tradition begun by Elise's father and mother, Grant and Amy Mitsch. Their 1993 color catalog not only pictures over 60 of the 300 varieties they grow, but also explains the difference between the terms narcissus, jonquils and daffodils. There are twelve divisions (as defined by the Royal Horticultural Society) within the world of daffodils, and the Havens supply bulbs from eleven of those divisions. Wait 'til you see the variety of shapes and sizes and colors possible! Oregon's daffodil growers are among the nicest people I talked with as I prepared this book. They shared the names of their competitors, and indeed all work together to inspire enthusiasm for daffodils, just as Murray Evans and Grant Mitsch cooperated during their lifetimes. I'm impressed!

Oregon Trail Daffodils

41905 S.E. Louden Road
Corbett, Oregon 97019
☎ *503/695-5513*

Hours *Daily 8-5 (March through mid-May) or by appointment*
Accessible *No*
Mail Order
Catalog *Free*

Diane Tribe, a 4th-generation daffodil enthusiast and another of Murray Evans' nieces, grows 400 varieties of daffodils. The collection includes both show daffodils and garden varieties, but concentrates on the former. She and her husband Bill offer tours of their fields in spring to see the flowers in bloom. They are seriously into their own hybridizing. Their stock came from her uncle and from East Coast varieties supplied by a friend in Virginia, Bill Panel. All of their daffodils are grown from seed. Noting the painstaking research that goes into the subject, she explains, "It takes seven years to determine if a variety is show quality!

Each spring hundreds of thousands of visitors from across the country enjoy the vibrant tulips abloom in the Skagit Valley! The display garden at Roozengaarde with its familiar windmill is one of the highlights. Roozengaarde is a division of Washington Bulb Company, which is the largest grower of tulips, daffodils and iris in the world and is responsible for ninety-five percent of the bulbs grown in the Skagit Valley. The Roozen family has been in the bulb business since the late 1700s. Their catalog not only offers tulips, hyacinths and daffodils, but also fritillary, glory of the snow, allium, summer snowflake and several other lesser-known bulbs. Each bulb they ship is inspected and packaged locally to ensure "top size." Orders must be received by August 31, but you can purchase bulbs at their store during September, October and November. Anytime you're in the area, the gift store is a gardener's delight with home accessories, gifts and fresh-cut flowers. They have an annual sale from mid-December through New Year's. Restrooms and outdoor tables make Roozengaarde a favorite picnic destination. From I-5, take Kincaid Street (exit # 226) and go west to the first stoplight. Take a right, then continue over the bridge and take a left onto Wall Street. Wall makes a quick right turn and becomes McLean Road. Go about three miles and turn left on Beaver Marsh.

DESTINATION ☆
Roozengaarde

1587 Beaver Marsh Road
Mount Vernon, Washington 98273
☎ *206/424-8531*

Hours *Daily 9-5:30*
(March, April & May);
Mon-Sat 9-5 (June through Feb)
Accessible *Yes*
Mail Order
Catalog *Free*

Since 1934, this family business has been growing tulips, daffodils, crocus, hyacinths and miscellaneous unusual bulbs. The VanLierop family invites visitors to join them as they celebrate the return of spring and "walk through our living catalog." Each season offers an inspiring new collection of home and garden decorations at the retail store where they sell cut flowers and garden gifts in addition to a terrific collection of bulbs.

VanLierop Bulb Farm, Inc.

13407 80th Street E.
Puyallup, Washington 98372-3608
☎ *206/848-7272*

Hours *Mon-Fri 9-4:30 (Feb through mid-June & Mid-Sept through October)*
Accessible *Yes*
Mail Order
Catalog *Free*
FAX *206/848-9142*

West Shore Acres

956 Downey Road
La Conner, Washington 98273
☎ 206/466-3158

Hours Daily 10-6 (mid-March through April), Mon-Sat 10-5 (second week in Sept through third week in Oct); orders March through July
Accessible Yes
Mail Order
Catalog Free

Tulips, daffodils, crocus and hyacinths are listed by variety in West Shore Acre's catalog. Their retail shop sells flowers in bulbs in spring and fall, along with vases and baskets. A beautiful display garden on the channel surrounds a 1906 Victorian home here. It's a joy to visit.

Wooden Shoe Bulb Company

33814 S. Meridian Road
Woodburn, Oregon 97071
☎ 503/634-2243

Hours Phone hours 8-4; field open late March and early April (depending upon weather) 9-dusk
Accessible Yes
Mail Order
Catalog Free
Mailing address P.O. Box 127
Mt. Angel, Oregon 97362
FAX 503/634-2710

The Iverson family (which includes eighteen grandchildren) warmly welcomes the public to their thirty-acre tulip field each spring. Here you'll tiptoe through 115 varieties, buy fresh cut tulips and, no doubt, place a big order for your own garden. The descriptive catalog offers tulips and daffodils sure to please serious gardeners. They also offer a "Beginners Special." What a nice gift idea! From I-5, take Woodburn Exit #271. Go east 6 miles on 214 and 211 toward Molalla. Turn right (south) on Meridian for a mile and a half, then left on Newman for another half-mile. Follow the signs.

Iris for Late-spring

Aitken's Salmon Creek Garden

608 N.W. 119th Street
Vancouver, Washington 98685
☎ 206/573-4472

Hours Daily during daylight hours (April through June); 8-5 (July through Oct.)
Accessible Difficult on grass paths
Mail Order
Catalog $2 (refundable)
FAX 206/576-7012

Barbara and Terry Aitkin's extensive hybridizing program has resulted in award-quality tall bearded iris. They also grow a wide selection of beardless Japanese, Siberian, Spuria, Pacific Coast and species iris from around the world. Their color catalog displays mouthwatering choices. Bearded iris orders are shipped Mid-July through August and the beardless from August through October. During the "off" season the Aitkins bring gardening activities indoors with orchids.

Japanese and Siberian Iris are part of the perennial garden at Caprice Farm. See page 184 for complete listing.

Caprice Farm Nursery

15425 S.W. Pleasant Hill Road
Sherwood, Oregon 97140
☎ *503/625-7241*

"We are a small retail mail-order nursery specializing in the finest Siberian and Spuria iris," say Tom and Ellen Abrego. They publish a price list describing 51 varieties of Siberians, which are well-suited to water gardens. They've 35 delicate-looking, clump-forming Spurias, which are, in fact, very rugged and drought-tolerant. Chehalem Gardens is primarily a mail-order business. "We offer excellence in product and service. Our garden is open in May, on weekends only. It's best to call ahead." Iris are shipped in August and September. Take Highway 99W out of Newburg toward McMinnville. After passing through Dundee, turn right on Trunk Road proceed up the hill one mile.

Chehalem Gardens

19105 N.E. Trunk Road
Dundee
☎ *503/538-8920*

Accessible *Yes*
Mail Order
Catalog *Free*
Mailing address *P.O. Box 693*
Newberg, Oregon 97132

In April, May and June, you'll find 250 acres of iris on display at Cooley's, which is one of the two largest iris nurseries in the country! Sixty-four years in the trade, this retail and mail order company is still very much a family-operated business. Its garden is open free to the public and its 80-page color catalog pictures over 300 gorgeous varieties of bearded iris. They offer quantity discounts and let you choose your own "bonus" plants. Select collections are sold at substantial savings. All orders include cultural instructions. They have a nineteen-minute video on tall bearded iris and offer lectures and seminars by request. May-June issues of national magazines carry advertising specials.

Cooley's Gardens Inc.

11553 Silverton Road N.E.
Silverton, Oregon 97381
☎ *503/873-5463 or 1-800/225-5391*
(orders only)

Hours *Daily 8-5 (May through October);*
Mon-Fri 8-5 (November through April)
Accessible *Yes*
Mail Order
Catalog *$4 (refundable)*
Mailing address *P.O. Box 126*
Silverton, Oregon 97381
FAX *503/873-5812*

Schreiner's Gardens

3625 Quinaby Road N.E.
Salem, Oregon 97303
☎ 503/393-3232
or 1-800/525-2367 (orders only)

Hours Mon-Fri 8-5
Accessible Yes
Mail Order
Catalog $4 (refundable)
FAX 503/393-5590

Since 1925, three generations of Schreiners have been growing and hybridizing bearded iris. The other of the nation's largest retail iris growers is listed second in this book because S follows C. (See previous page.) Schreiner's offers a huge, colorful "Iris Lovers Catalog," packed with scrumptious-looking flowers in every possible hue. The fertile Willamette Valley is obviously a most hospitable place for iris! In 1991 Schreiner's won six out of eleven awards of merit bestowed by the American Iris Society for new introductions in tall bearded iris. The catalog includes terrific collections and "Red Star" quantity discounts. A free instruction booklet comes with each order. The viewing gardens are open daily from May through first week in June from 8 a.m. until dusk.

Walsterway Iris Gardens

19923 Broadway
Snohomish (Maltby), Washington 98290
☎ 206/485-6470 or 668-4429

Hours Daily 9-5 (mid-May to mid-Sept)
Accessible Yes
Mail Order
Catalog $1

"Most of our customers come out to gardens from mid-May to mid-June to select their iris varieties, and then they come back to pick them up after digging in July," says Mrs. Walster. Her two-acre iris collection includes 600 varieties of tall bearded iris and an extensive selection of Japanese and Siberians. You are welcome to bring a lunch and use the picnic tables on the property. This home business thrives on a comfortable, relaxed approach. The catalog, which does not picture the iris, is nonetheless quite descriptive. From 405, take the Monroe exit. Follow Highway 522 (center lane) six miles to the first signal light. Take a left and follow the signs.

Lilies to Light-up the Summer Garden

Bob and Dianna Gibson present about 250 varieties of lilies in the two color catalogs they produce each year. Over 500 varieties, including Asiatic, trumpet, Oriental hybrids and nursery-propagated species, are being tested at any given time. They carry alstroemeria (Peruvian lilies), and the catalog notes that *Alstroemeria aurantiaca* is invasive and should only be planted on the edge of civilization! I appreciate that kind of honesty! The Gibsons offer small but nice selections of evergreen daylilies and astilbe as companion plants. They are in the process of developing a five-acre display garden, which are welcome to visit from mid-June through August on Thursdays, Fridays and Saturdays. They ask that you send a written request, including SASE, and let them know the number of people and cars to expect.

B&D Lilies

330 P Street
Port Townsend, Washington 98368
☎ *206/385-1738*

Hours *Mon-Fri 9-5; Sat 10-4*
(June 20-Aug 30)
Accessible *Yes, but limited in field*
Mail Order
Catalog *$3 (refundable)*
FAX *206/385-9996*

Primarily a mail-order nursery, Lilies and More is a family operation whose focus is on developing different color forms of West Coast American hybrids for the garden market. Their descriptive catalog presently lists Asiatics, Orientals, trumpets and Aurelian varieties and species hybrids. Owner Billie Mathieu says we can look forward to miniature trumpets, Orienpets, tetraploid varieties and a wide selection of up-facing Orientals in future catalogs.

Lilies and More

12400 N.E. 42nd Avenue
Vancouver, Washington 98686
☎ *206/573-4696*

Hours *By appointment only*
Accessible *No*
Mail Order
Catalog *$1*
Mailing address *P.O. Box 65157*
Vancouver, Washington 98665-0006

The Lily Pad

5102 Scott Road N.W.
Olympia, Washington 98502
☎ 206/866-0291

Hours Mon-Fri 8-5
(telephone orders only)
Accessible No
Mail Order
Catalog $1

"We are a small-scale, family-operated business. To maintain quality and to assure best-adapted stock to the Northwest, we're always upgrading our selection and looking for the best and newest cultivars for Northwest gardens," says Jan Detwiler. The catalog lists Asiatic, Aurelian and Trumpets and Oriental Hybrid lilies. It has a section of rare and unusual hybrids for the collector and a section of discount bulb collections. "Although we don't offer a tour, our flowers are on display at local farmers' markets during the bloom season. Call for exact times and locations."

Lindel Lilies

5510 239th Street
Langley, British Columbia V3A 7N6
☎ 604/534-4729

Hours Display Garden open Sun-Fri
(June-Sept)
Accessible Yes
Mail Order
Catalog $2 (refundable)
FAX 604/534-4742

Lindel Lilies offers a wide selection of garden hardy Asiatic, Martagon, Trumpet and Oriental hybrids as well as species lilies. Bulbs are available for both fall and spring plantings. "We can help with your selection and growing questions," say Del and Linda Knowlton, noting that their "only business is growing and selling lilies." They claim the largest selection available in Canada. The Knowltons are often asked to conduct seminars at garden clubs and create displays at flower shows.

Into the Fall with Dahlias

Connell's Dahlias

10216 40th Avenue E.
Tacoma, Washington 98446
☎ 206/531-0292

Hours Mon-Fri 9-5 (Oct through April)
or by appointment
Accessible Yes
Mail Order
Catalog $2

Connell's color catalog lists over 400 top dahlia varieties, including 15 to 25 new cultivars each year and most of the American Dahlia Society's "fabulous fifty." An instruction sheet accompanies each order, and the catalog offers both a monthly guide and the booklet, *Dahlias Today*. The Show Garden (*10616 Waller Road E.*) is open from August 15 though September during daylight hours. Labor Day weekend and the weekend before are peak times at the garden; dahlia experts will be standing by to answer questions and take orders.

"We grow only the best, we discard the rest," says David Jack, whose specimen mail order nursery is a third-generation family venture that has been in business in the scenic Fraser Valley since 1920. Ferncliff grows top selections of dahlias, glads, daylilies, iris and peonies. (David ships only the dahlias to the U.S.) Each year he offers three to five new giant dinnerplate introductions and several excellent new garden dahlia varieties. The field plantings and show gardens are open to the public during the peak bloom periods (iris from April until June, peonies in late May and June, and acres of dahlias from mid-August to early-October). Take Highway #7 two miles east of Mission, to the Dewdney Trunk Road at Hatzic Esso station, turn north up the hill a quarter-mile, then east (right) on Henry Avenue to the end. Take a left on McTaggart Street, then a right at the sign.

Ferncliff Gardens

8394 McTaggart Street
Mission, British Columbia V2V 6S6
☎ *604/826-2447*
Hours *Mon-Fri 8-5, Sat 9-4*
(March 15 through Oct 15); Mon-Fri 8-5
(Oct 15 through March 15)
Accessible *No*
Mail Order
Catalog *Free*
U.S. Mailing address:
David Jack
P. O. Box 66
Sumas, Washington 98295
FAX *604/826-4316*

"We grow 350 varieties of exhibition-quality dahlias suitable for serious dahlia hobbyists and home gardeners" says Patti Eckoff, who loves to "talk dahlias." She offers advice on everything from planting to lifting and storing. "We have a continuing development program with at least a thousand seedlings undergoing evaluation. The seedlings are always an interesting part of a tour of our garden – a preview of coming attractions. Bring your cameras and take home a memory!" Selection is best in September when you can view the dahlias in bloom.

Sea-Tac Dahlia Gardens

20020 Des Moines Memorial Drive
Seattle, Washington 98198
☎ *206/824-3846*

Hours *Daily 8-dusk*
Accessible *Partially*
Mail Order
Catalog *Free with SASE*

Swan Island Dahlias

995 N.W. 22nd
Canby, Oregon 97013
☎ *503/266-7711*

Hours *Mon-Fri 9-4:30*
Accessible *Yes*
Mail Order
Catalog *$3*
Mailing address *P.O. Box 700*
Canby, Oregon 97013

Just when the rest of the landscape is late-summer drab, Swan Island is a spectacular sight with forty acres in bloom. The fields are open every day from dawn until dusk from August until the first frost. The company is the largest retail grower in the U.S. All its varieties are labeled. The Gitts family hosts an Indoor Dahlia Festival on the Saturday, Sunday and Monday of the week before Labor Day and throughout Labor Day weekend. Over 15,000 cut flowers in big, splashy arrangements help you select the shapes, colors and sizes to fill a special niche in the garden. The 52-page color catalog tells you everything you need to know about growing these festive Mexican natives. Plant selection is best in August and September, and orders are shipped in the spring.

Perennial Border, circa 1911

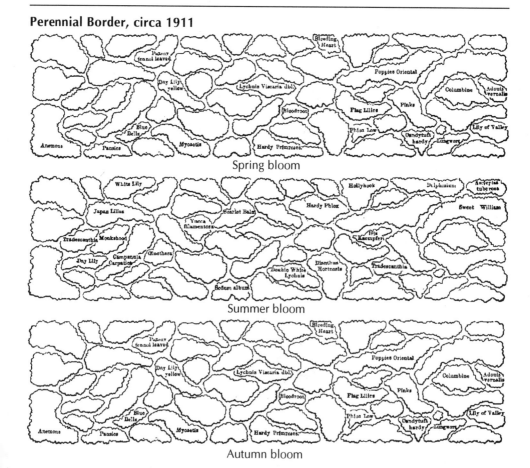

Spring bloom

Summer bloom

Autumn bloom

Chapter Seven
The Edible Landscape

*"Supermarkets are all right,
but it's much more fun
to shop for food in nature"*

.....Euell Gibbons

Designing with Edible Plants

The latest thing in gardening circles is landscaping that both pleases the eye and teases the palate! And why not? There's nothing inherently homely about food plants. Who's to say that pear trees are less attractive than maples or that grapevines don't measure up to clematis? Why not plant parsley as a lacy border, strawberries as ground cover, purple basil as a colorful filler in the perennial bed? Attractive edibles integrated with ornamentals make for a better use of limited garden space, and they make a landscape more interesting.

If you've never grown edible plants, experiment for the fun of it! Good soil is key to successful food crops. Remember, too, that you're making a commitment to managing without chemical pesticides. "With the advent of new technologies, gardeners have more control over disease, pests, even the weather," says Washington gardener Stephen Weedman, whose company, Grown Naturally, supplies organically-grown fruits, nuts, herbs and vegetables to markets and restaurants in Longview. He and his partners, Mark Chadwick and Jerry Lokan have developed an "arsenal" of resources for keeping their edibles healthy.

These organic gardeners' secrets include choosing disease resistant varieties and using crop rotation and companion planting. In winter, they plant cover crops, which they dig back in to enrich the soil. They also add liberal amounts of organic compounds to the soil, encouraging worms, spiders and microorganisms to flourish.

"Microorganisms exist in a symbiotic relationship with plants," says Stephen. "These workhorses add their own body secretions to the soil, enhancing and breaking down the compounds. Then they die, adding more nutrients. Without microorganisms, air, water and nutrients become less available, and plants become more susceptible to disease and insects." 🌿

Fruits, Nuts & Berries

The Pacific Northwest is one of the best places on earth to cultivate fruits, nuts and berries. Having easy access to these wholesome plants in your garden allows you to harvest at the exact moment of ripeness. The produce is fresh and the price is right!

Apple, pear, apricot, plum, cherry, peach and fig trees are lovely shade trees for small gardens. Walnut and chestnut trees provide a canopy for larger landscapes. If your space is limited or you have a bare wall to cover, fruit trees can be espaliered (preferably against a south-facing wall). Many of the berry bushes make attractive hedges. Creeping blueberries and strawberries are splendid ground covers.

A number of the sources in this section specialize in varieties suitable for gardens west of the Cascades where cool summers slow the ripening process. They offer catalogs packed with information to help you make your selections. Most of them sell excellent tools, organic supplies and books. 🦋

Catalog Sources for Fruit-bearing Trees, Shrubs & Vines

Over a hundred varieties of red, white, pink and black currants and fifty varieties of gooseberries are available from this mail-order source. The company also offers jostaberries (a cross between gooseberries and currants) and the golden, red and purple-fruited Cornelian cherry dogwoods. Place your order in the fall or early winter. The plants are shipped bare-root.

A.I. Eppler, Ltd.
P.O. Box 16513
Seattle, Washington 98116-0513
☎ *206/932-2211*

Hours Mon-Fri 10-5
Mail Order
Catalog $3

Located on the plateau at the foot of Mt. Rainier, Buckley Nursery Garden Center, is one of the most complete sources for bare-root fruit and nut trees and small fruits in Western Washington. The company's list ranges from apples to walnuts, and it includes such edibles as horseradish and rhubarb, plus a good selection of grapevines. "We are a complete regional garden center, but our biggest business is in the fruit trees and deciduous shrubs we ship throughout the region from February through April," says owner Don Marlow.

Buckley Nursery Garden Center
646 North River Avenue
Buckley, Washington 98321
☎ *206/829-1811*

Hours Daily 9-5
Accessible Yes
Mail Order
Catalog Free

Burnt Ridge Nursery & Orchards

432 Burnt Ridge Road
Onalaska, Washington 98570
☎ *206/985-2873*

Hours *By appointment only*
Accessible *No*
Mail Order
Catalog *Free; send a U.S. or $.40 Canadian stamp*

The catalog's tag line reads, "Specializing in unusual trees, shrubs and vines that produce edible nuts and fruits." And what an extensive list it is – new varieties of familiar plants and plants I didn't even know are edible! While the majority of the business is in mail-order edibles, Michael Dolan and his wife Carolyn are rapidly expanding into unusual ornamentals and Northwest natives. "We offer a large selection of rare fruiting plants suited to the Northwest such as mulberry, paw paw, persimmon, loquat, fig, jujube, kiwi and mayhaw. We also grow a wide variety of common fruits, such as apples, pears, plums, cherries, peaches and apricots, with an emphasis on varieties well-adapted to our maritime climate. We sell all the different nut trees that will grow in Washington: chestnut, Persian and black walnut, pine nut, almond, northern pecan, hickory, heartnut, butternut, monkey puzzle, hazelnut and ginkgo." In the fall they sell nuts and a hand-cranked nutcracker that can open the shells nearly as fast as the hopper is filled. Selection of plants is best in winter and spring; shop for small fruits summer and fall. All produce is certified organic. Ask for directions when you call for an appointment.

C&O Nursery

P.O. Box 116
Wenatchee, Washington 98807-0116
☎ *509/662-7164*

Hours *Mon-Fri 8-5, Sat 8-4 (March & April); Mon-Fri 8-5 (May through Oct); Mon-Fri 8-5, Sat 8-noon (Nov through Feb)*
Accessible *Yes*
Mail Order
Catalog *Free*
FAX *509/662-4519*

C&O, which was begun in 1906, is a third-generation family business located in downtown Wenatchee. The company is well-known for the fruit trees it ships throughout the U.S. and Canada. Its catalog lists over one hundred different apple, pear, peach, plum, prune, cherry, apricot and nectarine varieties.

Cloud Mountain Farm & Nursery is located along the western edge of the Cascades, twenty miles east of Bellingham on the west-facing slopes of Sumas Mountain. "Better fruit-growing country is hard to imagine," say Tom and Cheryl Thornton about their twenty acres of nursery stock and orchards. "We have been in business for 15 years, through the extremes in temperature and rainfall, and have been striving to gain a better understanding of regional microclimates. Our staff combines many years of experience and expertise in helping you choose the appropriate plants for your home. The catalog provides a wide range of fruiting plants and lists ornamentals for the landscape. However they do not ship the ornamentals and don't ship any plants into Canada. Visit this seasonal nursery for weekly specials on select trees and shrubs. They offer several excellent free workshops in spring.

Cloud Mountain Farm & Nursery

6906 Goodwin Road
Everson, Washington 98247
☎ 206/966-5859

Hours *Thurs-Mon 10-5, Sun 12-5
(Feb through mid-June);
Thurs-Sat 10-5 (Sept and Oct)*
Accessible *Yes*
Mail Order
Catalog *$1*
FAX *206/966-0921*

"We have a wide selection of fruit trees that produce well west of the Cascades," says Bob Hartman. "Most of our customers prefer to come to the nursery to pick out their trees. During the fruiting season and on into the fall we have fruit available for people to taste before purchasing the trees. In fact we encourage people to come taste the fruit." He offers plants on a number of different rootstocks, allowing customers to select the ultimate size of their trees from dwarf to standard size. The company has begun offering rootstocks for people who would like to try grafting or budding their own trees. "People may call for gardening advice at any time," says Bob. "Sorry, but we can't ship to Canada."

Hartman's Fruit Tree Nursery

713 21st Street S.E.
Puyallup, Washington 98372-4758
☎ 206/848-1484

Hours *Sat 8:30-dark
(mid-Nov through mid-April).
Will take calls any time during the year.*
Accessible *Yes*
Mail Order
Catalog *Free*

Moon's Nursery

P.O. Box 1097
Oroville, Washington 98864
☎ 509/476-3188

Hours Mon-Sat 9-5
Accessible No
Mail Order
Catalog $1
FAX 509/476-3188

Owner Hong Suk Moon is pioneering the propagation of Korean pears in the U.S. His registered *A-Ri Rang* variety boasts fruit weighing over a pound! He carries several other varieties of Oriental pears and the appropriate pollinators. The nursery, which is located in the Okanagan River Valley near the Canadian border, also offers Japanese apples and walnut trees grafted on Russian rootstock, plus premium varieties of peach, plum, nectarine, apricot and cherry trees. It's a wholesale operation, but he is willing to ship to non-commercial growers in the U.S. and Canada, with a minimum order of four trees.

Northwoods Nursery

27635 S. Oglesby Road
Canby, Oregon 97013
☎ 503/266-5432

Hours Tues-Sun 10-5 (Jan through May);
closed in summer;
open by appointment during the fall.
Phone or fax orders accepted
Mon-Fri 9-5, Sat 9-12 (Dec through June)
Accessible No
Mail Order
Catalog Free
FAX 503/266-5431

Northwoods Nursery offers gardeners and orchardists a wide selection of hard-to-find, easy-to-grow dwarf fruit trees, nut trees, berries, vines and beautiful ornamentals. The company has both a well-accepted retail store and well-known mail-order division that serves the U.S. and Canada. "Aside from fine varieties of apples, cherries, peaches, plums, berries, we offer more exotic selections such as American and Asian persimmons, kiwi hardy to minus 40-degrees, Asian pears, hardy figs, extremely rare grafted paw paw trees and much more," says owner, Kathy Fives. Master gardeners as well as eager novices look to the informative 56-page catalog for such plants as passionflowers, hardy eucalyptus, bamboo and old roses. The retail store is also a good source for ornamental grasses, ground covers, native plants and a good selection of vines, as well as containers and books. In spring they offer classes and lectures on grafting, pruning and new plant varieties. From Canby, take Highway 170 south toward Marquam about three miles, turn right on Gribble Road to the end. Turn left on Oglesby and look for the nursery about 100 yards ahead on right.

Puget Sound Kiwi began as a home garden project and evolved into a small-scale nursery. Its founder began taking cuttings from about 200 parent plants and "letting them take root at their own pace." Bob Glanzman believes that growing kiwifruit is perhaps the most exciting gardening adventure you'll ever try. Kiwifruit (*Actinidia deliciosa*) and other fruiting vines of this plant family make fine ornamental plants and produce an abundance of fruit. Cats find a substance in all *Actinidia* vines to be attractive like catnip," he says. He advises customers to plan ahead and train the vines on a sturdy arbor! Selection is best in May.

The Puget Sound Kiwi Co.
1220 N.E. 90th Street
Seattle, Washington 98115
☎ *206/523-6403*

Hours *Call for message*
(April through July)
Mail Order
Catalog *Free with SASE*

"We specialize in disease-resistant cultivars for organic growers in the Pacific Northwest," say the staff at Raintree. "We offer a wide variety of fruits, nuts, berries, bamboo and other plants for the edible landscape, including many flavorful varieties of apples, pears, plums, peaches. We also have unusual fruiting plants that do well in our region – figs, medlars, loquat, pineapple guava, gooseberries, blueberries, kiwis, quinces, pomegranates, serviceberries, currants and passion vines." The company also offers citrus trees, which make great container plants in the Northwest. The free 72-page catalog includes an informative backyard grower's guide and a page on creating a habitat for birds and wildlife. It's packed with expert gardening advice, plus an array of books, tools and organic supplies. You'll find markdowns in May. Write or call for the dates of free fruit growing classes. From I-5, take exit 71 (just south of Chehalis) and travel 24 miles east to Butts Road.

Raintree Nursery
391 Butts Road
Morton, Washington 98356
☎ *206/496-6400*

Hours *Sat & Sun 10-4:30*
(mid-Dec through mid-May);
or by appointment
Accessible *No*
Mail Order
Catalog *Free*
FAX *206/496-6465*

Van Well Nursery

1000 North Miller Street
Wenatchee, Washington 98807
☎ *509/663-8189*

Hours *Mon-Fri 8-5*
Accessible *Yes*
Mail Order
Catalog *$1*
Mailing address *P.O. Box 1339*
Wenatchee, Washington 98807
FAX *509/662-9336*

Van Well's catalog offers a complete line of quality fruit trees, including several patented varieties. The varieties are well-described and listed in order of ripening at Wenatchee. Large commercial growers account for most of this mail-order company's sales, but orders from home gardeners are welcomed. The trees are shipped by UPS (surface or air), and selection is best in March and April.

The Herb Garden

Throughout the millennia, mankind depended upon herbs for food, dyes, cleaning products, cosmetics and medicine. Many of the earliest writings, on clay tablets and papyrus, were herbals that described useful plants – where they could be found and how they could be preserved. No home garden was without its herbs. Then in the nineteenth century, commercial products replaced traditional herbal remedies, and herb gardens almost disappeared from the landscape.

When I set up housekeeping in the early '60s, the only culinary herbs I knew were those available on grocery shelves, dried and bottled. In the last few years there has been an explosion of interest in fresh cooking herbs that add exquisite flavors without salt or fat. These ancient, beneficial plants are once again being utilized for personal health and beauty, and there's new enthusiasm for herbs as decorative elements and for freshening the air.

Their soft colors, interesting textures and wonderful fragrances are enough to recommend herbs in the garden. They are among the easiest plants to grow, so they're rewarding for a beginner. Herbs are highly decorative in perennial borders, and because they require little space, they're ideal in containers on small terraces and on sunny window sills in urban apartments.

Traditionally, herbs were arranged in formal gardens. Most herbal books offer photographs and drawings of historical patterns – knots, stars, circles, cartwheels, diamonds, squares-within-a-square. Today, enthusiasts are recreating Chinese medicinal gardens and "literary gardens," based on herbs mentioned in the Bible or the works of Shakespeare. 🌾

Sources for Herbs & Herbal Crafts
Washington

Thirty-seven years of experience in growing herbs and her status as a Master Gardener have made Verona Latta popular on the lecture circuit. The display garden at her farm features over 500 species of herbs and everlastings, plus lots of perennials, ground covers, fruits and ferns. The company she founded manufactures herbal vinegars, which are sold at farmer's markets throughout the region. Her store, Heartstrings, in South Bend, markets wreaths, baskets, soaps, skin care products, jellies, syrups, mustard and seasoning blends, all fabricated from herbs. It also carries related ceramics and jewelry. The store is in a Victorian building surrounded by a pretty herb and perennial garden. The nursery at the farm hosts a herbal luncheon the second Saturdays of July, August and September. Reservations are limited to 25, and the events include making a herbal wreath.

Bears Herbs Hearts & Flowers
81 E. Raymond-Willapa Road
Raymond, Washington 98577
☎ *206/942-2122*

Hours Daily except Wed & Sat 10-dark
(April through Oct)
Accessible No

Two acres of gardens surround "Bell House," the home of one of Sequim's pioneer families, now a charming gift shop. They've a wonderful selection of herbs (including elephant garlic), plus annuals, ground covers, house plants, perennials, roses and seeds. Cedarbrook Farm makes herb vinegars, nine scents of potpourri, garlic braids, moth repellents, holiday wreaths and arrangements. You'll find garden books and baskets, baskets, baskets. Send for class information and the company's gift catalog, which is mailed in October.

Cedarbrook Herb Farm
986 Sequim Avenue S.
Sequim, Washington 98382
☎ *206/683-7733*

Hours Daily 9-5
(March through Dec 24th)
Accessible No
Mail Order
Catalog $2 gift catalog
(they do not ship plants);
$1 class schedule

Fairie Herbe Gardens

6236 Elm Street
Tumwater, Washington 98501
☎ 206/754-9249

Hours Tues-Fri 10-4,
weekends and holidays 1-6
(Mar 15 through Oct);
or by appointment
Accessible Yes

Owner David Baird is a real gardener, and his half-acre city lot will stimulate your imagination as to the many ways herbs can be used in the landscape. It features a culinary garden and a fragrance garden where heliotrope, lemon balm, lavender and other scented herbs delight the nose. For visual appeal, there's a formal medieval paradise garden and an ever-changing blue and yellow garden. Over 400 varieties of herbs and other hardy perennials are identified here, including many cultivars of English lavender and thyme and mint, plus old-fashioned garden plants no longer grown as herbs. He sends out a brochure announcing the dates for several workshops he teaches and for the spring sale and open house weekends in June and July, where you'll find his best prices of the year. From I-5, take exit # 102 (Trosper Road) and travel east to Capitol Way. Turn right; proceed south to X Street and turn left. Fairie Herbes is at the corner of X and Elm.

Fairlight Gardens

30904 164th S.E.
Auburn, Washington 98002
☎ 206/631-8932

Judy Jensen's interest in herbs has generated a garden and gift shop. She also teaches herbal crafts. See complete listing on page 165.

The Herbfarm has become an institution. Even *The New York Times* has raved about this place! Begun in 1974 from an old wheelbarrow parked under a tree and a hand-lettered sign that read, "Herb Plants for Sale," the company now employs 35 people and includes a nursery, shop, school, gourmet restaurant and mail-order business. This is one of the few firms equipped to ship herb plants. There are seventeen meticulously groomed display gardens here. Selection is best from late April to early July. The Visitor's Guide published every April and September lists herbal and general gardening products, activities and class schedules. The Herbfarm offers hundreds of classes on cooking, growing and crafting with herbs. Mother's Day weekend, when the nursery offers a free plant for moms, and Father's Day weekend, which launches the annual Microbrewery Festival, are special here. And, such events as the Scarborough Faire & Llama Festival during the July 4th weekend, the Harvest Festival with its demonstrations of old-time American living (Labor Day weekend) and the Great Pumpkin Celebration (the two weekends before Halloween) provide wonderful family entertainment. From I-90, take exit 22 (east of Issaquah). Go north through Preston toward Fall City. About three miles from the Freeway exit, turn left across the green bridge over the Raging River (S.E. 328th). Follow the signs.

DESTINATION ☆
The Herbfarm

32804 Issaquah-Fall City Road
Fall City, Washington 98024
☎ *206/784-2222*

Hours *Daily 9-6 (March through Oct);*
Daily 9-5 (winter)
Accessible *Yes*
Mail Order
Catalog *Free Visitor's Guide;*
$3.50 Plant List includes $2 coupon
FAX *206/789-2279*

Patterns for herb gardens, circa 1911

Rachel Dee Herb Farm

40622 196th Avenue S.E.
Enumclaw, Washington 98022
☎ *206/825-2797*

Hours *Tues-Sat 10-5*
(March through Oct)
Accessible *No*
Mail Order *(herbal gifts)*
Catalog *Free*

"We are a working herb farm," says Ivonne Brown, who invites visitors to stroll through her display gardens and experience the excitement of herbs by sniffing, pinching and tasting. "Some gardens simply must be a nibble-your-way-through experience. We have a gift shop which features dried flowers, seeds, wreaths, herbal baths, garden tools, books and potpourri ingredients. We also have an herbal food line of jams, jellies and vinegars, which we sell at the Pike Place Market in Seattle, by mail-order, and in the shop. When the world worries, there is the peace and solitude of the garden. We hope to leave this message with our customers." May through August are the best months for visiting the gardens, and you'll find mark-downs in September and October. Special events include classes and workshops.

Silver Bay Herb Farm

9151 Tracyton Boulevard
Bremerton, Washington 98310
☎ *206/692-1340*

Hours *Tues-Sat 11-5*
(March 15 through Dec 23);
Sun 11-5 (June through Sept & in Dec)
Accessible *Yes*

Silver Bay is a tranquil, secluded world of its own where you can stroll through fragrant herb gardens, enjoy views of the Olympic Mountains, walk the beach, or celebrate special occasions. Browse in the large gift shop for books, seeds, herbal crafts and supplies. "My hope is to provide a peaceful getaway for my customers and to share the rich world of herbs with them," says Mary Preus. "Our Northwest Chef's picnics in the summer under the large gazebo give customers a chance to talk with noted Northwest chefs and enjoy delicious meals in a relaxed atmosphere. In addition to numerous classes, the farm sponsors a Spring Fest held the Friday and Saturday before Mother's Day, an Autumn Fest in September and a Holiday Fest the first weekend in December. There's always a good sale in conjunction with these festivals.

Oregon

In addition to a big selection of herbs, this small home-based business offers a charming gift shop, a well-maintained display garden, popular classes and herbal refreshments. During their annual events (Herb Festival the first two weeks in May and Holiday Open House during the first two weeks in November), you'll find consigned, juried crafts and art by local artisans, plus special culinary treats and herbal displays. Call or write to get on the mailing list for classes and specific festival dates. From I-205, take the Stafford Road exit and travel south on Stafford to Newland Road.

Barn Owl Nursery

22999 S.W. Newland Road
Wilsonville, Oregon 97070
☎ *503/638-0387*

Hours *Wed-Sat 10-5 (April through July);*
Wed & Sat 10-5 (mid-Sept through mid Dec)
Accessible *Yes*

Here's another mail-order source for herbs. See complete listing on page 220.

Brentwood Park Organics

20301 S. Mattoon Road
Estacada, Oregon 97023
☎ *503/631-8013*

These fourth-generation herbalists offer the largest lavender collection on the West Coast, many drawn from a large gene pool of pre-1960 plants. They have herb articles and books that date back to 1930. You'll find forty-eight different mints, a rosemary that's hardy to zero-degrees (named for the nursery) and much, much more. "We've been growing organically since 1973 and have been organically certified since '84," says Barbara Remington. Events throughout the year include March Merrymint Days, the Sweet Violet Social in April, a Tasting Tea on the Saturday before Mother's Day (try a lavender cookie), a Lemon Social and Basil Bash in August, a Harvest Faire in November and, of course, their popular Christmas Open House. Call for information about activities and the courses they teach at Portland Community College.

Dutchmill Herb Farm

6640 N.W. Marsh Road
Forest Grove, Oregon 97116
☎ *503/357-0924*

Hours *Wed-Sat 12-6*
(March through Dec);
or by appointment
Accessible *Yes*

Goodwin Creek Gardens

P.O. Box 83
Williams, Oregon 97544
☎ 503/846-7357

This mail-order-only source specializes in perennials and native American herbs, many of which were historically considered medicinal. (Owners Jim and Dotti Becker make no claims about the curing-power of the plants, but their catalog makes interesting reading) See complete listing on page 189.

Nichols Garden Nursery

1190 Old Salem Road
Albany, Oregon 97321
☎ 503/928-9280

Hours Mon-Sat 9-5
Accessible Yes, via ramp into store, but difficult on grounds
FAX 503/967-8406

"We have attractive display gardens incorporating a liberal use of herbs in the landscaping and we love for people to visit," says Rose Marie Nichols McGee. In the company's All American Selection Garden you'll find the best of the herb, vegetable and flower varieties introduced in the past few years. The Nichols Family has been growing herbs and vegetables in the Willamette Valley since 1950. Everything available in the catalog (see page 224), is also for sale here at their nursery.

Idaho

The Peaceable Kingdom

8375 Rapid Lightning Creek Road
Sandpoint, Idaho 83864
☎ 208/263-8038

Hours Fri, Sat & Sun 10-5
(May through Nov)
Accessible Partially
Catalog $10 per year for newsletter/catalog

Lois Wythe "grows, forages, processes and sells" herbs and dried florals. She offers workshops, herb garden planning and organic gardening classes. The gift shop, Mole Hole II, offers crafts and products from the farm, including blueberries, prunes and elephant garlic. A Pioneer Culinary Herb Garden, Shakespeare Garden, Butterfly and Bee Garden, Theme Herb Garden and a vegetable garden surround the house and workshop. From Sandpoint, take Highway 200 N.E. to the Colburn-Culver Road, seven and a half miles to the Northside School. Turn right onto Rapid Lightening, go two miles, passing the Pack River General Store to the first mailbox on the right. Watch for #8375 and turn right.

British Columbia

DESTINATION ☆

Ravenhill Herb Farm

*1330 Mt. Newton X Road
Saanichton, British Columbia V0S 1M0*
☎ *604/652-4024*

Hours Sun 12-5 (April through Aug 25)
Accessible Yes
FAX 604/652-4024

On a superb site overlooking a verdant valley bounded by forest-clad hills and the Saanich inlet/fjord, visitors can meet Andrew Yeoman and Noel Richardson. Most of the plants these herb enthusiasts sell can be found growing in their demonstration garden. They also offer Noel's herb cookbooks and both happily answer culinary/gardening questions. The farm is an oasis for the city dweller with its sheep, goats, geese, chickens and peacocks. Ask about the several art shows and don't miss the annual craft sale on the third Sunday of November. By auto, the nursery is 25 minutes north of Victoria and ten minutes from the airport and Butchart Gardens.

Fresh Veggies

It's easier to plant and tend vegetables in a conventional rectangular patch, but if you don't have space to spare, veggies can be grown successfully amidst an ornamental landscape. Historically, farmer's wives mixed flowers with vegetables, so urban gardeners are simply reversing the trend when they tuck squash into the flower bed. Most beginning gardeners make the mistake of thinking too big, anyway. One plant can produce an astounding amount of food!

If you're starting a traditional vegetable garden, double-digging is the time-honored way to prepare the soil. Begin by digging a trench two-feet-wide and eighteen-inches-deep at one end of the bed. Transfer the soil to other end. Line the bottom of the trench with composed manure. Start digging the next trench, filling the first trench half-full of soil from the second trench. Work the soil and compost together and add a second layer of compost to the trench. Then put the remainder of the soil from the second trench into the first, and fork the top layer. Repeat the process in consecutive trenches. To retard weeds and reduce watering, mulch the garden when the plants are about three-inches tall. Expect insect damage. Plant a little extra to compensate.

The Seattle Tilth Garden Guide, a month-by-month planning calendar, tells you what to plant and when to plant it. The calendar contains garden and pest management tips, vegetable and herb charts, a bibliography, and varietal recommendations. At just $5 (plus tax and postage), it's quite a bargain! A non-profit membership organization, Seattle Tilth is devoted to organic gardening, urban ecology and building a sense of community. You can reach them by phone at 206/633-0451.

The sources listed in this section supply especially fine vegetable plants to give gardeners a head start on the season. ❧

Sources for Vegetable Starts

Washington

Black Lake Organic Farms and Garden Store

4711 Black Lake Boulevard S.W.
Olympia, Washington 98512
☎ *206/786-0537*

Hours *Daily 9-6; closed Mondays in January and all major holidays*
Accessible *No*

The emphasis here is on organic supplies. They've been "all-organic" since 1980. "We sell our own vegetable starts and offer fruit, nut and some ornamental trees, plus plants for attracting wildlife and supplies for feeding and housing wildlife (birdhouses, feeders, bird seed, bat boxes, etc.)" says Gary Kline. The company carries seeds, tools and books for gardeners of all interests. Staff members offer consultations on all-organic lawn care and landscaping with no synthetic fertilizers or pest controls. They freely give advice in the store or over the phone. They are located three miles south of Highway 101 on Black Lake.

Canyon Country Gardens

15116 Canyon Road E.
Puyallup, Washington 98373
☎ *206/535-6788*

See page 249 for information about this company's vegetables and their canning expertise.

Fruitdale Nursery

552 Fruitdale Road
Sedro Wooley, Washington 98284
☎ *206/856-1877*

Vegetable starts number in the hundreds here. See complete listing on page 250.

The Garden Shed in Ballard is another excellent all-organic garden store. "We offer everything necessary for a natural garden – seeds, soil amendments, fertilizers, and organically approved and ecologically soft pest controls", says Debra Byrne. The company sells certified organically grown herbs and vegetable starts, including many unusual and hard-to-find varieties. "We're small and independently owned. We try to deal with other Northwest companies that are committed to organics. We don't carry cheap, rip-off "organic" fertilizers that are 90% chicken coop waste and 10% contamination. Our fertilizers are blended specially for Northwest soils by Down-to-Earth, Whitney Farms, and Pacific Organics. Our pest control products come from companies that have demonstrated a long-term commitment to the environment. We're committed to offering the best-quality plants, fertilizers and a large selection of fine-quality tools at an honest price."

The Garden Shed
5905 24th Avenue N.W.
Seattle, Washington 98107
☎ *206/783-9412*

Hours Mon-Sat 9-6, Sun 10-5 (April through Aug); Tues-Sat 10-6, Sun 10-3 (Sept through March)
Accessible *Yes*
FAX *206/783-9412*

Hillcroft offers herbs and such specialty vegetables as European lettuces. All its edibles are grown from seed and tailored for coastal N.W. climatic conditions. See full listing on page 173.

Hillcroft Nursery, Inc.
9430 195th N.E.
Redmond, Washington 98053
☎ *206/885-9520*

Artichokes, bok choy, pac choy, mizuna greens, red and green shiso, Japanese cucumbers are some of the unusual vegetables you'll find here. They have a fine selection of herbs at this general nursery, as well. See complete listing on page 331.

Mano's Earlington Greenhouses
13043 Renton Avenue S.
Seattle, Washington 98178
☎ *206/255-7744*

☆DESTINATION
Tillinghast Seed Company

623 Morris Street
La Conner, Washington 98257
☎ *206/466-3329*

Hours *Mon-Sat 9-5:30, Sun 11-6*
Accessible *No*
Mail Order

"Coffee is always on at Tillinghast." It's comforting to know that some things don't change. The oldest seed company on the West Coast maintains its original seed bins, from which folks still scoop out seeds for cover crops and grasses. It's still a great source for canning supplies and candy sticks. Well, there have been a few subtle changes... You'll discover a gourmet kitchen store with blended coffees, a floral shop and year-around Christmas attic. More than ambiance attracts people to this 1885 building. Vegetable starts and fruit trees are big draws, not to mention the herbs, roses, rhodies and perennials. At the end of the growing season there's the annual Open House and Pumpkin Festival in late October. Although the company no longer publishes a catalog, you can phone-in orders – seeds for herbs and Oriental vegetables in addition to "garden varieties," flowers for drying, seeds for winter gardening, wildflowers and meadow mixes.

Oregon

Brentwood Park Organics

20301 S. Mattoon Road
Estacada, Oregon 97023
☎ *503/631-8013*

Hours *Mon-Sat 9-5 (April through Aug); or by appointment (fall and winter)*
Accessible *Yes*
Mail Order
Catalog *$1*
Mailing address *P.O. Box 1227 Clackamas, Oregon 97015*

This certified organic farming operation sells starts for over 250 different varieties of herbs, vegetables and flowers, including several edible flowers. They distribute their products to nurseries in Portland, Eugene and Seattle. They make all their own soil mixes and employ thousands of lady bugs and praying mantises to take care of the aphids and other pests. They ship organic pest controls and beneficial insects throughout the U.S., guaranteeing live delivery of the bugs. They also ship herbs in 4" pots or plug trays. Merchandise is marked down in August and September. To visit the nursery, take the Park Place exit from I-205. Go east to the second light and take a right on Redland Road and follow it past the Redland Store to Mattoon Road. Make a left and follow Mattoon to Circle Diamond Ranch. At the sign for the ranch, turn left and follow the gravel road down to the green barn.

See listings on pages 216 and 224.

Nichols Garden Nursery

1190 Old Salem Road
Albany, Oregon 97321
☎ *503/928-9280*

Dollie Rasmussen's nursery purveys the same varieties of vegetable plants you'll find in her U-pick garden. See complete listing on page 255.

Rasmussen Farms

3020 Thomsen Road
Hood River, Oregon 97031
☎ *503/386-4622*

This is where Territorial Seed Company's varieties are trialed and selected. "We offer vegetable starts of all the seeds we sell, plus fruit trees, bedding plants and roses," says Julie Johns. The nursery offers seminars on gardening topics throughout the year. Call for information. See page 226 for information about Territorial's catalog.

Territorial Seed Company

20 Palmer Avenue
Cottage Grove, Oregon 97424
☎ *503/942-9547*

Hours *Mon-Sat 8-5:30, Sun 9-4*
(March through June);
Mon-Sat 8-5:30 (July through Feb)
Accessible *Yes*
FAX *503/942-9881*

Idaho

Edward's Greenhouse is an excellent source for herbs and vegetable starts. See complete listing on page 190.

Edward's Greenhouse

4106 Sandcreek Street
Boise, Idaho 83703
☎ *208/342-7548*

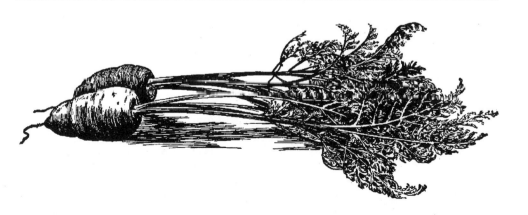

Starting from Scratch

Catalogs available from the sources in this section offer the most tempting array of herbs, vegetables and flowers imaginable! In recent years, seed companies have introduced new vegetable varieties bred for cold hardiness and a shorter period from germination to production. These factors really count if you're trying to raise several crops in a single season or hope to grow a lot of produce in a limited amount of space.

The compressed peat pellets available in most catalogs make it easy for a fledgling gardener to start plants from seed. They are not very expensive, and they allow you to transplant rooted seedlings, peat and all, directly into the ground without disturbing the plant. Some gardeners prefer to start seeds in sterilized plastic pots or flats. Even egg cartons will work.

☞ **Money-saving Tip: Seeds are cheap. Don't be afraid of failure; for every seed that doesn't germinate, three others will.**

Always read the directions on the back of the seed packet. Some seeds need light to germinate; others require darkness and need to be covered or set in a closet until the first sprouts appear. If you don't have a greenhouse, you can place seedlings in a tray in a large south-facing window, but you may need to supplement sunlight with artificial lighting. Water the seedlings well, allow the soil to drain, and enclose the tray in a clear plastic bag. You probably won't need to water again. Be sure to turn the tray daily so the plants won't lean toward the light.

It takes six to eight weeks to get tomatoes, onions, eggplant and peppers ready for the garden from seed. Cabbage, broccoli and cauliflower need four to five, while squash and cucumbers require only about two. Count back from the date it's safe to transfer tender, young plants into your garden. Cool-weather crops such as broccoli, cabbage, cauliflower and onions can go in early, but such favorites as tomatoes, cucumbers, squash and peppers shouldn't be planted in the garden until the weather becomes consistently warm.

Add in an extra week for "hardening-off," the period when you set your transplants outdoors in a protected area during the day and bring them in at night. Gradually increase the number of hours the plant remains outdoors. When planting, be sure the soil is well-cultivated and moist. Choose a cloudy day to plant or provide shade and mist for the transplants. If you've grown the seedlings in a peat planter, be sure to cover the peat with a little soil, otherwise it will act as a wick and dry out the roots. 🌺

Catalog Seed Sources

Abundant Life Seed Foundation is a non-profit corporation. Its purposes are to "acquire, propagate and preserve the plants and seeds of the native and naturalized flora of the North Pacific Rim, with particular emphasis on those species not commercially available; to provide information on plant and seed preservation; and to aid in the preservation through cultivation." The seeds offered are open pollinated and fungicide-free. The list includes herbs, vegetables and grains as well as a number of native trees, shrubs and wildflowers. A twenty dollar membership supports the foundation, its test gardens and the World Seed Fund. Members receive a subscription to the seed catalog and book list for a year, plus three informative newsletters.

Abundant Life Seed Foundation

P.O. Box 772
Port Townsend, Washington 98368
☎ 206/385-5660

Hours Mon-Fri 9-1
(telephone orders and information)
Mail Order
Catalog $2
FAX 206/385-7455

You've seen the affable and knowledgeable Ed Hume on TV and you've seen his products in garden centers, but did you know his company offers a terrific catalog? In its pages, you'll discover packaged and bulk seeds for vegetable, herb and flower gardens, plus lawn seed and wildflower mixes. The edible varieties are selected for short season climates. Such offerings as the Purple Queen bush bean, Ingot carrot, Sweet Slice cucumber and Olympia spinach have produced excellent results in the company's test garden. The catalog also includes dahlia and gladiolus bulbs, fall cover crop mixes, bird and slug deterrents, garden fabric, liquid kelp concentrate and a wonderful array of books, booklets and videos.

Ed Hume Seeds
P.O. Box 1450
Kent, Washington 98035

Mail Order
Catalog $1 (U.S.), $2 (Canada)

Fungi Perfecti

P.O. Box 7634
Olympia, Washington 98507
☎ 206/426-9292

Hours Mon-Fri 9-4
Mail Order
Catalog $3
FAX 206/426-9377

Okay, so we're not talking seed catalog here, but I couldn't find any other logical place for this listing. Mycophiles will be delighted with this mail-order company's selection of organically cultured mushrooms. Fungi Perfecti offers a variety of mushroom patch kits for indoor and outdoor cultivation. Each kit arrives with an instruction booklet and a guarantee.

Good Seed Co.

Star Route, Box 73A
Oroville (Chesaw), Washington 98844
☎ 509/485-3605

Hours Daily 9-5
(closed June, July, Nov & Dec)
Mail Order
Catalog $1

This mail-order-only firm caters to Northern mountain gardeners, providing 100% open pollinated seeds, with a good selection of heirlooms. You'll find several varieties of potatoes and garlics, Old World and pre-Columbian beans and grains you're unlikely to find elsewhere. The company has a Colonial Herb Collection and seeds for a Pioneer Vegetable Garden, as well as some nice old-fashioned flowers, wildflowers, cover crops, plus a few trees and berry-producing shrubs.

Nichols Garden Nursery

1190 N. Pacific Highway
Albany, Oregon 97321
☎ 503/928-9280

Hours Mon-Sat 9-5
Mail Order
Catalog Free
FAX 503/967-8406

"Our 72-page catalog offers a broad and interesting selection of vegetable, herb and flower varieties," says Rose Marie Nichols McGee, whose family has been in the business for over forty years. The Nichols' serve up some new and unusual vegetables and includes a large selection of Oriental veggies, as well as vigorous garden flowers and wildflowers. One section is called "The Competitor's Corner." If you're hoping to grow the biggest pumpkin (or several other giant vegetables), here's the source. Look here also for hops, roots and bulbs. The catalog features five pages of tools and culinary supplies, plus home-brew and wine making supplies. The section, "Nichols Rural Bookstore" has a selection of publications most bookstores do not stock.

This small family-operated organic vegetable farm located high above the Kootenai River Valley offers several varieties of seed potatoes. "Grown in fertile soil, these potatoes will yield approximately fifteen pounds per pound planted, provided that fertility is maintained and some attempt is made to control insects," says David Ronniger. His firm also offers sunchokes, garlic, onions and cover crops. You'll find books, including a cookbook, natural mineral salt and all the cultural information on potatoes you'll ever need. They cannot ship to Canada, but direct Canadian customers to Becker's Seed Potatoes (R.R. #1, Trout Creek, Ontario P0H 2L0). Selection is best from December through May, and you'll find markdowns after May 1.

Ronniger's Seed Potatoes

Star Route 47
Moyie Springs, Idaho 83845

Mail Order
Catalog $2

Jan Blüm (pronounced bloom) founded this heirloom-variety seed company in 1981, and her passion has paid off in overwhelming success. She writes in her 1993 catalog (which is charming from cover to cover, by the way) that the rapidly-growing business required her to move into Boise, hire a large staff and computerize. Having retrenched, she says, "I am a country woman, and my gardens are here – not in town." Noting that she has suspended phone service and no longer promises one-day service, she maintains that Seeds Blüm is to be "a small concern operated from a rural, agrarian point of view." The catalog is about a philosophy of life, and it will please every gardener who wants to grow vegetables and prepare meals the old fashioned way. It's laced with recipes, crafts and gift ideas, as well as seeds for veggies, grains, herbs, vines and flowers. You may even want to become one of her area advisors or "seed guardians," responsible for growing one variety every year and saving the seeds.

Seeds Blüm

Idaho City Stage
Boise, Idaho 83706
☎ *208/342-0858 (recorded message)*

Mail Order
Catalog $3
FAX 208/338-5658

Seeds Trust/ High Altitude Gardens

4150B Black Oak Drive
Hailey, Idaho 83333
☎ *208/788-4363*

Hours *Daily 9-5*
Accessible *Yes*
Mail Order
Catalog *$2*
FAX *208/788-3452*

Vigorous short-season varieties of vegetables are available here. "Most varieties that are hardy enough to thrive in high, cold climates are equally successful at low elevations," say owners Bill and Barbi McDorman. They note that sixty-day tomatoes are especially good for people who have a summer home where they spend only a couple of months and for gardeners with limited space who want multiple crops in a single season. The couple traveled to Siberia in 1989 and brought back seeds for both vegetables and wildflowers. They've since introduced more than thirty varieties of Siberian tomatoes. Their catalog includes vegetable and wildflower seeds from several continents, native grass seed, pest controls, tools and irrigation equipment. I'm especially drawn to the colorful wildflowers pictured in this book.

Territorial Seed Company

P. O. Box 157
Cottage Grove, Oregon 97424
☎ *503/942-9547*

P. O. Box 225
Vancouver, British Columbia V5X 3E8
☎ *604/322-5266*

Mail Order
Catalog *Free*
FAX *503/942-9881*

Territorial's varieties are trialed on their research farm and selected for Maritime Northwest gardeners. "We offer the highest quality vegetable, herb and flower seed to the home gardener," says Julie Johns. "We guarantee our seed to germinate and offer refund or replacement." The 95-page 1993 spring catalog is chock-full of garden tips and planting charts. It includes a good selection of biological and trap-method pest controls and organic fertilizers. The catalogs (which come out twice a year) offer tools, irrigation equipment and season-extenders in the form of row covers and portable greenhouses. They have three pages of garden books that cover everything you need to know about edible landscaping.

Chapter Eight

The Specialty Garden

*"We are the children of our landscape;
it dictates behavior and even thought
in the measure to which we are
responsive to it."*
.....Lawrence George Durrell

Rock Gardening

A rock garden is potentially a work of art. It may be a beautiful solution for a problem slope or a carefully created mound that brings character to otherwise uninteresting terrain. However, the hodgepodge of plants and rocks so often tossed together in the hospitable Northwest has given rock gardening a bad name. That's a pity.

Done well, a rock garden recalls the hand of nature. Having worked with rock for thousands of years, the Japanese subscribe to basic principles of design that can and should be applied to rock gardening. Japanese garden masters are taught to respect the grain of each stone. By observing the manner in which geologic forces shape formations in nature, they carefully align the rocks to "flow" in the same direction, and they half-bury the boulders to impart "rooted" appearance. Completed, the rocks appear to have been unearthed by wind and water.

These elegant man-made outcroppings provide a fitting environment for a number of low-growing plants. The most commonly used ground covers in rock gardens are alpines, plants that flourish above the timberline. Other suitable subjects include heathers, dwarf rhododendrons, dwarf conifers, ground-hugging succulents, miniature bulbs and perennials that form low tufts of leaves.

When selecting plants for a rock garden, the first factor is to consider each plant's ecological needs. Although alpines and other rockery plants grow within a wide range of natural habitats, they generally require sandy, well-drained soil. If you have a shady site, start with plants that naturally coexist in cool, woodland environments. If the site is sunny, pick sun-loving species normally found in an open rocky meadow.

The rock garden should be seamless, like a tapestry, with a rich composition of forms, textures and hues. It's important to design with an overall color scheme in mind, massing at least five of a species together. Use plants with unique forms, such as dwarf conifers, as singular accents. It's also necessary to understand how these vigorously spreading plants compete for space. Leave room for future spread, filling in with compatible annuals the first year or two, if necessary.

The sheer number of species adaptable to rock gardens can be bewildering, even to an expert. For a beginner's source book, my rock gardening friends recommend *Miniature Gardens* by Joachim Carl. They also report that there will soon be a new edition of Link Foster's *Rock Gardening*, which has long been the Bible of dedicated rock gardeners (all text, no pictures). It's a very specialized field. You'll find Rock Garden Societies in most cities with members willing to share knowledge and experience. 🌺

Sources for Alpines & Other Rock Garden Plants

"I specialize in dwarf conifers, alpine plants and container gardening," says Leanette Bassetti, who invites enthusiasts to visit her display rock garden. Groups and individuals are welcome to bring lunch and eat under the crooked arbor. They'll also enjoy her trough and container garden and the perennial, annual and shade gardens. Mrs. Bassetti is a popular speaker at garden organizations where she gives slide shows on the development of rock gardens, alpine plants and container gardens. Her various garden rooms, which make ideal settings for small weddings, are available for rent June through August.

DESTINATION ☆
Bassetti's Crooked Arbor Gardens

18512 N.E. 165th
Woodinville, Washington 98072
☎ 206/788-6767

Hours Fri 10-3 (mid-April through Oct);
or by appointment
Accessible Yes
Mail Order
Catalog Free plant list

Chehalis Rare Plant Nursery offers dwarf conifers, alpine and rockery plants, and general nursery stock including ferns, ground covers, perennials, deciduous trees and shrubs. Owner Herb Dickson writes, "My specialty is *Primula*, hardy species and hybrids with emphasis on the auriculas. I have developed a new type of flower in the garden auriculas where the center color extends out into the petals, leaving a small band or fringe of color on the edge." He sells seed by mail and plants at the nursery only. The seed offerings include show and exhibition alpine primroses and garden auriculas by separate colors.

Chehalis Rare Plant Nursery

2568 Jackson Highway
Chehalis, Washington 98532

Hours Daily 9-dark
Accessible No
Mail Order
Catalog $.50 (seed list)

Tony and Judy Tilley offer dwarf perennials and lots of little woodland and rockery plants. See complete listing on page 177.

Galbraith Gardens

1650 Galbraith Lane
Bellingham, Washington 98226
☎ 206/671-0704

Heather Acres

1199 Monte-Elma Road
Elma, Washington 98541
☎ 206/482-3258

Bob and Alice Knight are known throughout North America for their mail-order selection of heaths and heathers. Not only "old favorites," but also many new and rare cultivars are in production at Heather Acres, the couple's very special nursery thirty miles west of Olympia. See full listing on page 153.

Jackson Nursery

31805 N.E. George Road
Camas, Washington 98607
☎ 206/834-2555

Hours Sat, Sun & Mon 9-dark
Accessible Yes

"You have to crawl on your hands and knees above timberline to see these plants in nature," says Horace Jackson, pointing to such wonderful scree plants as drabas, gentians and saxifrages. He has hybridized a striking yellow-gold lewisia, and he maintains three little greenhouses full of other rare alpines. If you don't have a rock garden, you might like to grow these tiny plants in one of the attractive troughs he makes from hollowed-out local rocks. His nursery also offers an interesting selection of Japanese maples and bonsai. It's very hard to find, so get explicit directions.

Lamb Nurseries

101 East Sharp Avenue
Spokane, Washington 99202
☎ 509/328-7956

Lamb's catalog features hardy perennials and rock garden plants. See page 182 for complete listing.

Mt. Tahoma Nursery

28111 112th Avenue E.
Graham, Washington 98338
☎ 206/847-9827

Hours Sat-Sun 10-6 Sept through June;
by appointment only at other times
Accessible No
Mail Order
Catalog $1

"We are a small specialty nursery involved in the selection, propagation and selling of choice rock garden and woodland plants," says Rick Lupp. "We offer a wide selection of Washington State native alpines as well as plants from all over the world." Rick notes that the plants will be on their own roots (no grafts). You'll also find a good selection of troughs at the nursery. It's located in the lower foothills of Mt. Rainier, (Mt. Tahoma to Native Americans), where the temperature may fall as low as minus-twelve degrees Fahrenheit. All of the rock garden perennials, dwarf shrubs and grasses listed in this interesting catalog have proven hardy at the nursery. Some are available in very limited quantities.

Grahame Ware's company supplies seeds of Western alpines to thousands of Canadian and U.S. gardeners. See complete listing page 133. He teaches a "most eclectic" class on rock gardening at Okanagan University in Vernon.

Natural Legacy Seeds & Rare Plants
R.R. #2, C-1 Laird
Armstrong, British Columbia V0E 1B0
☎ *604/546-9799*

Donald Howse is a collector of unusual garden plants with a special emphasis on specimens for the rock garden. All of his plants are shipped in the containers in which they have been grown, and he prides himself in supplying plants generous in size relative to their age and growth rate. The catalog offers a large selection of hardy dwarf conifers (some quite rare) and a nice selection of broadleaf trees, shrubs and vines. Other sections of the catalog feature perennials, Japanese iris, saxifrages, sempervivums and sedums, plus collector's cases and container gardens. Mr. Howse welcomes visitors to his nursery and gardens, but requests that you make an appointment since his business is primarily wholesale.

Porterhowse Farms
41370 S.E. Thomas Road
Sandy, Oregon 97055
☎ *503/668-5834*

Hours *By appointment only*
Accessible *Yes, on gravel*
Mail Order
Catalog *$4*
FAX *503/668-5834*

See complete listing on page 246. Among the outdoor plants listed in Dr. Burl Mostul's catalog are cacti and lewisias.

Rare Plant Research
9527 S.E. Wichita
Milwaukie, Oregon 97222
☎ *503/652-0433*

Owners Chris and Joe Schugmann offer compact hardy flowering perennials and subshrubs for the rock garden, including a small selection of choice dwarf species rhododendron and dwarf conifers on their own roots. See complete listing page 133.

Schugmann's Nursery
4300 Mosquito Lake Road
Deming, Washington 98244
☎ *206/592-2989*

Siskiyou Rare Plant Nursery maintains a rock garden display and purveys an enormous array of alpine plants, dwarf conifers, Japanese maples and trough/container plants. See complete listing in Collector's Plants on page 265.

Siskiyou Rare Plant Nursery
2825 Cummings Road
Medford, Oregon 97501
☎ *503/772-6846*

Squaw Mountain Gardens

*36212 S.E. Squaw Mountain Road
Estacada, Oregon 97023*
☎ *503/630-5458*

*Hours Mon-Fri 8-4:30 (March-Sept);
by appointment in fall and winter*
Accessible *No*
Mail Order
Catalog *Free*

"We carry the reference collection of *Sedum, Sempervivum, Jovibarba, Rosularia* and *Orostachys* for the North American Plant Preservation Council," reports Janis Noyes. "We also have a wide selection of companion rock garden plants and are always on the search for the unusual." Squaw Mountain offers over 1200 varieties selected to add beauty to the landscape, rock garden or planters. They've a number of native ground covers including vancouveria and wild ginger. They also feature hardy garden ferns, with several tropical varieties available, as well. Plant selection is best from April through July. "We will provide a presentation of slides and informative talk to interested garden organizations," she adds. The 1993 catalog lists nineteen books on rock gardening.

Stone Crop Gardens

*2037 S.W. 16th Avenue
Albany, Oregon 97321*
☎ *503/928-8652*

*Hours Wed and Sat 10-6
(March through Oct);
all other times by appointment*
Accessible *Yes*
Mail Order
Catalog *Free*
FAX *503/757-7645*

The folks at Stone Crop Gardens specialize in hardy succulents for the Northwest. They grow eighty varieties of sedums, an equal number of the sempervivums, and twelve jovibarba species. They are building significant collections of rosularia, hardy Northwest cacti, lewisia, cyclamen, saxifrage and other rock garden plants. Everything they grow is available by mail year-round. While some are natives, most are alpine plants from Europe or Asia and all are grown in unheated growing houses or outdoors. The original stock came from the wonderful thirty-year collection of Helen Payne in Dallas, Oregon. Their catalog is an excellent reference guide to the subject.

Trans-Pacific Nursery

*16065 Oldsville Road
McMinnville, Oregon 97128*
☎ *503/472-6215*

See page 247 for details on this company's unusual collection.

Water Gardening

Quiet or dancing, no other element adds as much pleasure to a garden as water. The very words we use to describe its sights and sounds – bubbling, gurgling, rushing, trickling, shooting, spilling – suggest water's magical ability to play on our emotions. Flowing lazily along a natural stream, water is relaxing; tumbling down rocks, it has the power to excite. Be it fountain, fish pond, reflecting pool, bog or stream, a water feature and its attendant plants seem to cool the hottest summer day.

A water feature may also serve utilitarian purposes. A naturally occurring depression, which could be a liability in the landscape, can be widened into a charming little bog. A rock-lined stream bed that channels water away from the house may suggest a pleasing creek, even when dry. Swimming pools and spas can be designed to appear as natural ponds or formal fountains, thus serving decorative as well as practical functions.

Fishponds, which were much in vogue early in this century, fell out of favor in the '50s, primarily for maintenance reasons. They're popular once again, partly because improved materials have made them less expensive to build and easier to maintain. Traditional geometric garden pools are usually constructed of reinforced concrete and capped with brick or cut stone. Often they will incorporate a fountain. Naturalistic free-form ponds can be made with inexpensive PVC pond liners or pre-formed fiberglass. To get maximum effect, a water feature should be placed where it will reflect sky, trees and flowers. Add colorful koi and special-effects lighting, and you have a real treasure. Let your imagination run free. You may even want a bridge to cross or an island to conquer.

Whatever shape the water takes, gardening possibilities in and around the pool include a range of delicate and colorful plants that would seem out-of-place in a dry landscape – luscious ferns, bog plants and water lilies. A few words of caution, however. Do not dam or alter a natural stream that runs through your property without a permit; observe carefully how nature builds her waterways (natural-looking streams and ponds are difficult to achieve); and remember that children can drown in a few inches of water. Check regulations in your municipality before beginning construction. Secure your pool or pond from the moment you begin digging the hole! 🌿

Sources for Plants, Fish & Fountains

Washington

Evergreen Gardens & Gifts

7216 27th Street W.
Tacoma, Washington 98466
☎ 206/565-9369

This full-service garden center specializes in ponds, koi and water plants. See complete listing on page 353.

Kimura Nursery

3860 N.E. Bel-Red Road
Bellevue, Washington 98008
☎ 206/881-6508

Kimura Nursery offers a large stock of water plants. See complete listing on page 338.

Misty Valley Water Gardens

702 10th Street S.E.
Puyallup, Washington 98372
☎ 206/848-9473

Hours Sat 10-4 (April through Sept.); or by appointment
Accessible Yes
Mail Order
Catalog Free

Misty Valley specializes in select, unusual water plants. This small nursery is a good mail-order source for several varieties of water iris and lilies, rushes and such floating water plants as parrot's feather, tropical water hyacinth and floating hearts. All plants are shipped bare-root. Plants picked up at the nursery are potted and ready to place in your pond. The catalog describes the specific needs of each plant.

☆DESTINATION
Moorehaven Water Gardens

3006 York Road
Everett, Washington 98204
☎ 206/743-6888

Hours Wed-Mon 10-6 (April through Oct); Fri-Mon 10-4 (Nov through March)
Accessible Yes

Twenty years of experience maintaining two acres of water gardens should qualify Chris and Val Moore for calling themselves the Northwest's pond experts! Word-of-mouth has always been their best advertisement, and visitors love the place with its splashing, gurgling ponds. They offer more than fifty varieties of water lilies, plus imported and domestic fish that range in price from $3 to $5,000 – "Imagine that!" says Chris. "Spring is especially noisy between croaking frogs, screaming peacocks, whistling pheasants, squawking geese and a roaming, gobbling turkey. Bring ear plugs." They offer advice to both "would-be" and experienced water gardeners and always send customers home with lots of handouts.

Here's one of the top sources for ponds and fountains, water plants and other aquatic supplies in the Seattle metropolitan area. You can choose from fifty varieties of tropical and hardy water lilies (many are intoxicatingly fragrant) and over one-hundred bog plants, plus pond-hardy goldfish and koi to enliven the garden. The owner, Dianne Tolgerson, is enthusiastic about her subject. She freely offers advice and holds seminars on pond construction and the maintenance of water plants.

Oasis Water Gardens

404 S. Brandon
Seattle , Washington 98134
☎ 206/767-9776

Hours Tues-Sun 10-6
(April through Sept);
Tues-Sat 10-4 (Winter)
Accessible Yes

The water gardening headquarters in their area, Pioneer West offers pools, fountains, pumps, books, fish, plants and expert advice. See complete listing on page 355.

Pioneer West

710 N. Tower
Centralia, Washington 98531
☎ 206/736-3872

"Although we offer a full line of green goods (annuals, perennials, shrubs and trees), most of our customers come for the aquatic plants and Koi. We offer a wide selection of hardy water lilies (usually 25 varieties or more) as well as marginal or bog plants," says Jan Bahr. Customers also enjoy walking around the large earthen ponds on the property and looking at the water lilies in bloom. The height of the season is June and July, although one is likely to see some blossoms anytime from mid-May through September.

Roadhouse Nursery

12511 Central Valley Road N.W.
Poulsbo, Washington 98370
☎ 206/779-9589

Hours Tues-Sat 9:30-5:30, Sun 10-5
(March-Mid-Nov)
Accessible Yes
Catalog Free price list

Sky Nursery & Garden Center

18528 Aurora Avenue N.
Seattle, Washington 98133
☎ *206/546-4851*

Sky Nursery has developed a reputation as pool and pond specialists, and they've a good selection of water plants. See complete listing on page 332.

Soos Creek Gardens

12602 S.E. Petroritsky Road
Renton, Washington 98058
☎ *206/226-9308*

Hours Wed-Mon 10-6 (April-Nov 15); by appointment (Nov 15-March)
Accessible Yes, with exceptions

"We maintain several acres of garden area with easy trails throughout," say Helmut and Lourdes Brodka. "Our specialty is water plants. We have several natural ponds and many little pools, where we grow over 60 varieties of hardy bog and water plants. We've possibly the largest selection in King County. Our emphasis is on native and natural landscaping, which also includes many unusual and difficult-to-find plants. Most of what we sell can be seen in the garden as full-grown examples. Our plants are always low-priced because we grow everything in our own fields and ponds. We offer additional discounts for large purchases. We like to show our customers through our garden and explain where plants grow best (or not so well)."

Tsugawa Nursery & Watergardens

410 Scott Avenue
Woodland, Washington 98674
☎ *206/225-8750*

This lovely Japanese nursery carries everything for the water garden and offers periodic seminars that "take the mystery out of raising koi and water plants." They carry imported koi, blue shubunkins, red cap fantails, ryukins and calico orandas. See complete listing on page 363.

Oregon

The exterior of this business is unpretentious, to put it kindly. Inside, you'll be wowed by the fourteen water features, the water and bog plants of all descriptions, the fish, the fountains. I couldn't believe my eyes! Before I had a chance to visit, owner G. W. Bunch had told me that his company was "the largest dealer of koi and water gardens and pond-related items on the West Coast." Well, he wasn't kidding. At night the gardens are lighted; so if you really want to be knocked-out, call about hours for night viewing. Besides all the decorative accessories, including *Henri Studios* statuary, there are *Rain Jet* fountains, *Sequence* and *Little Giant* pumps, and underwater lights, *Argent* pond treatment products and *Permalon* pond liners up to an acre in size available here. There's also a complete bonsai garden with finished bonsai for sale. Although the company did not have a retail catalog as this book went to press, it ships to customers throughout the region.

DESTINATION ☆
Clearwater Fish & Pond Supply, Inc.

19800 S.W. Farmington Road
Aloha, Oregon 97007
☎ *503/649-7211*

Hours *Tues-Fri 10-7, Sat & Sun 10-6*
Accessible *Yes*
Mail Order
FAX *503/649-1476*

"We specialize in the creation of naturalized water features and try to bring the tranquillity and soothing effect of a mountain stream and pond into our clients' yards," says Eamonn Hughes. "We not only design and construct these systems, but also sell a full line of water garden supplies, including hard-to-find rubber pond liners. New to the company in 1994 is a large selection of water plants (60 varieties). Call for information about the water garden seminars held each month, March through September, and one-day, hands-on workshops offered every three weeks from April through September.

E.F. Hughes Water Gardens

25289 S.W. Stafford Road
Tualatin, Oregon 97062
☎ *503/682-2827*

Hours *By appointment*
Accessible *No*
Mail Order
Catalog *Free*
FAX *503/682-2827*

Ponderings Plus

3360 N. Pacific Highway (Hwy. 99)
Medford, Oregon 97501
☎ *503/773-3297*

Hours Mon-Sat 9-5:30
(open on Sundays during April, May and
June); Mon-Sat 10-4:30 (winter)
Accessible Difficult on gravel
FAX 503/734-2017

The three dedicated gardeners who own this co-op nursery search high and low for the water plants and unusual perennials, annuals, vines, bamboo and other grasses that make their store special. In addition to their large selection of plants for ponds and bogs, they've got fountains, pumps, liners and rocks. A new shipment of koi and goldfish arrives each week during the "pondering season." The nursery shares space with and displays Rogue River Rustics' delightful willow furniture (listed on page 288). You'll find books and assorted garden ornaments here as well. Call about classes in pond construction and their Summer Water Lily Festival in late July and early August.

Sunrise Water Gardens

5211 E. Evans Creek Road
Rogue River, Oregon 97537
☎ *503/582-0442*

Hours Fri-Sun 19-6 (April-Oct)
Accessible Yes
Mail Order
Catalog $2

Sunrise Water Gardens is an experience. One can browse along the shores of its ponds and glimpse nature at her finest, where flower gardens meet lovely water lilies and lush green water plants. "We offer everything for the pond from the flexible UVL-resistant liner to an excellent selection of koi and goldfish and hardy water lilies in pinks, reds, yellows, whites and changeables. We hold the secret to clear healthy pond water – an organic product that clears your water in six to eight weeks and is non-toxic to humans, fish, plants and birds," say Tom and Mary Hench. Selection is best in summer, and they always have a special on some plant or fish. The couple give guided tours throughout the season to garden clubs and teach seminars on pond culture. "Weddings and club meetings here are enhanced by Mother Nature."

British Columbia

Water features are the specialty here, of course, and Great West serves the needs of landscape projects from small backyard ponds to estate-size lakes. The company carries all the components needed – pre-formed ponds and vinyl liners, *RainJet*, *PEM*, and *Hydrell* fountains, specialty pumps and nozzles, lighting, etc. They have a fine selection of *Henri* statuary and fountains, plus up-scale bronze and concrete garden ornaments by *Austin Sculptures*, *Florentine Craftsmen* and *Ornements de Parterre de Lanaudiere*. You'll find all the books you could want on the subject of water gardening, but you'll need to look elsewhere for the fish and plants.

Great West Fountain Technology

#127- 7011 Elmbridge Way
Richmond, British Columbia V7C 4V5
☎ *604/ 270-8118*

Hours *Mon-Sat 9-5:30, Sun 11-4*
(May through Oct); Mon-Sat 9-5
(Nov through April)
Accessible *Yes*
Catalog *Free catalog sheets*
from manufacturers
FAX *604/270 2892*

Mandeville Gardens keeps a fine selection of water garden plants. See complete listing on page 390.

Mandeville Gardens

4746 S.E. Marine Drive
Burnaby, British Columbia V5J 3G6
☎ *604/434-4111*

Greenhouse & Interior Gardening

To me, a home is incomplete without house plants to brighten bare walls, spill from bookshelves and flower on table tops. Plants are useful for camouflaging architectural flaws. You can use a grouping to fill one end of a long narrow room, to divide space in an overly large room or to soften a corner. And, I like big fluffy ferns for warming-up an empty fireplace in summer.

I first learned the visual impact of indoor plants years ago when friends bought a house with a huge formal living room. Like most young couples, they couldn't afford much in the way of furnishings, so they invested in several large ficus trees. The "garden room" effect was so pleasing that they never did buy the fine furniture they had originally envisioned.

In choosing house plants, it's important to consider the scale of both the room and the plants. Too many small plants can make a room look "fussy." On the other hand, huge plants or plants with large leaves may look menacing in a small space.

Tropical plants are literally life-savers for people who spend long hours confined indoors. They not only provide vital oxygen, but also raise a room's humidity level, which is a gift to anyone who suffers with dry skin. Used in large numbers, house plants have even been shown to cleanse the air of noxious household chemicals.

A two-year study by NASA and the Associated Landscape Contractors of America proved that 'Janet Craig', 'Warneckii' and marginata dracaenas, peace lily, English ivy, mother-in-law's tongue, green spider plant, golden pothos and bamboo palm are among the best plants for removing concentrations of chemicals from the air. The researchers estimated that fifteen to twenty potted plants of these species can purify the interior of a typical 1,800-square-foot house. The other good news is that these common plants are easy to grow and among the most attractive for interior plantscaping.

☞ **Money-saving tip: Inspect house plants carefully before making your purchase.**

Most house plants are grown outdoors in California, Florida or Hawaii. Good plant shops and garden centers acclimatize these tropical plants for several weeks before offering them to the public. By gradually reducing light, moisture levels and withholding fertilizer, they prepare the plant for the drier conditions and lower light levels of a home environment.

Avoid plants that have brown edges on the leaves (an indication of sun scald or excessive fertilizer), pale or yellow leaves (a sign of improper watering), sparse or leggy plants (a symptom of abnormally forced growth) and roots that grow above the soil surface or out the drainage hole (a sure sign of having become root-bound). Inspect both the undersides of leaves and the places where the leaves join the stem for insects. A "bargain" plant is no bargain if it expires within a week or spreads an insect infestation to your existing plants.

It's probably a good idea to place a new plant in quarantine in any case. To reduce the shock of moving it into a dry environment, mist the foliage every day with tepid water. Also it's good practice to flood new plants with water to flush out salts that may have accumulated from heavy fertilizing by the grower. Run a slow stream of water through the soil for a full five minutes and let the plant drain thoroughly. (A bathtub or shower works well for this task.) Periodically, I run water through all of my house plants to prevent the build-up of salts.

It's normal for a few older leaves at the bottom to die as the plant adjusts to new conditions. Instead of pinching-off yellowed leaves, allow them to drop naturally; nature has a mechanism for sealing the wound. If the plant loses a lot of leaves, you're probably watering too much or have placed the plant where it isn't getting enough light. If it dies within the first month in spite of your TLC, take it back and ask for a replacement.

You'll find a wealth of unusual indoor plants in the specialty nurseries listed below. Most of the large garden centers also have fabulous house plant departments these days. The ferns and potted palms favored in Victorian times are popular once again, and the options only begin there. With worldwide transportation swift and cheap, exotic species from tropical regions and deserts all over the world are available to the discriminating shopper. Never has there been such a vast array of colorful blossoms, fanciful leaf patterns, and marvelous plant-forms from which to choose. 🌺

Sources for Tropicals & Exotics
Washington

Barbara and Terry Aitkin report that their burgeoning orchid collection has allowed them to share a few. They've cattleyas, dendrobiums and moth orchids (phalaenopsis). Barbara notes that these plants grow well under lights and on window sills and that they bloom during wintertime. See listing on page 196.

Aitken's Salmon Creek Garden
608 N.W. 119th Street
Vancouver, Washington 98685
☎ 206/573-4472

Larry Bailey's mail-order business was founded for the purpose of supplying named exhibition auriculas and "blue ribbon" primroses to growers who find it difficult if not impossible to find the older florist-type plants. The company is not open to the public, but shipments of auricula are sent mid-spring and mid-fall, while the julianas and acaulis are only shipped in spring. Mr. Bailey notes that the hobby of growing florist primulas is truly a leisure time activity for those who are looking for a slower pace of life.

Baileys'
P.O. Box 654
Edmonds, Washington 98020

Mail Order
Catalog Free

Baker & Chantry Orchids, Inc.

18611 132nd Avenue N.E.
Woodinville, Washington 98072
☎ *206/483-0345*

Hours *Daily 10-5*
Accessible *No*
Catalog *$1*
Mailing address *P.O. Box 554*
Woodinville, Washington 98072

Will Chantry has developed a fine reputation for his tropical and sub-tropical species and hybrid orchids. "Growing orchids is not a hobby," explains Mr. Chantry. "Its an incurable disease!" His selection within the royalty of the plant world varies with the seasons, but it's always lovely. He even boards orchids for customers. Ask to be put on the mailing list to receive notice of the four annual special events, which are held in spring, during the July 4th weekend, Labor Day weekend, and for nine days starting at Thanksgiving. The open houses include refreshments, drawings and good prices on the plants.

Chieri Orchids

2913 9th Street North
Tacoma, Washington 98406-6717
☎ *206/752-5510*

Hours *By appointment only*
(after 4 p.m. or on weekends)
Accessible *No*
Mail Order
Catalog *Free*

Pat Pettit grows orchids from the high Andes cloud forests – wonderful masdevallias, odontoglossums (tooth-tongued) and miltonias (pansy orchids). She ships to customers and says the plants "love living indoors in the Northwest." Her selection is best from winter through spring.

Enchanted Garden

1524 Pike Place
Seattle, Washington 98101
☎ *206/625-1205*

Hours *Mon-Sat 9-5:30, Sun 11-3*
Accessible *Yes*

Enchanted Garden specializes in bromeliads, orchids, cacti and insectivorous plants. Venus fly traps and pitcher plants are available in spring. The company maintains an excellent selection of orchids and bromeliads year-around. The owner, Doreen Locati, is one of the Northwest's most knowledgeable vendors. She and her staff offer advice and free instruction sheets with each purchase. "We know how to grow what we sell." The shop is in the Pike Place Market, on the east side of the street.

Indoor Sun Shoppe has been in business 23 years, selling products guaranteed to brighten up a gloomy day. It offers a wide selection of unusual house plants, including cactus, carnivorous plants, herbs and orchids, plus a full-spectrum of indoor lighting. You'll also find seeds, books, specialty soils and fertilizers and organic supplies in this little store, which is known and loved for its relaxing environment complete with library and coffee bar. There's free parking in the rear; enter on 9th N.E.

Indoor Sun Shoppe

911 N.E. 45th
Seattle, Washington 98105
☎ *206/634-3727*

Hours *Mon-Fri 10-7, Sat & Sun 12-6*
Accessible *Yes*

Molbak's carries tropical greenery in sizes ranging for two-inch pots to twelve-foot trees. The range of species is equally diverse, from common house plants to exotic materials you would expect to find in a public conservatory. See complete listing on page 355.

Molbak's

13625 N.E. 175th Street
Woodinville, Washington 98072
☎ *206/483-5000*

See complete listing on page 251. Cacti and succulents are also part of the landscape at this bonsai nursery.

Mt. Si Bonsai

43321 Mt. Si Road
North Bend, Washington 98045
☎ *206/888-0350*

Exclusively an air plant nursery, Owens Gardens sells *Tillandsia* (the largest genus of the bromeliad family) to nurseries and gift shops throughout the country. Although the greenhouses are not open to the public, Barb Owens sells by mail-order throughout the nation and takes her products directly to the public at flower shows, fairs and festivals. Call for information about planned appearances in your area or write for a catalog describing these interesting plants that cling to cliffs and tree branches in their native Latin American environments.

Owens Gardens

P.O. Box 906
Monroe, Washington 98272
☎ *206/794-6422*

Hours *Mon-Sat 8-7*
(phone access only)
Mail Order
Catalog *Free*

Price-Ragen Co.

517 E. Pike
Seattle, Washington 98122
☎ *206/329-8155*

2245 Carillon Point
Kirkland, Washington 98033
☎ *828-6393*

Price-Ragen's interior plants are probably the largest (in both size and selection) you'll find in the Northwest. In case you wonder how to get home with a 18-foot-tall ficus, Price-Ragen delivers. See complete listing on page 293.

Shinoda Floral

18306 83rd Ave, S.E.
Snohomish, Washington 98290
☎ *206/668-8585*

Hours *Mon-Sat 9-6 (summer);*
9-5 (winter)
Accessible *Yes*
Mail Order

Shinoda is one of the premier wholesalers of African violets in the country. The company, which is also known for its European baskets and dish gardens, sells and ships to the public through this retail store. Shinoda does not offer a catalog, but says that you can order any exotic plant you want. They've a huge selection of the hundreds of African violets bred and grown by the company, plus all kinds of tropicals including birds of paradise, papaya, citrus trees, orchids and evergreens. In summer, they carry annuals and perennials, ground covers, roses and lots of flowering shrubs.

Tropical Foliage Unlimited

210 Wells Avenue S.
Renton, Washington 98055
☎ *206/277-0922*

Hours *Mon-Fri 10-5, Sat 10-3*
Accessible *Yes*

Sandra Nishio receives shipments at least twice a month to keep her 4000-square-foot space stocked with tropicals – from two-inch starts to twelve-foot trees. All of the plant material (which comes from Florida, California and Hawaii) is shade-grown specifically for Northwest growing conditions. She takes a lot of pride in her work; she asks questions and tries to direct customers to plants suitable for the growing conditions in their homes.

Verkist Orchid Floriculture

156 Kline Road
Bellingham, Washington 98226
☎ *206/734-1926*

Hours *By appointment only*
Accessible *Yes*

Bruce Verkist grows cattleya orchids from seed. He has hybridized a number of yet-unnamed varieties of this showy genus, which he's happy to offer to other enthusiasts.

Oregon

Blossom Creek Greenhouse

Owner Ann Starns grows over 200 different orchid cacti and 300 bromeliads. She has desert cacti, tillandsias, night-blooming cerus, and Christmas and Thanksgiving cacti. You'll also find succulents and tropical patio plants, such as bougainvillea.

989 S.W. 5th
North Plains, Oregon 97133
☎ *503/647-0915*

Hours *By appointment only*
Accessible *Yes*
Catalog *Free*

Interior Scapes

Customers come from as far away as Portland and Eugene to this 4,000 square-foot showroom in downtown Salem to find large tropical plants and handsome containers from around the world. "Interior Scapes combines our love of tropical plants with interior design and architecture to create landscapes for your home or office that are both breathtaking and functional," says owner Michael Jones. "With our guaranteed maintenance services, you can keep your interior landscape at its peak. We also offer a variety of outdoor containerized plantings of the same high caliber, complete with drip systems." Check out the company's plant sales in June and August. Phone or drop in for advice; house calls are by appointment.

233 Commercial Street N.E.
Salem, Oregon 97301
☎ *503/364-4937*

Hours *Mon-Fri 10-5, Sat 11-5*
Accessible *Yes*
FAX *503/364-4139*

Northwest Garden & Topiary

Orchids and tropical greenery greet visitors to this little jewel box. See complete listing on page 316.

805 N.W. 23rd Street
Portland, Oregon 97209
☎ *503/222-9939*

The Plant Peddler

Lisa Brending specializes in cacti and bromeliads and carries 600 other tropical foliage plants, including staghorn terns, air plants, orchids, gardenias and large specimen Norfolk pines and dracaenas. Even if it's not in stock at her small store, she'll try to find whatever you're seeking.

1001 E. Burnside
Portland, Oregon 97214
☎ *503/233-0384*

Hours *Tues-Sat 10-5:30*
Accessible *Yes*

Portland Nursery

9000 S.E. Division
Portland, Oregon 97266
☎ *503/788-9000*

The selection of tropical plant material is breathtaking at this branch of Portland Nursery! See complete listing on page 367.

Rare Plant Research

9527 S.E. Wichita
Milwaukie, Oregon 97222
☎ *503/652-0433*

Hours *By appointment only*
Accessible *No*
Mail Order
Catalog *$1*

Dr. Burl Mostul explains that the purpose of Rare Plant Research is to search, study and propagate rare or possibly endangered plants. Most are succulent plants from tropical areas around the world. He collects seed and then grows the plants to sell, sending plants to botanical gardens and herbarium specimens to herbaria. "Many of the plants are new to science and most are new to the horticulture," he says. Among the outdoor plants listed in his catalog are cacti and lewisias (the largest selection in the U.S.A.). The sale of plants funds future expeditions to remote botanically interesting areas. Dr. Mostul presents educational slide shows on botanical expeditions and on special plant families.

Red's Rhodies

15920 S.W. Oberst Lane
Sherwood, Oregon 97140
☎ *503/625-6331*

Mail Order
Catalog *Free (vireya and orchids only)*

"Red" Cavender is well-known for native azaleas, but he also grows vireya rhododendrons and pleione orchids (a.k.a. windowsill or crocus orchids). These small, easy-to-grow bulbs thrive indoors or outdoors, west of the Cascades. He notes that the tropical rhododendrons are especially adaptable to hanging baskets and that the orchids are nice in rock gardens. Both are excellent greenhouse plants that enjoy an outdoor vacation in summer, and both are available by mail-order.

Stagecoach Farms Nursery

3900 South Stage Road
Medford, Oregon 97501
☎ *503/776-3544*

Known for its wide selection of indoor specimen plants, Stagecoach Farms stocks over two hundred cymbidium orchids. Call for information about seminars on the care of house plants and the special requirements of cymbidiums. See complete listing on page 379.

Trans-Pacific is a collector's nursery for conservatory gardeners. The stock is rare and exotic, including many endangered species. "We're continually bringing in new things, most recently from a collecting trip to Mt. Kilimanjaro," says Jackson Muldoon. "Items range from the very tropical to sub-arctic alpine, with a large middle ground of marginally hardy, but very unusual container plants. You'll also find bonsai starts, water plants and a smattering of succulents and terrestrial orchids." The catalog descriptions make wonderful reading. One entry says, "A plant that is just about as outrageous as a plant can get on planet earth. Long green curls, spirals and coils of rush-like leaves explode out from the center..." It's obvious that Mr. Muldoon enjoys his work!

Trans-Pacific Nursery
16065 Oldsville Road
McMinnville, Oregon 97128
☎ 503/472-6215

Hours Tues-Sat 10-5, Sun 10-3
Accessible No
Mail Order
Catalog $2

Cacti and succulents are the specialties here. As wholesale suppliers, Roy and Gerry Foss don't ship to customers, but they are happy for retail customers to stop by and shop. Much of their stock is grown from cuttings. They have lots of hanging baskets filled with burro tails, rosary vines, senecio and stapelias. The greenhouses are located a mile east of Highway 101. Turn right at the one-mile post on Highway 20.

**Yaquina Nursery
and Greenhouses, Inc.**

Highway 20, Mile Post 1
Newport, Oregon 97365
☎ 503/938-7287

Hours Daily 9-6
Accessible No
FAX 503/265-9876

Idaho

Lee's Nursery is well known for a large and varied selection of house plants, which includes Hawaiian-grown orchids, Arizona cacti, tillandsias from Mexico and Central America and an array of tropical trees and flowering plants of all sizes. See complete listing on page 385.

Lee's Nursery

1650 Highway 200 E.
Sandpoint, Idaho 83864
☎ 208/263-1411

British Columbia

Chanthorn Orchids

17223 2nd Avenue
Surrey, British Columbia V4A 5A8
P.O. Box 8061 #64
Blaine, Washington 98230
☎ 604/535-7186

Hours By appointment only
Accessible Yes
Mail Order
Catalog Free
FAX 604/535-7186

For more than twenty years Niya Arkell's firm has been importing orchids from Thailand into the U.S. and Canada. The company has greenhouses in Surrey, British Columbia and Ferndale, Washington. Its catalogue lists vandas, cattleyas, dendrobiums and Thai species orchids. "Customers include many collectors attracted by the broad selection of plants, low prices and prompt service," she says, adding that with each orchid you receive instructions on growing and caring for these lovely plants.

Country Garden Ltd.

10015 Young Street N.
Chilliwack, British Columbia V2P 4V4
☎ 604/792-6612

You'll discover a marvelous selection of tropical foliage and flowering house plants at this destination garden centre! See complete listing on page 393.

Home Grown Plants & Hydroponics

1963 S. Ogilvie
Prince George,
British Columbia V2N 1X2
☎ 604/563-6828

Hours Mon-Sat 10-5
Accessible Yes
Mail Order
Catalog Free

"As specialists in hydroponics equipment and supplies, we cater to the indoor gardening enthusiasts and believe service is what counts," says Mary-Lee Tucker. In addition to a variety of tropicals, her company offers bonsai, ferns herbs, seeds and garden books. "We also provide interior plant maintenance and design for office and residential situations. Watch for monthly specials, and don't hesitate to ask for advice."

Southlands Nursery Ltd.

6550 Balacava Street
Vancouver, British Columbia V6N 1L9
☎ 604/261-6411

A large atrium greenhouse filled with exotic tropicals and blooming plants is the centerpiece of this gorgeous garden centre. See complete listing on page 389.

Container Gardening

Plants in handsome containers add significantly to the graciousness of an outdoor seating area. The design ideas that work for placement of house plants apply equally well to container plants on a deck or patio. One good decorator trick is to mass potted plants on both sides of a glass door or low window wall, doubling the impact inside and out. Container plants may be used as focal points in the landscape or to lend warmth to entrances and frame gateways.

Bonsai is the ultimate in elegant container gardening. To see some of the country's finest bonsai, visit the Pacific Rim Bonsai Collection adjacent to the Rhododendron Species Botanical Garden in Federal Way, Washington. You'll find bonsai available at the Foundation's annual sale (see page 272). Several bonsai nurseries in the region specialize in this ancient art form. (Listings begin on page 256.) They not only sell plants, containers and tools, but also offer patient instruction year-round.

Containerized plants require more attention than plants in the ground. Generally, they need regular doses of fertilizer and periodic repotting. If the roots become too large for the pot size, the plant can't store enough water to sustain itself. In warm weather, container plants may need daily watering. The upside to gardening in containers is that not a precious drop of water is wasted to surrounding soil. By adding biologically harmless polymers to the soil, you can reduce by 75% the water needs of containerized plants. 🌺

Sources for Patio Plants

Washington

Family owned and operated, Canyon Country Gardens specializes in hanging baskets, planters, bedding annuals and perennials. They produce vegetable garden starts and offer recipe/canning ideas, as well as expert advice about the varieties they've chosen to grow. Selection is best at this seasonal nursery in May and June. You'll find merchandise marked down at the end of the season; they're often sold out by mid-July.

Canyon Country Gardens
15116 Canyon Road E.
Puyallup, Washington 98373
☎ *206/535-6788*

Hours Daily 9-5
(April through mid-July)
Accessible *Yes*

Fall City Greenhouse and Nursery

34006 Fall City-Snoqualmie Road S.E.
Fall City, Washington 98024
☎ 206/222-6492

Hours Daily 10-6
Accessible Yes

"Most of our business is in container gardening, reports Larry Stacey. "Customers can bring in their empty baskets or pots February through April and we'll plant them up with colorful flowers." Seasonal sales at this lovely nursery take place in July and August and again in November.

☆DESTINATION
Flower World

19127 99th Avenue S.E.
Snohomish, Washington 98290
☎ 206/481-7565

Hours Daily 9-5; open until 8 on Fridays
(April through June)
Accessible Yes, on gravel
FAX 206/668-1586

Its name is not a misnomer – the sheer volume of plants in five acres of greenhouses at Flower World is overwhelming! The company describes itself as a "Costco-type" garden center. "We offer a tremendous assortment and variety of plants at little over wholesale prices, and we can do this because we grow almost 80% of our plants," says the owner. Of special mention are the hundreds of varieties of fuchsias. In April and May there is a "fuchsia blossom" table set up on weekends, with an expert standing-by to answer questions. Flower World is worthy of a visit any time of the year, but springtime, when thousands of flowering baskets are at their peak... Well, you'll just have to see it for yourself! The house plants also bring people in by the droves; good quality, good prices.

Fruitdale Nursery

552 Fruitdale Road
Sedro Wooley, Washington 98284
☎ 206/856-1877

Hours Daily dawn to dusk
(April until mid-July), Tues-Sat 8-4:30
(mid July through March)
Accessible Yes

Fuchsia and ivy geranium hanging baskets are the specialty here. Baskets of double impatiens, trailing begonias and campanulas are available in abundance. They've all kinds of annuals in pots to brighten decks or condo balconies and zillions of bedding plants. The varieties of vegetable starts number in the hundreds – fifteen kinds of cabbages, for example, and tomatoes and cucumbers and peppers and more.

This student-run venture features plants grown by the students. From fall pansies and mums to poinsettias and wreaths at the holidays, the stock turns to house plants and dish gardens in winter. Then fuchsia, geranium and begonia baskets and bedding plants are available in the spring.

Interlake Plant Store, Interlake High School

16245 N.E. 24th
Bellevue, Washington 98008
☎ 206/455-6027

Hours Mon-Fri 7:30-4
(Sept through June)
Accessible Yes

"We have the nicest begonias and fuchsias in town," says Donna Legato. "Our bedding plants are reasonably priced and of good quality." The nursery specializes in flowing baskets of fuchsias, begonias, lotus vines, lobelias, geraniums and impatiens. They're at their peak in May and June. You'll also find shrubs and flowering trees, fruit and nut trees, house plants, perennials and roses here.

Legato's Garden

13506A N.E. 72nd Avenue
Vancouver, Washington 98686
☎ 206/574-8875

Hours Daily 9-6 (Feb 10-Sept 1)
Accessible No

The specialty at Mano's is seasonal color – vibrant primroses in January, Valentine baskets, Easter lilies and Asian lilies, hanging baskets for summer, and poinsettias for the holidays. They offer classes in moss basket making, hold a rose care and pruning clinic in March, and sell house plants at 25 to 40% off in October. Also see listing on page 331 .

Mano's Earlington Greenhouses

13043 Renton Avenue S.
Seattle, Washington 98178
☎ 206/255-7744

Hours Mon-Sat 9-6, Sun 10-5
Accessible Yes
FAX 206/255-4621

Mollgaard began as a wholesale greenhouse and has expanded to include retail sales of its ornamental potted plants. They've a huge selection of bedding plants, seasonal plants in containers and hanging baskets. The company sells cedar containers and provides custom planting on request. You'll also find house plants within the extensive inventory.

Mollgaard Floral

4406 132nd Street N.E.
Snohomish, Washington 98290
☎ 206/337-1835;
223-9340 (from Seattle);
1-800/562-0403

Hours Mon-Sat 9-6, Sun 10-5
(spring & summer); Mon-Sat 9-5
(fall & winter)
Accessible Yes
FAX 206/338-3855

Pearson's Nursery

26626 132nd Avenue S.E.
Kent, Washington 98042
☎ *206/631-3743 or 206/630-4786*

Hours *Tues-Fri 9-6:30, Sat-Sun 9-5*
(mid-March through July)
Accessible *Yes*

"Customers come to our retail greenhouses from all over the Northwest because we grow over a hundred varieties of fuchsias, including new introductions each year," says Helen Pearson. "We also grow zonal, ivy, miniature and scented geraniums (always the new and unusual), a wide selection of begonias in pots and hanging baskets, and lots of plant choices for garden and container plantings. We give growing tips and advice on selection and design. We want our customers to be successful gardeners and to have a good time shopping in our nursery." Merchandise is marked-down in July. Write for information about the company's fuchsia catalog.

Peninsula Gardens

5503 Wollochet Drive N.W.
Gig Harbor, Washington 98335
☎ *206/851-8115 or 1-800/622-8700*

One full-time person does nothing but create hanging baskets and planted containers at this big, beautiful garden center. See full listing on page 351.

Pepper's Greenhouse

1203C Havekost Road
Anacordes, Washington 98221
☎ *206/293-2213*

Hours *Daily (except Wed) 10-6*
(April through June);
by appointment during rest of year
Accessible *Yes*

Judy Pepper reports that this is the twenty-fourth year for this family-run nursery. Hanging baskets are their specialties, and the nursery seeks out new and unusual bedding plants. The annuals go on sale in early July. Throughout the season you'll find a large selection of rhodies, as well. They carry bulbs, conifers, ferns, fruits and berries, ground covers, herbs, house plants, perennials, roses, shrubs, trees and vines, plus containers, fountains and other garden ornaments.

Squak Mt. Greenhouse & Nursery

7600 Renton-Issaquah Road S.E.
Issaquah, Washington 98027
☎ *206/643-0601*

Seasonal color at grower's prices is Squak Mountain's featured attraction. See complete listing on page 338.

Sunflower Greenhouse grows its own annuals, and the year culminates with five hothouses full of poinsettias. You'll find lots of containers and a staff willing to create container gardens to go! See complete listing on page 332.

Sunflower Greenhouse & Garden Center, Inc.

1900 N.E. 150th Street
Seattle, Washington 98155
☎ *206/367-5440*

Nyle Verkist's specialty is annuals and patio plants. He offers lots of colorful hanging baskets and completed containers, plus pots and plants for you to create-your-own. Expect to find primroses, fuchsias, geraniums (thirty varieties) and poinsettias in their respective seasons. The nursery is also experimenting with several dozen perennials. Stay tuned.

Verkist Gardens

156 Kline Road
Bellingham, Washington 98226
☎ *206/734-1926*

Hours *Mon-Sat 9:30-5*
Accessible *Yes*

A large-scale grower, Windmill features pansies, primroses, fuchsias and poinsettias. The selections are strong in a whole range of bedding plants. See complete listing on page 353.

Windmill Nursery

5823 160th Avenue E.
Sumner, Washington 98390
☎ *206/863-5843*

Oregon

Forty-five varieties of scented, miniature and Martha Washington geraniums are featured here. You'll find hanging baskets and bedding plants, plus a sampling of landscape plants that includes ferns, ornamental grasses, ground covers, herbs and vegetables. "Because the nursery is at our home in the country, our overhead is low, which is reflected in the prices," says owner Danita Shattuck. She holds a Season's End Sale in early-July and offers "green-thumb advice" throughout the season.

DanCin' Bloomers Greenhouse

29827 Highway 99E
Shedd, Oregon 97377-9775
☎ *503/491-3927*

Hours *Tues- Sat 10-6*
(March through mid-July)
Accessible *No*

Egan Gardens

9805 River Road N.E.
Salem , Oregon 97303
☎ *503/393-2131*

Hours *Mon-Sat 9-6, Sun 10-5*
(March through mid-July);
Mon-Sat 9-5, Sun 10-5
(mid-July through Sept.)
Accessible *Yes*
FAX *503/390-9020*

Originally a wholesale operation, Egan Gardens has become *the place* for flower-lovers since they opened a retail side of the business a few years ago. Ellen Egan says, "The mainstay of our spring sales is zonal geraniums – we do 65,000 of them. We also make 2,000 ivy geranium baskets, 2,000 fuchsia baskets and a good assortment of other hanging baskets from the typical to the occasional off-the-wall. Hey, we like to experiment! We keep our material coming on fresh all summer. Our pride and joy is mixed planters (both ready-made and custom); we strive for appealing forms, luscious color combinations and interesting textures. This is *art*." Egan Gardens times the perennial crops so the plants reach blooming season without becoming stressed and overgrown. "While it's impossible to grow all perennials, we grow a wide variety and add some new, different and kind of weird things to the list each year," she notes.

Goose Creek Nursery

30750 S.E. Jackknife Road
Eagle Creek, Oregon 97022
☎ *503/637-3867*

Hours *Daily 9-6*
(closed Saturdays May through Oct)
Accessible *No*
Catalog *Free*

"We specialize in fuchsias and geraniums. Our main feature is a fuchsia tree, up to two-feet in height," explains Ollie Hager, who notes that his 330 varieties of fuchsia become available in early February. The stock includes a good selection of hardy varieties. He can be found at various farmers markets on Saturdays during the growing season, so he suggests you call before coming if you're traveling a long distance.

In late-April and May, you can select from Dollie Rasmussen's 1,200 hanging baskets. If you wish to create your own, she offers help based on "many years of experience!" In addition to the hanging baskets and patio container gardens, Rasmussen Farms features U-cut flowers (perennials April through July and annuals July through September) and U-pick vegetables throughout the growing season. The nursery also sells seeds, bulbs, ferns, ground covers, perennials, herbs and roses. "This is a working farm. Our vegetable starts are the same varieties we plant in our own garden," says Dollie. Watch for the annual sale, which begins the week prior to the Fourth of July.

Rasmussen Farms

3020 Thomsen Road
Hood River, Oregon 97031
☎ *503/386-4622*

Hours *Daily 9-6 (April-Dec)*
Accessible *Yes*

"Wisteria Herbs and Flowers offers a large and varied selection of herbs, scented geraniums and out-of-the-ordinary annuals. See complete listing on page 187.

Wisteria Herbs and Flowers

5273 S. Coast Highway
South Beach, Oregon 97366
☎ *503/867-3846*

Idaho

Boise Botanical offers lots of hanging baskets and colorful annuals, herbs and perennials for seasonal displays in containers, plus an excellent selection of house plants. See complete listing on page 318.

Boise Botanical

712 N. Orchard Avenue
Boise, Idaho 87306
☎ *208/343-5900*

Two people work full-time creating custom-made container plantings during the spring and early summer at Edward's Greenhouse. See complete listing on page 190.

Edward's Greenhouse

4106 Sandcreek Street
Boise, Idaho 83703
☎ *208/342-7548*

British Columbia

Country Garden Ltd.

10015 Young Street N.
Chilliwack, British Columbia V2P 4V4
☎ *604/792-6612*

The vast selection of indoor and outdoor container plants here culminates in a Christmas extravaganza with acres of poinsettias on display in the greenhouses. See complete listing on page 393.

Island Sun Greenhouses

8185 Island Highway
Fanny Bay, British Columbia V0R 1W0
☎ *604/335-0315*

Hours *Daily 9-6 (April through Aug)*
Accessible *Yes*
FAX *604/335-1135*

According to Gardens West magazine, this Vancouver Island company has been a "best kept garden secret." The secret is out! Arlene and Graham Wallace, who have been creating spectacular moss hanging baskets since 1984, now deliver their wares to residential and business customers in the Victoria area and over on the mainland, as well.

Sources for Bonsai

Washington

Bonsai Northwest

5021 S. 144th
Seattle, Washington 98168
☎ *206/242-8244*

Hours *Thurs-Sat 10-5*
Accessible *No*
Mail Order
Catalog *$2*
FAX *206/244-2301*

From starters to finished trees, Bonsai Northwest has a fine reputation in the field. The company ships indoor and outdoor plant materials all over the country. It keeps over a thousand different styles of imported pots in inventory and offers tools, books and all related materials. Most of the plant materials are imported from Japan, Korea and China, including Japanese white pine, satsuki azalea, wisteria and ginkgo. They've tropicals too – such plants as serissa, ficus and sweet plum.

Evans Nursery

6612 Tieton Drive
Yakima, Washington 98908
☎ *509/966-0698*

Hours *Mon-Sat 8-6, Sun 9-5*
(Feb through Dec)
Accessible *Yes, except restrooms*
Mail Order
Catalog *Free*

Larry Evans collects native alpine fir (*Abies lasiocarpa*) for world-wide distribution as bonsai subjects. Dug from private land at 7,000 foot elevation each September, the plants are wind swept by Mother Nature into gnarled and twisted forms. They grow only a quarter-inch per year, and a tree with a 3/8-inch trunk may be fifty years old. See complete listing for Evans Nursery on page 358.

Charlie and Ruth Anderson offer classes, books, containers and plant materials for beginning and advanced artists. They have over a thousand trees in containers waiting for enthusiasts to train. For those who prefer to purchase a completed piece, the couple offer finished bonsai. Selection is best in March and October.

Harbor Crest Bonsai

7595 N.E. High School Road
Bainbridge Island, Washington 98110
☎ *206/842-4148*

Hours *by appointment*
Accessible *Gravel makes difficult*

Kimura Nursery is well-known in the Seattle area for its bonsai classes, which include instruction classes for beginners and such advanced subjects as the miniature landscapes of the *Saikei* and Chinese *Penjing* traditions. The nursery stocks imported Japanese bonsai and sells all of the traditional plant materials, containers, tools and books for creating your own. For $15 a year, you can join the Bonsai Club, which entitles you to a 15% discount on all classes and supplies, as well as discounts on other nursery materials. See full listing on page 338.

Kimura Nursery

3860 N.E. Bel-Red Road
Bellevue, Washington 98008
☎ *206/881-6508*

"We offer the finest selection of indoor and outdoor bonsai in the Northwest," says David Dewire. "We take pride in our one-on-one relationships with customers, so that our product can be enjoyed an entire lifetime, or two. We offer care and maintenance services free for the life of the customer." You'll find the widest variety from April through June and again in late-fall.

Mt. Si Bonsai

43321 Mt. Si Road
North Bend, Washington 98045
☎ *206/888-0350*

Hours *Daily 10-5*
Accessible *Yes*
Mail Order
Catalog *$1*
FAX *206/888-4002*

Max Braverman makes one-of-a-kind containers (see listing on page 307), and his wife, Kate Bowditch, works with plants. You'll find exquisite finished bonsai (both tropical and winter-hardy) and bonsai containers at the nursery. Materials go on sale during Columbus Day weekend. Call for a class schedule.

Pine Garden Bonsai Company

20331 SR 530 N.E.
Arlington (Oso), Washington 98223
☎ *206/435-5995*

Hours *By appointment*
Accessible *No*
Mail Order
Catalog *$2 (hand-made containers)*
FAX *206/435-5995*

Oregon

Bonsai Artworks

1014 N.E. Ainsworth
Portland, Oregon 97211
☎ 503/281-7445

Hours By appointment
Accessible Yes
Mail Order

"We do real tropical bonsai from a list of tropicals that includes schefflera, mimosa, portulacaria, bougainvillea and five varieties of ficus," says Percy Hampton. The firm also offers native outdoor bonsai – maples, pines, spruce, elms, azaleas, etc. Plant selection is best April through October. Although Mr. Percy does not have a catalog, you can request plant materials by phone, and he'll ship the order.

Bonsai Village

23735 N.E. Airport Road
Aurora, Oregon 97002
☎ 503/678-1215

Hours Mon-Fri 8-4:30
Accessible Yes
FAX 503/678-1216

Ed Wood is a noted, knowledgeable rock gardener. His wholesale nursery is not really set up for retail business, but if you are looking for unusual pre-bonsai plant materials, you are welcome to come out and shop. He has lots of dwarf perennials and what he calls "oddball alpines" suitable for bonsai. Mr. Wood invites "garden viewing" in April, May and October.

Cascade Bonsai Works

P.O. Box 291
Sweet Home, Oregon 97386
☎ 503/367-4387

Hours By appointment only
Accessible No
Mail Order
Catalog Free

Don Pope and Dan Zwierzyna make fine American bonsai and miniature landscapes (*Saikei*). Their panel landscapes, which contain up to a tiny hundred trees, are especially lovely for courtyards, decks and small garden settings. Call for an appointment or look for their creative compositions at Portland Saturday Markets and the farmer's markets in Beaverton and Eugene. They supply bonsai to many of the garden centers in the region.

Clearwater Fish & Pond Supply, Inc.

19800 S.W. Farmington Road
Aloha, Oregon 97007
☎ 503/649-7211

See page 237 for the complete story on this fabulous find.

While Greer Gardens specializes in rhododendrons and azaleas for the landscape, seven pages of its catalog are devoted to bonsai. The plant materials are drawn from a wide spectrum of suitable species. See complete listing in Collector's Plants, page 264.

Greer Gardens
1280 Goodpasture Island Road
Eugene, Oregon 97401
☎ *503/686-8266*

Look for Diane Lund's Wee Tree Farm, the bonsai area at Garland Nursery. She has everything needed for bonsai hobbyists – pre-bonsai plants, pots, tools, wire and soil – as well as completed bonsai. "We import the traditional earthenware bonsai pottery from Japan and also have a line of plastic containers good for bonsai and other plant material. Our cast iron wind chimes from Japan have a beautiful sound," she adds. She conducts workshops in the spring and fall.

Wee Tree Farm at Garland Nursery
5470 N.E. Highway 20
Corvallis, Oregon 97330
☎ *503/753-6601*

Hours *Mon-Fri 9-6,*
Sat 9-5, Sun 10-5
Accessible *Yes*

British Columbia

This nursery carries bonsai, special perennials, trees and shrubs. Owner Peter Wams maintains contacts with growers in his homeland in the Netherlands. He and his wife, Inge, believe that their finished bonsai (indoor and outdoor), bonsai starts and bonsai dishes are among the best on Vancouver Island. They pride themselves on personal contact with their customers and offer free advice in the customer's garden, plus expert pruning skills. The nursery is situated about three hours north of Victoria.

All Season Nursery
6760 Island Highway
Bowser, British Columbia V0R 1G0
☎ *604/757-8803*

Hours *By appointment only*
Accessible *Yes*

Japan Bonsai

3170 Cambie Street
Vancouver, British Columbia V5Z 2W2
☎ *604/876-5700*

Hours *Tues-Sun 10-6*
Accessible *No*
Mail Order
Catalog *$2.50*
FAX *604/536-8799*

With over 40,000 bonsai and pre-bonsai in stock, Tak Yamaura's inventory includes tsukumo cypress, shimpaku juniper, Japanese mound juniper, Japanese larch, five-needle white pine, Korean lilac and satsuki azalea, to mention a few. The company also grows tropical and sub-tropical bonsai and carries a complete line of Japanese bonsai tools and ceramic and mica pots. Call to get the dates for classes (beginner as well as advanced) and seasonal sales each spring and fall.

Takamatsu Bonsai Design

1529 W. 4th Avenue
Vancouver, British Columbia V6J 1L6
☎ *604/737-2204*

Hours *Tues-Sun 12-6*
Accessible *Yes*
FAX *604/737-2010*

"We are arguably the best in Canada in bonsai," states Gerard Sanders. "We teach, we grow, we care. Purchasing a tree is the beginning of a relationship – we provide maintenance, baby-sitting, pruning service and conduct classes at the introductory level or advanced level. Only the right books and tools. All pots are #1 Japanese. We give free advice on anything that grows."

Chapter Nine
Collector's Plants

*"I know a bank whereon the
wild thyme blows,
Where oxslips and the
nodding violet grows
Quite over-canopied with
luscious woodbine,
With sweet musk-roses,
and with eglantine...*
.....Shakespeare, *A Midsummer-Night's Dream*

Rare Plant Nurseries

The nurseries in this category have three things in common: uncommon plant materials, a wide spectrum of plants from trees to vines, and mail-order service. They offer the discriminating gardener a wealth of varieties and a wealth of information. Reading their catalogs is like taking a class in horticulture! 🌸

✪DESTINATION
Collector's Nursery

16804 N. E. 102nd Avenue
Battle Ground, Washington 98604
☎ *206/574-3832*

Hours *By appointment only*
Accessible *Yes*
Mail Order
Catalog *$2*

The morning I spent at this nursery, Diana Reeck and Bill Janssen graciously shared with me their fascination with the unique, the rare and the beautiful within the plant kingdom. "We are always on the lookout for elusive botanical treasures," said Diana. Some of the plants they offer come from their own expeditions to wild places, and others are acquired through the exchange of plants or seed from other collectors in this region and throughout the world. They are quick to emphasize that they *do not* collect plants from the wild, but rather take seeds or cuttings in order to propagate and make known some of our less common native plants. In addition to offering a wide selection of unusual perennials, vines, trees and shrubs, Bill is involved in a hosta hybridizing program and Diana is developing a line of Pacific Coast iris. They both say, "The more we learn, the more there is to learn."

✪DESTINATION
Colvos Creek Farm

P.O. Box 1512
Vashon, Washington 98070
☎ *206/441-1509*

Hours *By appointment only*
Accessible *No*
Mail Order
Catalog *$2*

"We want to expand the idea of what a Northwest Landscape can be and to exploit the mild climate fully," says landscape architect Michael Lee. "Northwest plantings should stand out for their eclectic character rather than bland predictability. Our catalog offers a wide range of uncommon plants, with an emphasis on natives and drought-hardy material," he adds. The depth of his collection is apparent when one realizes that the listings include twenty-eight species of maple, eighteen arctostaphylos, thirty-nine hollies and twenty-nine willows. Of his fifty-seven oak species, half are evergreen! While

continued on next page--

his offerings are primarily shrubs and trees, a number of uncommon perennials appear as well. Rare materials are represented in such plants as a shrubby form of tanbark oak, a blue-green sprawling redwood and a boxwood from tropical Africa. Selection is best in the fall.

Forestfarm is one of the Northwest's nationally known sources for wonderful conifers, ferns, ornamental grasses, ground covers, perennials, species roses, shrubs, trees and vines. Among the listings are a good number of Western natives. The nursery is strictly a mail-order source. The owners, Ray and Peg Prag, wrote to me saying, "In 1937 the great plantsman E.H. Wilson said, 'my plea is for quality and variety.' We at Forestfarm try to provide both at a reasonable price. Although we started growing plants in 1974, every year we're amazed anew at the richness and diversity of the plant world. Growing plants is our great joy and we raise over 2,000 different kinds. And despite a growing number of customers, we try to treat each of them like we treat each of our plants— with special care. If some of the wonderful letters we get back are any indication, they appreciate it. Someone from Massachusetts wrote, 'I've dealt with at least sixty nurseries in the past ten years and you have very few peers and no superiors.' And from Indiana: 'Thanks for your beautiful plants. The care in packing and growing are evident to me.' We couldn't be happier about it because we've never yet met a gardener we didn't like."

DESTINATION ✫
Forestfarm

990 Tetherow
Williams, Oregon 97544-9599
☎ *503/846-6963*

Mail Order
Catalog $3

✯DESTINATION
Gossler Farm's Nursery

1200 Weaver Road
Springfield, Oregon 97478
☎ *503/746-3922*

Hours *By appointment only*
Accessible *Partially*
Mail Order
Catalog *$2*

"We carry a large selection of unusual trees, shrubs, vines and perennials, including the largest selection of *Hamamelis* (witch hazel) anywhere," say Marjory and Roger Gossler, a mother and son whose excellent selections of deciduous flowering trees and shrubs include magnolias, hydrangeas and stewartias. One very special cultivar, *Magnolia stellata rosea* 'Jane Platt' was named after the late Portland collector. The catalog also lists a fine selection of companion plants, plus conifers, ferns and bulbs. "We have a three-acre display garden that contains 3,500 different varieties," they add, noting that selection is best from September through March. The Gosslers are popular on the lecture circuit, giving talks on such subjects as winter gardens, magnolias, perennials and ornamental grasses.

✯DESTINATION
Greer Gardens

1280 Goodpasture Island Road
Eugene, Oregon 97401-1794
☎ *503/686-8266*

Hours *Mon-Sat 8:30-5:30, Sun 11-5:30*
Accessible *Yes*
Mail Order
Catalog *$3*
FAX *503/686-0910*

While Greer Gardens specializes in rhododendrons and azaleas, this nursery is a major mail-order source for unusual trees, shrubs and vines. Many species in this large collection are offered as specimen-size plants, which are shipped by air freight. The first two pages of Nancy and Harold Greer's catalog describe such rare and diverse plants as *Abeliophyllum distichum* 'Rosea' (pink-flowering Korean forsythia), *Aralia elata* 'Aureo-variegata' (Japanese angelia tree) and *Betula turkestanica* (Turkestan birch). And the list goes on for another one hundred pages. You'll find conifers, fruit and nut trees, ground covers, rock garden plants, and shrubs and trees for bonsai. The "frugal-dendron" page is very popular. No, this is not a new genus, but rather about thirty-five varieties of rhododendron offered at up to 50% off, with a minimum order of six plants.

Heronswood Nursery offers lots of choice plants that aren't normally encountered in the trade. "We specialize in Asiatic species as well as many others drawn from temperate climates worldwide. Our gardens are young, but enticing to the plant enthusiasts and collectors," says Dan Hinkley. "It is only through growing these plants ourselves that we can really know them. We welcome you to visit our nursery and garden, but, due to zoning restrictions, require that you make arrangements by calling or writing in advance." He and co-owner Robert Jones have organized their catalog listings by conifers, trees, shrubs, vines and perennials, making it extremely user-friendly. The catalog notes that some of the plants listed are grown by two other fine Northwest nurseries: the hydrangea cultivars from Keith Howe and trees, shrubs, perennials and grasses from Peter Ray at Puget Garden Resources.

DESTINATION ★
Heronswood Nursery

7530 288th N.E.
Kingston, Washington 98346
☎ *206/297-4172*

Hours *By Appointment Only*
Accessible *No*
Mail Order
Catalog *$3*

"Our unique nursery has been in business for 30 years serving the mail-order needs of gardeners around the nation and in Canada," says Baldassare Mineo. "We offer very large selections in alpine plants, dwarf conifers, Japanese maples and trough/container plants. Our beautiful display gardens are listed with the local Chamber of Commerce. They are filled with exciting plants from around the world. The plants bloom and go dormant at varying times, but there's always something to see. We hold 'Limited Collector Stock' sales on the first and last Saturday of each month except December and January." The catalog lists over a thousand plants, including hardy ferns, unusual bulbs, ornamental grasses, alpines to use as ground covers, native plants and wildflowers. Such shrubs as dwarf mountain laurel, dwarf pieris, dwarf rhododendron and a six-foot tall cut-leaf lilac are ideal for small gardens. The catalog's book section is an excellent source for beginning or advanced gardening information. Special events at the nursery include trough-building classes and slide lectures. They're always happy to offer horticultural advice to customers.

DESTINATION ★
Siskiyou Rare Plant Nursery

2825 Cummings Road
Medford, Oregon 97501
☎ *503/772-6846*

Hours *First and last Saturdays*
of each month
except Dec and Jan
Accessible *Yes,*
with some difficulty
Mail Order
Catalog *$2, refundable*

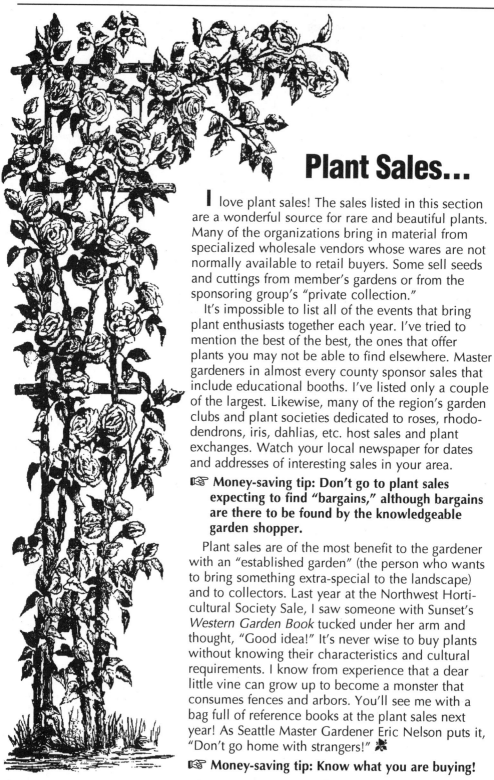

Plant Sales...

I love plant sales! The sales listed in this section are a wonderful source for rare and beautiful plants. Many of the organizations bring in material from specialized wholesale vendors whose wares are not normally available to retail buyers. Some sell seeds and cuttings from member's gardens or from the sponsoring group's "private collection."

It's impossible to list all of the events that bring plant enthusiasts together each year. I've tried to mention the best of the best, the ones that offer plants you may not be able to find elsewhere. Master gardeners in almost every county sponsor sales that include educational booths. I've listed only a couple of the largest. Likewise, many of the region's garden clubs and plant societies dedicated to roses, rhododendrons, iris, dahlias, etc. host sales and plant exchanges. Watch your local newspaper for dates and addresses of interesting sales in your area.

☞ **Money-saving tip: Don't go to plant sales expecting to find "bargains," although bargains are there to be found by the knowledgeable garden shopper.**

Plant sales are of the most benefit to the gardener with an "established garden" (the person who wants to bring something extra-special to the landscape) and to collectors. Last year at the Northwest Horticultural Society Sale, I saw someone with Sunset's *Western Garden Book* tucked under her arm and thought, "Good idea!" It's never wise to buy plants without knowing their characteristics and cultural requirements. I know from experience that a dear little vine can grow up to become a monster that consumes fences and arbors. You'll see me with a bag full of reference books at the plant sales next year! As Seattle Master Gardener Eric Nelson puts it, "Don't go home with strangers!" ✿

☞ **Money-saving tip: Know what you are buying!**

Regional Plant Sales by Season
Winter

Washington

This is the premier garden show in the Pacific Northwest! Two floors of the Convention Center are filled with gorgeous display gardens and commercial booths selling plants, seeds and garden-related items (furniture, pottery, art, etc.). On the upper level are educational booths, lecture halls and the Orchid Society Show and Sale. There's always a splendid lecture series with "big name" landscape designers and horticulturists from all over the world speaking on every imaginable garden topic. Admission is discounted after 5:00 p.m., and evenings tend to be the least crowded.

Northwest Flower and Garden Show

Washington State Convention Center, Seattle, Washington
Contact: Northwest Flower and Garden Show
☎ *206/224-1700*
for recorded information
(from late November through February)
or 206/789-5333 during other times of the year

Date: Usually second weekend in February (Wed through Sun)

Conservatory displays are removed and replaced with potted tulips, miniature roses, cacti, primroses and foliage plants. The sale helps fund the Conservatory. Used books donated by members assist the cause.

Seymour Botanical Conservatory Plant Sale

Contact: W.W. Seymour Botanical Conservatory
316 G Street
Tacoma, Washington 98405
☎ *206/591-5330*

Date: A weekend in early February (Saturday and Sunday)

Call for a free brochure that offers a selection of native plants from Mt. Tahoma nursery. Your order will be placed with the nursery by Snake Lake Nature Center and the plants will be delivered to Snake Lake for pick-up in mid-April. Proceeds benefit the Nature Center.

Snake Lake Nature Center Annual Native Plant Sale

Contact: Snake Lake Nature Center
1919 S. Tyler Street
Tacoma, Washington 98405
☎ *206/591-6439*

Date: Order between January and March; pick up plants in mid-April.

Weyerhaeuser Seedling Sale

Location: *Varies from city to city*
Contact: *Weyerhaeuser Seedling Sales Department*
Federal Way, Washington
☎ *1-800/732-4769*

Date: *Saturdays in February and March*

While you can purchase seedlings in quantities of 2,500 or more from Weyerhaeuser year-round, it's only during these Saturday sales in winter that you can purchase individual trees. Call the Seedling Sales Department for the date and location of a sale in your area.

Oregon

Weyerhaeuser Seedling Sale

Federal Way, Washington
☎ *1-800/732-4769*

Date: *Saturdays in February and March*

See previous listing.

British Columbia

Bloedel Floral Conservatory Free Day and Plant Sale

Contact: *Bloedel Floral Conservatory*
Queen Elizabeth Park
W. 33rd at Cambie
Vancouver, British Columbia V5X 1C5
☎ *604/872-5513*

Dates: *A Friday in January and March*

The Conservatory's little gift shop is open year around, but on the days the Conservatory is open free-of-charge, the walkways are lined with plants for sale. Species vary with availability but will usually include ferns, orchids and small palms.

VanDusen Botanical Garden Seedy Saturday

Contact: *VanDusen Botanical Garden*
5251 Oak Street
Vancouver, British Columbia V6M 4H1
☎ *604/266-7194*

Date: *First Saturday in February*

Seedy Saturday brings together about twenty-five exhibitors whose focus is on seed diversity around the world. A heritage seed exchange is the main event.

Spring

Washington

After years of hosting the Grandmother of all Plant Sales, the support organization for the Washington Park Arboretum has taken a new tack. Members now search-out extraordinary trees for the home gardener. They will also offer plants grown in the greenhouse from arboretum cuttings and special plants from members' gardens.

Arboretum Foundation Uncommon Tree Sale

Graham Visitors Center
Contact: *Arboretum Foundation
c/o University of Washington, XD-10
Seattle, Washington 98195*
☎ *206/726-1954 (recorded message)
or 325-4510*

Date: *mid-May*

Perennials, hardy ferns, dahlias, drought-tolerant plants, Japanese maples and colorful annuals abound at this sale, which is getting bigger every year.

Bellevue Botanical Garden Plant Sale

Wilburton School, Bellevue, Washington
Contact: *The Bellevue Botanical Garden
16023 N.E. 8th Street (mailing address)
Bellevue, Washington 98008*
☎ *206/462-2749*

Date: *A Saturday in late April or early May*

Plant sale aficionados eagerly await this three-day happening! Hard-to-find native plants, abundant herbs and perennials, trees, shrubs, roses and annuals are all featured here.

Children's Hospital Garden Sale

University Village, Seattle, Washington
Contact: *Children's Hospital
Guild Association
P.O. Box 5371, Mailstop CH23
Seattle, Washington 98105*
☎ *206/526-2153*

Date: *Usually the third week in April
(Tuesday, Wednesday and Thursday)*

The Specialty Nursery Association of Clark County is among the sponsors for this fair, which includes a display garden competition. You'll find all kinds of plants along with garden-related items such as planters and dried floral arrangements.

Clark County Home and Garden Idea Fair

*Clark County Fairgrounds, north of
Vancouver, Washington*
Contact: *Mari Eggebraaten*
☎ *206/256-0268*

Date: *Mother's Day Weekend, May
(Friday, Saturday and Sunday)*

Great Northwest Garden Fest and Plant Sale

Contact: Horticulture Department
Edmonds Community College
20000 68th West
Lynnwood, Washington 98036
☎ *206/640-1608*

Date: A weekend in May
(Friday and Saturday)

New ornamentals for the Pacific Northwest are featured at this sale. The specialty emphasis varies year to year.

Hulda Klager Lilac Gardens Sale

Contact: Hulda Klager Lilac Gardens
115 S. Perkin
Woodland, Washington 98674
☎ *206/225-8996*

Date: March and April

The Hulda Klager Lilac Gardens grow fifty different varieties of lilacs, and the plants are sold informally while supplies last (they usually sell out before the Open House in mid-April). Call the gardens to make sure someone will be there to dig-up a plant for you.

Lake Washington Technical College Spring Plant Sale

Contact: Don Marshall
Lake Washington Technical College
11605 132nd Avenue N.E.
Kirkland, Washington 98034
☎ *206/828-5621*

Date: The weekend before Mother's Day
(Friday and Saturday)

Fuchsia baskets, geranium baskets, house plants, bedding plants, herbs and vegetable starts are what this sale is about. Half the inventory is held back for Saturday's sale, so the merchandise won't be picked-over.

Master Gardeners of King County Plant Sale

Center for Urban Horticulture
Contact: Master Gardeners of King County
3519 S.W. 171st Street
Seattle, Washington 98166
☎ *206/296-3986*
to request an informational flier.

Date: A weekend in late April
(Saturday and Sunday)

Natives, perennials, annuals, vegetables, herbs, ornamental shrubs and trees, fruit trees and house plants are all available here, in conjunction with excellent lectures, demonstrations and information.

The Meerkerk Garden offers free admission on opening day, along with a large selection of rhododendrons for sale. Rhododendrons are sold throughout the spring and summer while supplies last.

Meerkerk Rhododendron Garden Sale

Contact: *Meerkerk Rhododendron Garden*
3531 S. Meerkerk Lane
Greenbank, Washington 98253
☎ 206/321-6682

Date: *A Saturday in late March*

Hard-to-find and hardy fuchsia varieties are available at bargain prices in two-inch and four-inch containers. About 12,000 dahlia tubers, representing about 400 different varieties are also featured at this sale. (The eleven fuchsia clubs in the Society each have plant sales as well; call Joan Hampton to find one in your area.)

Northwest Fuchsia Society Annual Spring Plant Sale and Puget Sound Dahlia Association Public Tuber Sale

Faith Lutheran Church, Seattle
Contact: *Joan Hampton*
Northwest Fuchsia Society
P.O. Box 33071
Seattle, Washington 98133-0071
☎ 206/364-7735
or Bill Batts
Puget Sound Dahlia Association
4007 52nd Avenue S.W.
Seattle, Washington 98116
☎ 206/937-6505

Date: *A weekend in March or April (Friday and Saturday)*

Growers bring in a wide assortment of ferns and companion plants for this very special sale, which is associated with the Fern Festival.

Northwest Horticultural Society Fern Sale

Contact: *Northwest Horticultural Society Isaacson Hall,*
Center for Urban Horticulture
University of Washington, GF-15
Seattle, Washington 98195
☎ 206/527-1794

Date: *A weekend in late May or early June (Friday and Saturday)*

Pomeroy Living History Farm Annual Herb Festival

Contact: *Pomeroy Living History Farm*
20902 N.E. Lucia Falls Road
Yacolt, Washington 98675
☎ *206/686-3537*

Date: *Third weekend in May (Saturday and Sunday)*

The setting makes this festival especially interesting. You'll find 400 different herb plants for sale.

Rhododendron Species Botanical Garden Spring Plant Sale

Contact: *The Rhododendron Species Botanical Garden*
P.O. Box 3798
Federal Way, Washington 98063
☎ *206/661-9377 (gift shop & general information); 838-4646 (from Seattle), 927-6960 (from Tacoma)*

Date: *A Saturday in early April*

While the gift shop is open throughout the year, The Rhododendron Species Foundation offers a spectacular range of species and hybrid rhododendrons and azaleas at this major garden benefit event. You'll also find ferns, alpine plants, trees, shrubs, heathers, perennials, bulbs and pottery.

Seattle Tilth Organic Edible Plant Sale

Contact: *Seattle Tilth Association*
4649 Sunnyside Avenue N.
Seattle, Washington 98103
☎ *206/633-0451*

Date: *Last Saturday in April*

Organic vegetable starts suitable for the maritime Northwest and raised by Seattle Tilth volunteers are among the star attractions here. Vendors also bring in herbs, edible flowers, medicinal plants, fruit trees, cane plants, woodland plants and flowers.

Skagit Valley Tulip Festival

Fields near Mount Vernon, Washington
Contact: *Skagit Valley Tulip Festival*
P.O. Box 1007
Mount Vernon, Washington 98273
☎ *800/4-TULIPS for a recorded message and to request a brochure or 206/428-8547 for more information*

Dates: *First three weeks of April*

Acres and acres of blooming bulbs attract thousands of visitors each year. Display gardens and shops throughout the county sell bulbs, cut flowers and gift items. Avoid the traffic and go during the week if you're can.

The society grows about a hundred varieties of chrysanthemums in the research farm's greenhouses. Most are garden varieties, but you'll also find some exhibition-quality. The plants usually sell by noon, so get there early.

Vancouver Chrysanthemum Society Spring Sale

Southwest Washington Research Station, Hazel Dell, Washington
Contact: *Dick Malpass*
☎ *206/574-4175*

Date: *First Saturday in May*

Two-year-old trees are sold to fund this group's promotion of good forest management on private lands. The twelve or more varieties of conifers are mainly suitable for windbreak and screens or Christmas trees. They offer a few landscape trees, as well.

Whatcom County Farm Forestry Association Annual Tree Sale

Northwest Fairgrounds (Horse Area); Lynden, Washington
Contact: *Tom Westergreen*
☎ *206/966-3605*

Date: *A Saturday in late March*

Excellent ornamental shrubs and trees are available here, along with other hardy plant materials, including perennials, bulbs and flowering woodland plants.

Whatcom Growers Association Spring Sales

Whatcom County, Washington (sale location varies)
Contact: *Chris Schugmann*
☎ *206/592-2989*

Dates: *A Saturday in late March or early April and a Saturday in May*

Oregon

Uncommon plants are the order of the day! You'll discover excellent rock garden specimens, ornamental trees, shrubs and herbaceous plants. Twenty wholesale vendors bring in plant materials not usually available to retail buyers, and volunteers propagate very special plants from the Berry collection. Seeds, books, pottery and other non-plant material are also part of the fare. Beginning in '94, day-long seminars will accompany the occasion.

Berry Botanic Garden Spring Plant Sale

Portland, Oregon (sale location varies)
Contact: *The Berry Botanic Garden 11505 S.W. Summerville Avenue Portland, Oregon 97219*
☎ *503/636-4112*

Date: *A Saturday in mid-April*

Bush's Pasture Park
Annual Benefit Plant Sale

Bush's Pasture Park, Salem, Oregon
Contact: Gretchen Carnaby
☎ 503/588-2410

Date: The weekend before Mother's Day
Weekend (Friday, Saturday and Sunday)

Lots of annuals and perennials to brighten your spring garden can be found here. The Friends of Bush Garden sponsor this sale, so you'll also find wonderful old roses.

Clackamas County Master
Gardeners Spring Garden Fair

Clackamas County Fairgrounds, Canby, Oregon
Contact: Adele Lehan
☎ 503/694-1055

Date: The weekend before Mother's Day
(Saturday and Sunday)

Vendors sell miniature roses, orchids, hardy perennials, vegetables, bedding plants and garden items such as bird houses and planters at more than 60 booths. Clinics, soil testing and educational displays round out the event.

The Hardy Plant Society of Oregon
Spring Plant Sale

Washington County Fairgrounds, Hillsboro, Oregon
Contact: Mary Hoffman, Secretary
☎ 503/656-1575

Date: The second weekend in April
(Saturday and Sunday)

Serious horticulturists come from all over the Northwest to examine the wares at this special sale. Out-of-the-ordinary perennials are the main attraction, but you'll also find distinguished herbs, shrubs and trees. The fifty vendors are all members of this organization, and most are landscape professionals who bring plants from their own specialty nurseries. The plants are labeled with Latin names, so come prepared.

Leach Garden Friends
Spring Plant Sale

David Douglas High School Cafeteria, Portland, Oregon
Contact: Leach Botanical Garden
6704 S.E. 122nd Avenue
Portland, Oregon 97236
☎ 503/761-9503

Date: A Saturday in April

Local growers and Friends of the Leach Botanical Garden offer a wide assortment of perennials, shrubs, trees and collectible plants at this popular event, which draws both beginning gardeners and serious horticulturists. The selection of native plants is exceptional. Participating specialty nurseries are encouraged to bring their rarest plants, as well as the newest introductions.

One of the highlights of the Wildflower Festival at Mount Pisgah Arboretum (six miles south of downtown Eugene) is the sale of unusual plants from member's gardens.

Mount Pisgah Arboretum Wildflower Festival

Contact: Mount Pisgah Arboretum
Buford Recreation Area,
off Seavey Loop Road
Eugene, Oregon
☎ 503/747-3817

Date: The third Sunday in May

Hundreds of fuchsias from two-inch pots to tree-sized, plus other donated plants and non-plant items can be yours with a nod of the head. Also, look for the one-of-a-kind items on the fixed-price table at this auction.

Oregon Fuchsia Society Plant Auction and Sale

Clackamas Park Friends Church,
Milwaukie, Oregon
Contact: Oregon Fuchsia Society
☎ 503/235-5844

Date: Third Tuesday in April

Members of The Dalles Art Association provide ornamentals and vegetable starts for this benefit. Get there early in the day; the best plants go quickly.

The Dalles Art Center Spring Plant Sale

Contact: The Dalles Art Center
220 E. 4th Street
The Dalles, Oregon 97058
☎ 503/296-4759

Date: The first Saturday of the Cherry Festival in April

Growers deliver native plants for home landscaping, and Master Gardeners are on hand to deliver advice.

Tryon Creek State Park Trillium Festival

Contact: Friends of Tryon Creek State Park
11321 S.W. Terwilliger Boulevard
Portland, Oregon 97219
☎ 503/636-4398

Date: The first weekend in April
(Saturday and Sunday)

British Columbia

Alpine Garden Club of British Columbia Spring Sale

William Griffin Center, North Vancouver, British Columbia
Contact: *Daphne Guernsey*
☎ *604/921-9740*

Date: *The first Sunday in May*

Alpine plants and seeds are the featured attractions. Look for gentians and primulas among other fine rock garden plants. The club also sponsors a worldwide seed exchange every year.

Horticulture Centre of the Pacific Spring Sales

Contact: *Horticulture Centre of the Pacific*
505 Quayle Road
Victoria, British Columbia V8X 3X1
☎ *604/479-6162*

Dates: *A weekend in March (Saturday and Sunday) & a weekend in late April or early May (Friday and Saturday)*

The March Sale offers a variety of perennials grown at the Centre. Perennials and hanging fuchsia baskets are available at the sale in April.

University of British Columbia Botanical Gardens Annual Perennial Plant Sale

Contact: *University of British Columbia Botanical Gardens*
6804 S.W. Marine Drive
Vancouver, British Columbia V6T 1Z4
☎ *604/822-3928*

Date: *A Sunday in May*

This is special! All the perennials offered for sale are propagated from plants found in the botanical gardens, so if you find a plant you love in the gardens, you'll likely find it for sale here.

University of Victoria Friends Plant Sale

McKinnon Gymnasium, University of Victoria, Victoria, British Columbia
Contact: *Betty Kennedy*
☎ *604/592-2070*

Date: *The first Sunday in May*

Ornamentals of all kinds are available at this sale: bulbs, perennials, annuals, bedding plants, rock and alpine garden plants and natives.

About 35,000 plants are sold during this one day – everything from geraniums to trees. "Pot luck" perennials from members' gardens are popular, as are the unusual, exotic plants from growers.

VanDusen Botanical Garden Annual Plant Sale

Contact: *VanDusen Botanical Garden*
5251 Oak Street
Vancouver, British Columbia V6M 4H1
☎ *604/266-7194*

Date: *The last Sunday in April*

Retailers bring in everything you need to turn your outdoor space into a garden room. Planters, furniture, paving stones and greenhouses are all temptingly displayed on the great lawn.

VanDusen's Garden Furnishings Sale

Contact: *VanDusen Botanical Garden*
5251 Oak Street
Vancouver, British Columbia V6M 4H1
☎ *604/266-7194*

Date: *The last weekend in May (Saturday and Sunday)*

Summer

Washington

Nursery-grown miniature rose bushes are available at a discount at this sale. You also can order miniature roses through the society during the spring and pick them up at the organization's meetings.

Seattle Rose Society's Mini Rose Sale

Crossroads Shopping Center, Bellevue, Washington
Contact: *Caroline Fredette*
☎ *206/723-7141*

Date: *A weekend in June (Saturday and Sunday)*

Bedding plants, foliage plants and cacti replace the Conservatory's normal displays for this benefit.

Seymour Botanical Conservatory Summer Plant Sale

Contact: *W.W. Seymour Botanical Conservatory*
316 G Street
Tacoma, Washington 98405
☎ *206/591-5330*

Date: *A weekend in early June (Saturday and Sunday)*

Oregon

Friends of Bush Garden Plant Sale

Bush's Pasture Park, Salem, Oregon
Contact: *Gretchen Carnaby*
☎ *503/588-2410*

Date: *Third weekend in July (Saturday and Sunday)*

The popular Salem Art Sale coincides with this event. You'll find wonderful herbs, some unusual house plants, perennials, annuals and old roses.

Fall

Washington

Arboretum Foundation Bulb Sale

Graham Visitors Center
Contact: *Arboretum Foundation*
c/o University of Washington, XD-10
Seattle, Washington 98195
☎ *206/325-4510 (recorded message) or 325-4510*

Date: *A weekend in October*

Unusual bulbs are purchased wholesale, sorted by members, and then sold to benefit the Arboretum Foundation. Donated plants and outdoor fall color plants are also available.

The Friends of the Conservatory Fall Plant Sale

Volunteer Park, Seattle, Washington
Contact: *Friends of the Conservatory*
1402 E. Prospect Street
Seattle, Washington 98112
☎ *206/322-4112*

Date: *late September*

A big tent on the lawn in front of the Conservatory makes a festive setting for this annual benefit. Tropical plants from all over the world are the featured attraction! Members propagate cuttings from the Conservatory and seek-out specialized nurseries to provide a wide range of greenhouse and indoor plants.

Perennials and house plants grown in the greenhouse are the main course here. The pottery shop next door to the greenhouse has its sale the same weekend, so you might pick up a pot to complement that new plant.

Friends of Manito Annual Plant Sale

Manito Park and Gardens, Spokane, Washington
Contact: Manito Park and Gardens
4 W. 21st Avenue
Spokane, Washington 99203
509/625-6622

Date: The third weekend in September (Saturday and Sunday)

Poinsettias, wreaths and tropical foliage baskets are among the goodies you can expect to find at this event. The items are products of educational projects, so they vary year to year and basket to basket.

Lake Washington Technical College Holiday Plant Sale

Lake Washington Technical College, Kirkland, Washington
Contact: Don Marshall
Lake Washington Technical College
11605 132nd Avenue N.E.
Kirkland, Washington 98034
☎ 206/828-5621

Date: Thursday night and Friday after Thanksgiving

A wealth of plant material (indoor and outdoor) is presented at this popular event. Books and educational seminars complement the varied and unusual plant selection, which includes a collector's corner, natives and plants to attract birds and butterflies. You'll also discover excellent containers and tools.

Northwest Horticultural Society Annual Plant Sale

Contact: Northwest Horticultural Society
Isaacson Hall,
Center for Urban Horticulture
University of Washington, GF-15
Seattle, Washington 98195
☎ 206/527-1794

Date: A weekend in late September (Friday and Saturday)

Here you can find all kinds of blooming plants for your fall garden as well as a large selection of trees, shrubs and perennials that should be planted in the fall.

Whatcom Growers Association Fall Sale

Whatcom County, Washington (site varies)
Contact: Chris Schugmann
☎ 206/592-2989

Date: A Saturday in early October

Oregon

Berry Botanic Garden Fall Plant Sale

Portland, Oregon (location varies)
Contact: The Berry Botanic Garden
11505 S.W. Summerville Avenue
Portland, Oregon 97219
☎ 503/636-4112

Date: A Saturday in early October

Rock garden plants, ornamentals and herbs (the unusual ones gardeners really search for) can be found at this sale, plus seeds, books, pottery and more.

Hardy Plant Society of Oregon Plant Sale

Washington County Fairgrounds,
Hillsboro, Oregon
Contact: Mary Hoffman, Secretary
☎ 503/656-1573

Date: The second weekend in September (Saturday and Sunday)

Many of the same member/vendors you met at the spring sale will be back in September with more fine landscape plants. Generally, plants at the fall sale are larger in size, and you'll find a nice selection of bulbs at this time.

Leach Garden Friends Fall Plant Sale

David Douglas High School Cafeteria,
Portland, Oregon
Contact: Leach Botanical Garden
6704 S.E. 122nd Avenue
Portland, Oregon 97236
☎ 503/761-9503

Date: A Saturday in September

A wide assortment of natives, perennials, shrubs, trees and collectible plants are available from the twenty or so specialty nurseries that display at this sale. Some of the plants come from the Leach Botanical Garden's own uncommon collection.

Mount Pisgah Arboretum Fall Festival and Mushroom Show

Contact: Mount Pisgah Arboretum
Buford Recreation Area, off Seavey Loop Road
Eugene, Oregon
☎ 503/747-3817

Date: Usually the last Sunday in October

The big wildflower festival at Mount Pisgah Arboretum is held too late for planting wildflower seed. The seeds are available in conjunction with the annual mushroom show.

Local growers and hybridizers donate bulbs, and member's contribute bulbs from their own gardens for this sale, which keeps the organization running and makes possible a spring daffodil show. The bulbs are sold at about half-price, and they are available in large quantities for naturalizing.

Oregon Daffodil Society Bulb Sale

Linn County Fairgrounds
Albany, Oregon
***Contact:** Leonard Forster*
☎ *503/491-3874*

***Date:** A Saturday in mid-October*

British Columbia

Alpine plants and bulbs are featured at this organization's fall sale.

Alpine Garden Club Fall Sale

VanDusen Botanical Garden
Vancouver, British Columbia
***Contact:** Daphne Guernsey*
☎ *604/921-9740*

***Date:** The third Sunday in September*

The Conservatory is open free to the public and the walkways are lined with plants for sale.

Bloedel Floral Conservatory Free Day and Plant Sale

***Contact:** Bloedel Floral Conservatory*
Queen Elizabeth Park
W. 33rd at Cambie
Vancouver, British Columbia V5X 1C5
☎ *604/872-5513*

***Dates:** A Friday in October and December*

Members of the Centre get first pick on Friday, but you'll still find a nice variety of perennials at the public sale during the weekend.

Horticulture Centre of the Pacific Fall Sale

***Contact:** Horticulture Centre of the Pacific*
505 Quayle Road
Victoria, British Columbia V8X 3X1
☎ *604/479-6162*

***Date:** A weekend in September (Saturday and Sunday)*

University of British Columbia Botanical Gardens Student Plant Sale

Contact: University of British Columbia
Botanical Gardens
6804 S.W. Marine Drive
Vancouver, British Columbia V6T 1Z4
☎ 604/822-3928

Date: A weekend in September (usually
Friday, Saturday and Sunday)

The Student Plant Sale started as a way to encourage the university students to have plants in their rooms. Now it's open to the public, and the plants are brought in by nurseries.

VanDusen Botanical Garden Tree-mendous Compost Sale & Uncommon Tree Sale and Festival

Contact: VanDusen Botanical Garden
5251 Oak Street
Vancouver, British Columbia V6M 4H1
☎ 604/266-7194

Date: The last weekend in October

Focusing on the urban forest, the VanDusen Botanical Gardens provides information, demonstrations and lectures on pruning and planting. On Saturday, rich mulch from the city compost is sold by the bag-full. On Sunday, the organization sells unusual trees (about 1,500 of them) to expand the diversity of the urban forest.

Chapter Ten
Garden Furniture

*"Sometimes I sits and thinks,
and sometimes I just sits."*
.....Old country saying

Please Be Seated

Garden furniture revives happy memories. I have old photographs of family picnics and children's tea parties held 'round a big outdoor table. My father taught me the constellations as we sat in canvas sling-back chairs in the backyard on starry summer nights. I loved to watch the world go by from my grandmother's porch swing and spend lazy Saturday afternoons reading in a hammock...

As people rediscover simple pleasures in a fast-paced world, garden furniture is back in style and better than ever! Visit any large furniture store or garden center today and you'll see outdoor sofas and chairs in a wonderful array of materials and finishes. There are dining tables and occasional tables, tea carts and etageres, bar stools and brightly colored market umbrellas – all reflecting a new penchant for flair and elegance.

You'll find traditional designs alongside every stylistic trend from art deco to postmodern. Fanciful Victorian styles are in vogue again, but now they're fabricated of steel, cast aluminum and all-weather resin wicker as well as wrought iron and wood. Northwest manufacturers are making faithful reproductions of classic English-style garden benches and wonderful new versions of the Adirondack chair. And to complement our casual Northwest lifestyle, they offer contemporary dining tables and chairs and well-crafted chaise lounges, porch swings and gliders.

Because many of the exotic hardwood species once used for garden furniture come from ecologically sensitive areas of the world, local designers are using domestic wood, which if properly selected and well-maintained, holds up as well as any tropical species. All of the regional manufacturers offer catalogs or brochures, and many are willing to customize orders to accommodate your special requests.

Garden shops and furniture dealers in the region feature cheerful metal and plastic patio furnishings from manufacturers all over the world. Take a look at the colors available! White, greens and earth tones remain garden favorites, but today's site furnishings also come in some wild and wonderful hues. In the right setting, pinks, purples and bright blues light up a garden. Cushions lend both pattern and color to seating areas, and here we are talking about a lot of choices. If the furnishings will be visible from indoors, be sure the colors complement your interior design as well as the exterior setting.

Your first priority should be comfort. Designers are responding to new consumer demands by studying human proportions and seeking the best fit for the widest possible range of human body types. While a garden bench need not be the ultimate in comfort, the chairs you use for dining and lounging should be as carefully selected as any that go into your home.

Manufacturers, both local and worldwide, are selecting materials and finishes for their durability. Wood will always be a favored material because of its natural insulating qualities – it doesn't get hot in the summer or cold in the winter. Designs in non-corrosive metals such as steel, aluminum (both cast and sturdy tubular forms) and welded wire-mesh are being offered with new electrostatically applied powder-coated paint finishes to provide a far-longer life span than simple paint. Furnishings made of high-tech plastics and resins treated with ultra-violet inhibitors are increasingly viable alternatives. Stone and concrete furniture, the most durable of choices, have a tendency to collect water and are generally considered less user-friendly than the other materials.

You'll also want to consider ease of maintenance and storage. If your furniture will be exposed to the elements, do not buy wood that has been sealed with a varnish or paint. Wood needs to breathe. An oil-based stain will protect the wood and allow it to expand and contract with changes in the weather. Wood furniture should be joined with brass, stainless steel or galvanized fasteners. In metal furniture, look for powder-coated finishes. If the pieces you are buying have webbed plastic seats, be sure the manufacturer offers replacement webbing. The metal parts can be kept sparkling with auto polish, but eventually the webbing will need to be replaced.

There are two ways to go. You can buy cheap, planning to discard the furniture when it falls apart. Or you can go for quality. It's hard to argue with the logic of stackable welded wire chairs that cost $4.95 apiece. (You've seen them at all the hardware stores, even the drugstore chains.) They're "knock-offs" of great-looking Italian chairs that sell for about $89. Sure, if you leave them outdoors, the welds break and the paint peels. They begin to rust after a season or two, but at that price, who can complain? They're handy to pull out when you're entertaining large crowds. If you keep garden furniture in storage except for when you use it, you can get away with benches and chairs and tables of lesser quality. But, for the furnishings you are going look at every day and plan to use year in and year out, buy the highest quality furniture you can afford.

☞ **Money-saving tip: Buy off-season.**

Most of the sources listed below have sales in late summer or early fall. I know it's hard to justify spending money on something you aren't going to use for several months, but you can save up to 50% just because a store needs to made room for other merchandise. Sometimes the sales begin as early as August or September, and these are often our sunniest months! During the season, check out such discount merchandisers as Best and Costco and other big home improvement stores. If you've shopped around and know what to look for in quality, you may unearth some real bargains at these places.

So, ladies and gentlemen, please be seated. 🌺

Northwest Furniture Manufacturers

Bald Peak Woodworks

24485 S.W. Scholls Ferry Road
Hillsboro, Oregon 97123
☎ *503/628-0894*

Hours *Fri-Sun 9:30-6 or by appointment*
Accessible *Yes*
Mail Order
Catalog *Free*
Mailing address *35566 S.W. Bald Peak Road*
Hillsboro, Oregon 97123

"Bald Peak Woodworks is a family owned business dedicated to creating the finest-quality outdoor wood products on the market today," says Janet Breslow, noting that all the company's furniture is hand-crafted in their workshop. "Our devotion to excellence in every piece we create will give you a product that will stand the test of time." The line includes Victorian porch swings, rustic garden benches, and table and chairs with a small signature heart-shape cut out of the back. They produce a Chehalem Mountain Lounger, which is their version of the Adirondack chair complete with a foot rest. They also make window boxes, hanging planters and patio containers, available in custom-made sizes and designs. The company is the Portland area representative for *Sunglo Solar Greenhouses* (See page 68) and they custom-build solarium room additions.

Cape Cod Comfys, Inc.

3413 Fremont Avenue N.
Seattle, Washington 98103
☎ *206/545-4309 or 1-800/842-0885*

Hours *Mon-Sat 10-6 (Jan through April);*
Mon-Sat 10-6, Sunday 12-5
(May through Dec)
Accessible *Yes*
Mail Order
Catalog *Free*
FAX *206/545-4520*

"We manufacture the most comfortable Adirondack-style furniture available," say the folks at Cape Cod Comfys. The company also offers an attractive line of companion pieces, such as swings and settees (elongated Adirondack chairs), traditional-style garden benches and round picnic tables with matching curved benches. All of their furniture is available in pine or cedar with stained or painted finishes. They make architectural birdhouses and whimsical garden ornaments too. You'll find special discounts during the Northwest Flower and Garden Show and again during the Fremont Street Fair in June.

Columbia Cascade Company is one of the world's largest manufacturers of commercial site furnishings and play equipment. Their sturdy products are used worldwide in urban beautification projects, and there is a place for these high-quality designs at fine homes, particularly their Restoration and Manor series. The company will sell to individuals at the same prices offered to contractors. Visitors to Portland will see hundreds of Columbia's *TimberForm Restoration* benches along the river front, at the convention center and in many of the city's public spaces. Several of the company's metal planters (offered in over 170 different colors) are also appropriate for use in private gardens. These are not inexpensive furnishings, but they are beautiful and should last several lifetimes. Call for the name of the representative serving your area. See play equipment listing on page 70.

Columbia Cascade Company

1975 S.W. Fifth Avenue
Portland, Oregon 97201
☎ *503/223-1157*

Hours *Mon-Fri 8:30-5*

Romantic twig furniture and birdhouses are the specialty here. Reminiscent of simpler times and hand-crafted to complement a country garden style, the line includes arbors, bakers racks, planters and plant stands, custom shelves and doll furniture. The "Princess Jane Collection" of furniture features high, rounded backs and the "Captain's Collection" is straight-lined. Each offers a choice of slat or twig seats. The company is located in the Mission British Columbia Royal Canadian Legion, and it is run by the Mission Association for Community Living to employ people with disabilities. "We are proud to offer products that never devalue and tend to stay in a family like fine art." Visit the workshop or call for a retail dealer in your area.

Great Canadian Basket Company

32965 Lougheed Highway
Mission, British Columbia V2V 1B4
☎ *604/826-9116*

Hours *Mon-Fri 8:30-5:30*
Accessible *Yes*
FAX *604/826-9611*

Humptulips Cedar Furniture

P.O. Box 133
Humptulips, Washington 98552
☎ 1-800/273-2564

Hours By appointment
Mail Order
Catalog Free

The craftsmen at this factory with a funny name make folding end tables and picnic tables, as well as round-backed Adirondack-style chairs and settees. About his furniture Lary Bohlman says, "I use only the finest Western Red Cedar for my furniture, buying it direct from sawmills and selling directly to the customer, thereby eliminating the middleman. I have done everything possible to make my furniture comfortable to the point that cushions are unnecessary. By using hardwood dowels and epoxy glue, the durability is beyond compare. Not having a retail showroom, I proudly bring my furniture to your home with no sales pitch or obligation. The product speaks for itself."

Rogue River Rustics

3360 N. Pacific Highway
Medford, Oregon 97504
☎ 503/734-2016

FAX 503/734-2017
Hours Mon-Sat 9-5:30
Accessible Yes
Mail Order
Catalog Free

"Noah" and Peggie von Brandt hand-craft traditional willow furnishings – romantic love seats and rounded-back armchairs, a delightful chaise lounge, several sizes of tables, plus an array of baskets and planters. They're willing to custom-make whatever your heart desires.

Sarita Furniture Ltd.

2365 Old Nanaimo Highway
Port Alberni, British Columbia
V9Y 7M1
☎ 604/723-1879

Hours Mon-Fri 8-4
Accessible No
Mail Order
Catalog $2
Mailing address Box 1269
Port Alberni, British Columbia
V9Y 7M1
FAX 604/723-1967

"Sarita Furniture attracts people who love wood, beauty, comfort, quality and outdoor living spaces," say owners Keith and Bernadette Wyton. "The furniture is crafted from Western red cedar, our local natural renewable resource that happens to be one of the finest woods in the world for outdoor use." Sold both by mail order and through fine garden centres in British Columbia and at City People's Garden Store in Seattle, Sarita furniture features classical designs with elegantly finishes. The catalog shows three bench and armchair styles, with benches available in several widths. It offers a choice of three dining tables, dining chairs, occasional tables, an adjustable lounge chair and a porch swing.

Sunrise Woodworks manufactures furniture that comes apart for winter storage and needs little storage space. The chairs fold, and the tables are designed with modular sections that allow you to change the shape and size within seconds. Fabricated of Western red or Alaska yellow cedar, the pieces are available unfinished or with custom finishes. They make a selection of planter boxes, custom-made patio railings and deck panels. Their portable *Pendalex*™ umbrella can be fitted with mosquito netting for camping, picnics or sleep-outs or as hot tub enclosures. The products are marked down in the fall.

Sunrise Woodworks Canada Corporation

#6A-3095 McCallum Road
Abbotsford, British Columbia V2S 4N3
☎ *604/850-3711*

FAX 604/850-3711
Hours *Mon-Fri 8:30-5, Sat 10-3,*
Sun by appointment
Accessible *yes*
Mail Order
Catalog *Free*

Jandon's basic porch swings, benches and gliders are elegantly simple and made to last. They've added a line of Victorian-style benches, swings and tables and handsome cedar arbors reminiscent of days gone by. The furniture is custom-constructed of clear woods (mahogany, redwood, cedar or painted fir) and available in a variety of sizes. The also offer striped or solid cushions and colorful outdoor swing covers.

Swings by Jandon

18595 N.W. North Star Drive
Banks, Oregon 97106
☎ *503/324-7154*

Hours *Mon-Sat 8-7*
Accessible *Yes*
Mail Order
Catalog *Free*

Mr. Clement makes highly refined benches, chairs, coffee tables, round dining tables and matching chairs. An expert woodworker, he crafts each piece of red cedar, employing mortise and tenon joinery and waterproof glue, then finishes it with two coats of oil. His signature is a decorative palmate leaf etched into wood. He ships the products throughout Canada and into the United States.

Timothy Clement

RR #2 S-38 C-17
Gibbons, British Columbia V0N 1V0
☎ *604/886-8218*

Hours *Mon-Fri 8-5*
Accessible *No*
Mail Order
Catalog *Free*

Union Design

P.O. Box 7032
Seattle, Washington 98107
☎ 206/545-9500

Hours By appointment
Mail Order
Catalog Free

The rolling countryside of Luberon, France inspired this collection's graceful sweeping curves. Union Design's hand-crafted settees, chaise lounges, armchairs, barstools and tables are painstakingly constructed out of Honduran mahogany. Each piece in this "gourmet" line makes a strong architectural statement. "We carefully match pieces in a set in order to compensate for natural color variations. All are assembled with mortise and tenon joinery," says George Rodzon. "Union Design brings to wood furniture an extensive knowledge of precision wood finishing and craftsmanship derived from our expertise in constructing the finest yacht interiors."

Washington Chair Co.

1885 North Zylstra Road
Oak Harbor, Washington 98277
☎ 206/675-2691 or 1-800/648-7405

Hours By appointment only
Accessible Difficult
Mail Order
Catalog Free

"We are a family-operated business doing what we love, loving what we do and delivering more than we promise," says Pacia Dixon. She and her husband Craig left successful careers in Bellevue and moved to a 1913 farmhouse on Whidbey Island where they now make heirloom-quality garden furnishings. They are devoted to traditional design and construction methods. Their Seaside Rockers and Gardener's Entry Bench (a little green-painted tool cache) are in high demand. They've a number of new pieces in production, including potting benches, sling chairs and barbecue accessory stands. The porch furniture has become as popular for use in kitchens and family rooms as for outdoor applications. To reach the workshop, take the Whidbey Island ferry and follow Highway 20 approximately thirty miles. Once you're past the Fort Ebey State Park exit, turn left on Zylstra Road and go another three and a half miles. Look for a sign on the left just north of "Cozy Place."

Bob and Betsey Searing design and build durable tables, chairs, benches, gliders, porch swings, tea carts and hammock stands. Each item is hand-fabricated from select red cedar or other native woods, and the pieces come fully assembled. "We can beat chain-store prices because we market directly to the public. We fully guarantee our products and solicit suggestions from our customers," say the Searings. The couple maintains a private showroom near Sea-Tac airport. Call for an appointment.

Yard Leisure
18032 2nd Place S.
Seattle, Washington 98148
☎ *206/242-9598*

Hours By appointment only
Accessible *Yes*
Catalog *Free flyer*

Retail Sources for Outdoor Furniture
Washington

Seattle Metropolitan Area

Tropitone, Brown Jordan, Homecrest and Woodard are a few of the furniture manufacturers you'll discover at this big outdoor living store. The company also carries *Telescope* director's chairs and *Grosfillex* resin furniture and planters. For shade-lovers there are umbrellas by *Parasol* and *California Umbrella*. They're stocking new lines of wood furniture and hammocks in '94. They've got barbecue grills, table accessories, windsocks and even toys and games for pools.

Al's Easy Livin'

1900 132nd Ave N.E.
Bellevue, Washington 98005
☎ *206/746-8004 or 622-7221 from Seattle*

FAX *206/747-5952*
Hours *Mon-Fri 9-6, Sat 10-6, Sun 12-5 (summer); Mon-Fri 9-5, Sat 10-5 (winter)*
Accessible *Yes*

Since 1948, this company has been known for casual wood furniture. They have lots of rustic wood benches, several more-ornate wood and iron benches, picnic tables, porch swings, Adirondack chairs, benches and side tables. Their lines are very reasonably priced. They ship to customers and maintain a mailing list for special sales.

Don Willis Furniture

10516 Lake City Way N.E.
Seattle, Washington 98125
☎ *206/524-9944*

Hours *Mon-Fri 9:30-8, Sat 9:30-6, Sun 12-5*
Accessible *Yes*
Mail Order
Catalog *Free*
FAX *206/524-0220*

Elco Fireplace & Patio

16151 Cleveland Street
Redmond, Washington 98052
☎ 206/881-8868

FAX 206/883-3815
Hours Mon-Fri 8-6, Sat 9-5
Accessible Yes
Mail Order
Catalog $2.50

Elco can custom-order a medium-priced line of aluminum furniture in your choice of 8 styles, 30 strap colors and 60 cushion fabrics, with delivery in three weeks. They also represent *Hatteras* hammocks, rope mesh tree and porch swings. Elco stocks a good selection of fire pits and barbecues, both free-standing and built-in models.

Garden Companions

23808 Bothell Highway S.E.
Bothell, Washington 98021
☎ 206/486-2530

Garden Companions offers the full line of *Kingsley-Bate* teak and a bright new line of metal garden furniture. See complete listing on page 313.

Garden Works

10632 N.E. 9th Street
Bellevue, Washington 98004
☎ 206/455-0568

In addition to this company's charming garden accessories, you'll find a nice selection of furniture made by local artisans. The company also carries hand-wrought iron garden furniture by *McKinnon and Harris*, which is inspired by early nineteen-century chinoiserie and Chippendale designs. See complete listing on page 313.

J.F. Henry

4540 California Avenue S.W.
Seattle, Washington 98116
☎ 206/935-5150

Hours Mon-Sat 9-6;
open until 8 p.m. on Fridays
Accessible Yes

This home accessory store features garden furnishings from March through August. They display a fine selection of wrought iron furniture from *Lyon-Shaw* year around and offer other manufacturer's lines ranging from complete patio sets to little cafe sets suitable for city balconies. The garden shop carries wind chimes and bells, garden animals, outdoor dining accessories, bird houses and feeders and lots more! Sometimes you'll find select garden merchandise included in the storewide July clearance.

Price-Ragen is one of those fabulous finds that, until recently, was available only to the design trade. Happily, they've expanded into retail sales and opened a large showroom in a big old building at Belmont and Pike, as well as an Eastside location. Price-Ragen stocks top-of-the-line garden furniture from *Lister, Summit* and *Triconfort* and *Santa Barbara* umbrellas. The garden furnishings are displayed with huge tropical plants and elegant accessories. Out back they offer a fine selection of landscape plants. "If it grows, we can get it," says Elizabeth Price. The showroom in Kirkland is smaller, but it too offers an array of gorgeous furniture and decorative accessories.

DESTINATION ☆
Price-Ragen Co.

*517 E. Pike
Seattle, Washington 98122*
☎ *206/329-8155*

*2245 Carillon Point
Kirkland, Washington 98033*
☎ *206/828-6393*

Hours *Mon-Sat 9-6; call for extended holiday and summer hours*
Accessible *Yes*
FAX *206/323-6440*

Weatherproof furniture is not what this company's name suggests, but several of the lines they carry are made to grace the garden. They stock *Lloyd/Flanders* all-weather wicker (made of resin) and metal furniture by *Tropitone, Brown Jordan, O.W. Lee, Lyon-Shaw* and *Woodard.* They also have Grosfillex and Allibert resin furniture, *Parasol* umbrellas, market umbrellas, and *Dayva* covers. And, they will ship to customers anywhere in the region.

Rattan Interiors

*1024 116th Avenue N.E.
Bellevue, Washington 98004*
☎ *206/455-1500*

*1191 Andover Park West
Seattle, Washington 98188*
☎ *206/575-2201*

Hours *10-6 Mon Sat 12-5 Sun*
Accessible *Yes*
Mail Order
Catalog *Manufacturer's brochures available*
FAX *206 575-0604*

In summer, three-fourths of the stock in this 15,000-sq.-ft. store is devoted to garden furnishings. They carry *Lloyd/Flanders, Tropitone, Woodard, Homecrest, Meadowcraft, Alu-mont, Samsonite, Lane/Venture, Allibert* and *Kettler.* They've a good selection of local wood furniture, plus *Finkel* cushions, *California Sunbrella, Hatteras* hammocks. You'll also find barbecue grills, garden ornaments, including *Henri Studio* stone furniture and fountains, and table accessories of all kinds.

Rich's Stoves, Spas and Patio

*16809 Highway 99
Lynnwood, Washington 98037*
☎ *206/623-2228*

Hours *Mon Fri Mon & Fri 10 8, Tues-Thurs 10-6, Sat 10-6, Sun 12-5*
Accessible *Yes*
Catalog *Manufacturer's brochures available*

Northwest Washington

The Greenhouse

1235 Cornwall Avenue
Bellingham, Washington 98225
☎ 206/676-1161 or 1-800/446-0104

Hours Mon-Thur 10-6, Fri 10-8, Sat 10-6,
Sun 11-5
Accessible Yes
Mail Order
Catalog Manufacturer's
brochures available

With a 12,000-square-foot display space full of home furnishings, the Greenhouse devotes half of the space to "summer furniture" – American-made solid wood *Telescope* director's chairs, medium-priced wood garden benches, *Lyon-Shaw* wrought iron, *Emu* wire furniture from Italy. They have pots, market umbrellas and garden gifts.

South Sound

Rattan Interiors

4027 Tacoma Mall Boulevard
Tacoma, Washington 98409
☎ 206/475-4950

See listing on page 293.

Eastern Washington

F.O. Berg/ Spokane Tent & Awning

East 410 Trent
Spokane, Washington 99202
☎ 509/624-8921

Hours Mon-Fri 8:30-5; Sat 10-5;
closed Sat in winter
Accessible Yes
Catalog Manufacturer's brochures
available
FAX 509/624-9780

Lloyd/Flanders, Tropitone, Telescope, Kettler, Homecrest, Alu-mont and *O.W Lee* are the big lines in a big showroom full of garden furnishings. They have umbrellas and cushions, windsocks, wind chimes and tableware too.

Pallis's furniture includes *Lloyd/Flanders* all-weather wicker, *Lyon-Shaw* wrought iron and *Samsonite* steel. They normally have select pieces of wood furniture and *Telescope* directors chairs and folding tables, as well. They've several lines of garden accessories, including *Austin* sculpture, bird feeders, wind chimes and specialty gift items. Above-ground pools are also a specialty here.

Pallis Pool & Patio

201 North Fruitland
Kennewick, Washington 99336
☎ *509/586-9108*

Hours *Mon-Fri 9-6, Sat 10-4; open Sun 12-3 (April through Oct)*
Accessible *Yes*
FAX *509/586-2836*

Central Washington

Spas and pool supplies are the main order of business here, but you'll also find complete lines of *Tropitone* aluminum and *Meadowcraft* wrought iron furniture, plus lots of patio accessories.

Central Washington Water

514 S. Wenatchee
Wenatchee, Washington 98801
☎ *509/663-1177*

Hours *Mon-Fri 9-5:30, Sat 9-3*
Accessible *Yes*

Southwestern Washington

Half this furniture store's 40,000-square-feet of floor space is devoted to outdoor furniture. You'll find many of the top lines in metal here – *Brown Jordan*, *Tropitone*, *Pacific Sun*, *Woodard*, *Lyon-Shaw* and *Winston*. They also carry *Kingsley-Bate* teak and *Mallin and Grosfillex* resin. To enhance the patio department, Sparks carries lots of garden ornaments, containers and fountains, as well. Watch for their annual Clearance Sale during the first two weeks in August.

Sparks Home Furnishings

1001 Broadway
Vancouver, Washington 98660
☎ *206/694-2571*

Hours *Mon-Fri 10-6, Sat 10-5, Sun 12-5*
Accessible *Yes*
Mailing address *P.O. Box 210*
Vancouver, Washington 98666

Oregon

Portland Metropolitan Area

☆DESTINATION
Fishel's

5 S.E. MLK, Jr. Boulevard
Portland, Oregon 97214
☎ *503/235-8941*

Hours *Mon-Fri 9-6, Sat 10-6, Sun 12-5*
Accessible *Yes*
FAX *503/235-8945*

Seventy-four years in business, Fishel's is an important name in garden furniture in the Northwest. Four floors of furnishings await the discerning shopper here! Selections in teak include *Jensen Jarrah, Lister* and *Barlow Tyrie,* and there are painted white wood pieces by *Summer Classics.* Smithsonian and Winterthur antique reproduction furniture and accessories from *Garden Source* add other traditionally styled choices. Among the metal lines, you'll find *Tropitone, Lyon-Shaw, Brown Jordan, Homecrest, Woodard, Winston* and *O.W. Lee.* In resins, Fishel's carries *Lloyd/Flanders* all-weather wicker, *Grosfillex* and *Allibert.* They have *California Umbrella* and *Basta Sole* umbrellas, too. The store is replete with displays that show how to furnish a welcoming "outdoor room."

Ludeman's, Inc.
12675 S.W. Beaverdam Road
Beaverton, Oregon 97005
☎ *503/646-6409*

FAX *503/646-8034*
Hours *Mon-Sat 9-6, Sun 12-5*
Accessible *No*

Ludeman's terrific furniture selection includes *Salterini* and *O.W. Lee* wrought iron; *Brown Jordan, Woodard, Homecrest* and *Alu-mont* aluminum; *Allibert, Grosfillex* and *Kettler* resin, plus lots of tables and benches in teak. They've got umbrellas, both metal and wood-framed and planters aplenty. Watch for their annual Anniversary Sale early August.

Oregon Garden Store
333 S. State Street
Lake Oswego, Oregon 97034
☎ *503/697-3635*

Oregon Garden Store carries English teak benches, redwood gliders, wrought iron patio sets, mahogany Adirondack chairs and porch swings. While you won't find big volume in this small shop, they can order from a number of sources. See complete listing on page 317.

The garden furniture in this boutique is especially select. Owner Ron Colvin picks the best from several manufacturers around the world, including *Kingsley-Bate* carved benches from Java, classic contemporary benches by *Summit* and graceful wrought iron pieces hand-crafted in Mexico and the Philippines. See complete listing on page 328.

Wildwood Garden Furnishings

7435 S.W. Capitol Highway
Portland, Oregon 97219
☎ *503/452-0301*

Willamette Valley

Spas and above-ground pools are the primary products here. Each spring the company orders-in several rail cars full of garden furniture – *Lloyd/Flanders* all-weather wicker, *Telescope* director's chairs, *Woodard*, *Alu-mont* and *Homecrest* aluminum. What they don't have in their large stock, they'll special order. If you're looking for bargains, watch for their clearance sale in fall.

Emerald Pool & Patio

1885 Highway 99 North
Eugene, Oregon 97402
☎ *503/688-1254*

2520 Silverton Road N.E.
Salem, Oregon 97303
☎ *503/370-9355*

Hours *Mon-Sat 9-5:30*
Accessible *Yes*
FAX *503/688-4572*

Southern Oregon

Tropitone and *Homecrest* aluminum furniture and *Lloyd/Flanders* all-weather wicker provide cheery choices in moderately priced furniture for dining and sitting outdoors beside the company's spas.

Pool & Patio Place

2728 Jacksonville Highway
Medford, Oregon 97501
☎ *503/773-6227*

Hours *Tues-Fri 9-5, Sat 9-3*
Accessible *Yes*

Eastern Oregon

Sunbrella, Brown Jordan, Homecrest and *Tropitone* are the main lines here. Look for big mark-downs from late summer through September.

Fireside Spa and Patio

424 N.E. 3rd
Bend, Oregon 97701
☎ *503/382-2597*

Hours *Mon-Fri 8-5, Sat 10-4*
Accessible *Yes*
FAX *503/382-3017*

The Lift

255 Century Drive
Bend, Oregon 97702
☎ 503/388-0022

Hours Daily 9-6 (April through Oct)
Accessible Yes

In summer you'll find *Brown Jordan, Lloyd/Flanders, Woodard, O.W. Lee, Alu-mont* and *Mallin* furniture, plus umbrellas and tableware. In winter, the focus shifts from the garden to the ski slope.

Idaho

Greenhurst Nursery & Garden Center

3209 S. Happy Valley Road
Nampa, Idaho 83686
☎ 208/466-5783

Mallin and *Lloyd/Flanders* are the casual lines you'll find at Greenhurst, while the benches, tables and chairs from *Windsor* and *Cane & Reed* (both high-quality manufacturers of wood furniture) fit a more formal garden. See complete listing on page 383.

Michael's Furniture Showplace

623 Americana Boulevard
Boise, Idaho 83702
☎ 208/344-8425

Hours Mon-Fri 10-9, Sat 10-6, Sun 12-5
Accessible Yes

At Michael's, the Patio Shop is open year-around, featuring garden furnishings by *Winston, Allibert* and *Lloyd/Flanders*.

British Columbia

Vancouver Metropolitan Area

All Seasons Pool & Patio

1-2900 Smith Street
Richmond, British Columbia V6X 2Z6
☎ 604/270-7803

Hours Mon-Fri 10-6, Sat 9:30-5 (year around); Sun 12-4 (May through August),
Accessible Yes

Tropitone, Meadowcraft and *Homecrest* aluminum, *Allibert* resins and *Telescope* folding furniture are the primary lines here. Owner Liska Miller always looks for new ideas in garden furnishings and tries to keep the store stocked with colorful choices for outdoor living.

The Avant Gardener

1460 Marine Drive
West Vancouver, British Columbia V7T 1B7
☎ 604/926-8784

The Avant Gardener carries teak, cedar and aluminum furniture, and their English trellis work may be just the ticket for completing a cozy sitting area. See listing on page 319.

"We specialize in only the finest quality outdoor furniture in aluminum, wrought iron and wood," says Janet O'Callagan. *Brown Jordan, Tropitone, Grosfillex* and *Woodard* are the store's premier manufactured lines. The store carries an extensive collection of gifts and accessories, and at Christmas it becomes a holiday boutique. Garden furniture is marked-down in April and August.

Courtyards Casual Furniture

2082 West 41st Avenue
Vancouver, British Columbia V6M 1Y8
☎ *604/261-4116*

Hours *Mon-Sat 9:30-5:30*
Accessible *Yes*

Elegant garden accessories are what you see first, but tucked in amongst the collectibles are top-of-the line benches and other select pieces of garden furniture. See complete listing on page 325.

Hobbs

2129 W. 41st Avenue
Vancouver, British Columbia V6M 1Z6
☎ *604/261-5998*

This lively 10,000-square-foot showroom is filled with casual furniture and handsome accessories. *Brown Jordan, Lyon-Shaw, Tropitone, Meadowcraft, Homecrest* and *O.W. Lee* are the big names in metal furniture here. They also carry *Kingsley-Bate* wood furniture, *Allibert* resin and *Basta Sole* market umbrellas. Home and Patio Gallery ships merchandise throughout British Columbia; in fact they've even supplied customers in Saudi Arabia!

Home and Patio Gallery

3430 Brighton Avenue, Suite 203A
Burnaby, British Columbia V5A 3H4
☎ *604/421-1688*

Hours *Mon-Fri 10-6, Sat 9:30-5:50,*
Sun 12-5
Accessible *Yes*
Mail Order
Catalog *Free*

Vancouver Island

Don't overlook this shop if you're looking for lovely garden benches. See complete listing on page 320.

Dig This

45 Bastion Square
Victoria, British Columbia V8W 1J1
☎ *604/385-3212*

Patio and Company

475 Gorge Road East
Victoria, British Columbia V8T 2W1
☎ 604/383-4511

Hours Mon-Fri 9-5:30, Sat 9-5;
open Sun 12-5 (May- Sept)
Accessible Yes
Mail Order
Catalog Manufacturer's brochures
available

You'll find two floors of rattan, wicker and wrought iron patio furniture in this spacious outdoor living store. *Tropitone* and *Mallin* aluminum, *Homecrest*, *Meadowcraft* and *O.W. Lee* wrought iron and *Lloyd/Flanders* all-weather wicker provide a wide range of choices for relaxing and dining. They've a nice selection of outdoor tableware, too.

The Okanagan

26th Street Kitchen & Bath, Ltd.

5201 26th Street
Vernon, British Columbia V1T 8G4
☎ 604/542-3399

FAX 604/542-3375
Hours Mon-Sat 8:30-5
Accessible Yes

In business for twenty-three years, two generations of the same family maintain a relaxing ambiance and well coordinated ideas for outdoor living here. They have spas, gazebos, shoji privacy huts, as well as patio furniture from mid-range to high-end lines. The outdoor furniture goes on sale at half-price in August.

Chapter Eleven

Garden Accessories

*"The Devil whispered behind the leaves,
'It's pretty, but is it Art?'"*
.....Rudyard Kipling

The Finishing Touch

Exteriors are as thoughtfully accessorized as home interiors these days. Envision a rear garden or entry court as an outdoor room. A large piece of sculpture might be used to punctuate the space and draw the eye, just as a fireplace compels attention in the living room. A water garden could fulfill the same purpose as a landscape

painting hanging on the wall. Billowy hanging baskets or handsome urns holding topiary trees might "finish" the space in the same way that lamps and objets d'art enliven and complete the room.

Design Tips

It's important to understand that exterior spaces are larger in scale than interior rooms. Even if an enclosed courtyard is the same size as an adjacent living room, the open sky makes the outdoor space seem larger. A small piece of art can easily become lost. To make a strong impact, garden accessories generally must be more massive than interior furnishings.

Keep in mind the viewpoint from which a piece of garden art will be seen. Consider not only its size, but also its shape. Remember that works of garden art don't exist in isolation, but rather they compete with other elements in the landscape and with one another. We've all giggled over front yards packed with pink flamingos, gnomes and whirly-gigs. If these pieces bring pleasure to the owners, who am I to cast stones? I have a friend (a fellow landscape architect) who owns a flock of plastic flamingos purchased when Woolworth's went out of business. All fifty of the birds alight for party occasions, and they are a hoot! However, I would generally suggest restraint and caution gardeners against cluttering the landscape with too many decorative objects in view from one spot.

A recirculating fountain might serve as kinetic sculpture, with water tumbling down a multi-level rock waterfall, bubbling up from a pool like an underground spring or pouring out of a piece of classical statuary. A delicate wall fountain, ceramic bowl filled with water lilies or a Japanese basin could be used to set the motif in a small garden. A plaque, clock or window box might brighten a bare wall. Whimsical pieces, like a garden sign or concrete bunny peering out of a planting bed, add elements of surprise. A birdhouse or wind chime attract the eye upward, while a sundial or birdbath could be used to focus attention on the center of a formal garden.

☞ **Money-saving Tip: If you cannot afford "important" garden art, one handsome potted tree or a grouping of plants in containers can function as sculpture.**

A few strategically placed pots might be used to separate a seating area from the dining area or to divide an overly large planting area. In working out an arrangement of plants, remember that the plants will show to best advantage if they are played against a wall. When the grouping is played against foliage, the pots will predominate.

You'll find handsome terra cotta pots in every imaginable shape and size and a wide array of wood, stone, concrete and glazed ceramic containers available from Northwest manufacturers and garden stores. The only word of caution I would interject here is to be sure that any clay container you buy is fired for outdoor use. Some of my favorite containers are glazed ceramics, which tend to deteriorate with cycles of freezing and thawing. I use these pots for the tropical plants I keep on the terrace in summer and move indoors for the winter.

Just as the Northwest is rich in plant materials, the selections in garden decorations are wondrous. Regional artisans and craftspeople are making fabulous pots, planters and window boxes, birdhouses and banners, wind chimes and bells, topiary and fountains. (For additional fountain sources, see Water Gardening, beginning on page 233.) There are fabulous garden emporiums and import shops that have quite literally brought the world to our doorsteps. And, the work of some of our local sculptors is finding acceptance in the best gardens in Europe and Asia. In this chapter you'll discover sources as varied and interesting as those from which you've found your home's interior furnishings. Don't just look within your own state or province; many of the companies ship their wares. 🦌

Northwest Manufacturers & Importers
Washington

Aw Pottery
21031 76th Avenue W.
Edmonds, Washington 98026
☎ *206/778-1227*

Hours Wed-Sat 10-5 (Feb through Sept);
by appointment (Oct through Jan)
Accessible Yes

This is quite a find! Until recently, the company served only the wholesale market. The owner, Lee Lang Aw, wrote to me saying, "The Aw family has been making pottery in China for generations and, since the 1940s, at our studios in Malaysia. We have retained our family and guild ties in China, where potters fire their wares in the kilns they have used for centuries. Every year we go deep into the provinces to find the unique products of each region. From some villages we buy fine hand-painted ceramics, from others we buy containers so rustic they appear to have been dug out of China's earth." You'll find containers, urns and tubs in a variety of shapes ranging from bonsai pots to giant fish ponds. Most are high-fired stoneware well-suited to Northwest gardens. "We welcome gardeners, designers, browsers and bargain hunters to our pottery gardens. Thanks to intensive customs searches, we have lots of seconds."

Bruning Pottery

2908 Sixth Avenue S.
Seattle, Washington 98134
☎ 206/623-2627

Hours Mon-Fri 9-5, Sat 10:30-4
Accessible Yes
Mail Order
Catalog Free

Larry and Judy Bruning manufacture handsome high-fired ceramic planters, pots and vases, ranging from three to fourteen-inches in width. Larry formulates his own glazes in a wide palette of colors. In addition to standard shapes, they've a wonderful selection of bonsai containers, ikebana trays and bulb bowls. Vases range from four-inches in height up to three-foot-tall floor vases. All are suitable for outdoor use. You'll find reduced prices on "seconds" at the studio.

Coppersmiths

P. O. Box 23416
Federal Way, Washington 98093
☎ 206/874-9373

Hours By appointment only
Mail Order
Catalog Free

"I am proud to be a coppersmith," says Kimball Smith, who became interested in window boxes in Europe. His beautifully shaped boxes come in lengths from 24 to 48-inches, designed to fit American-style windows. One of the few remaining smiths in America, he works in solid copper and makes his own tools and jigs. "I limit my labors to hand tools, mostly crafted from oak," he notes. "Copper will last lifetimes, so these window boxes can be handed down as heirlooms." The business is primarily mail-order, but you can set up a special appointment if you want to visit the workshop.

D.E. Dodroe & Co.

3224 S. Hudson
Seattle, Washington 98118
☎ 206/422-6481 or 1-800/929-1625

Hours Fri 9-5
Accessible No
Mail Order
Catalog Free

This busy workshop is not geared for walk-in trade. Most of their ornaments, fountains and paving accents are sold wholesale. However, the company is open to the public on Fridays. "All our pieces are created locally as original Northwest garden art," says Don Dodroe. "Inspiration comes from nature and classical art, with a dose of whimsy and a belief that the garden should be a place for interesting surprises. Our finishes resemble terra cotta, verdigris copper, lead, stone or aged bronze, so people are always astonished when we explain that each piece is cast and hand-finished in high-strength concrete. We are especially proud of the quality and detail in our work and how much fun people have with it."

In addition to the birdbaths, fountains, benches and planters one would expect to find at a place that casts concrete garden ornaments, Marco Luciano makes pedestals, stepping stones and other custom-designed architectural elements, such as pool surrounds. The quality of the product here is very good, and the staff is willing to spend time helping you achieve the look you want. If it can be made of concrete, this company will attempt to find or fabricate it.

Luciano Arts

4268 Aurora N.
Seattle, Washington 98103
☎ *206/634-2787*

FAX 634-3335
Hours *Mon-Sat 11-5*
Accessible *Yes*

Owner Maxine Means started this business with her late husband in 1950. "We stress quality of the workmanship," she says, noting that many of the statues and fountains, planters and benches were designed by her husband and that her company has the only molds for these pieces. "We have a working knowledge of landscaping, so we make a special effort to get the right item for our customer." The showroom is located in the Beach Basket Garden Center.

Means Ornamental Concrete

4121 Harborview Drive
Gig Harbor, Washington 98335
☎ *206/858-9291*

Hours *Mon-Sat 10-5, Sun 11-5*
Accessible *Yes*

MN's primary business is garden apparel (see complete listing as Kneezers, page 105), but they've introduced a new line of hand-crafted cedar planters, bench seats and window boxes, all reasonably priced and available through mail order. The company will take custom orders for planters up to eight-feet long.

MN Productions

P.O. Box 577
Freeland, Washington 98249
☎ *206/221-7995*

Nichols Bros. Stoneworks offers handsome English-design containers, urns, vases and pedestals made of reconstituted sandstone. They also make a line of whimsical little ornaments inspired by popular English designs – pigs, hedgehogs, rabbits, cats and toads cast in concrete with antiqued finishes. And, they fabricate pineapple and artichoke finials, which are hard to find and perfect for flanking a garden gate.

Nichols Bros. Stoneworks

20209 Broadway
Snohomish (Maltby), Washington 98290
☎ *206/668-5434*

Hours *Mon-Fri 8-5*
Accessible *Yes*
Mail Order
Catalog *Free*
FAX 206/483-5721

-continued on next page

Nichols Bros. Stoneworks

-continued

The pieces are in demand from landscape designers and fine garden shops throughout North America, but what many people don't know is that they'll ship to individual homeowners, as well. If you visit the factory, you may find finish-flawed pieces available at a discount.

Oriental Furniture Warehouse

1111 Elliott Avenue W.
Seattle, Washington 98119
☎ *206/286-3139*

Hours *Tues-Sat 10:30-5, Sun 12-4*
Accessible *Yes*

This shop buys Thai pots and Kmer vases, Chinese fish pots, garden seats and planters by the container-load. There's always a nice selection in the store, and you can get on the mailing list to receive notice of sales and new shipments.

Original Moss Animals

19401 94th Street E.
Bonney Lake, Washington 98390
☎ *206/845-3134*

Hours *Wed-Sat 10-6, Sun 9-3*
Accessible *Difficult on gravel pathways*

"Moss animals are conversation-pieces in any garden!" says owner Betty DuMont. "Our product is made of a steel-structured frame that's treated against rust. It's completely stuffed with moss and soil, then covered with a coat of moss with the roots to the inside so it continues to grow. Monofilament holds the topiary form in shape until the moss starts growing. You can plant any kind of low ground covers or ferns on them. They won't crush if children sit on them or they are treated roughly. We can custom make anything you want, planted or unplanted. Any size. We offer repairs and instructions for care." The business is located in a house at the end of the road off Highway. 410 (Sumner-Buckley Highway). Call for directions if you don't have a Pierce County map.

These stackable, interlocking planter systems are hand-crafted in "Ballard, U.S.A.," Seattle's Scandinavian neighborhood. Patio Patch planters are made of Western red cedar, They come fully assembled. Available with casters for ease-of-moving, they're ideal for small-space flower gardening and great for topiaries, herbs, vegetables and living Christmas trees. The planters can be ordered with attached trellises for vines or espaliers. The company sells by mail-order only (you can call any time of the day to leave a message), and it offers a five-year warranty on workmanship.

Patio Patch Planters

P.O. Box 70281
Seattle, Washington 98107
☎ *206/789-4937*

Mail Order
Catalog *$2 refundable with order*
FAX *206/789-4937*

"If you like birds and fish, my ceramic garden ornaments will turn your head," says Patricia Moodie. She makes a throughly weatherproof birdfeeder that looks like a tall Victorian house and another that resembles a lighthouse. She also crafts life-like ceramic koi for ponds, fountains or birdbaths. She'll copy the colorations and markings of your favorite fish. Her stoneware waterfall/planters recreate the effect of a stream in the forest – in miniature – a pleasant touch for a city balcony or an entranceway. The sizes, shapes and colors are your choice.

Patricia Moodie

W. 1725 9th #2
Spokane, Washington 99204
☎ *509/624-7952*

Hours *Daily 9-5*
Accessible *No*
Mail Order
Catalog *$3*

Max Braverman makes one-of-a-kind bonsai containers from chocolate-colored stoneware clays. They are shaped on a potter's wheel, then formed into ovals and rectangles. "The forms," he says, "range from delicate to ponderous. All are appropriate for bonsai." He makes his own glazes. Some, such as the Jun blue glaze, have been known since the Song Dynasty and others are his own formulas. Also see listing for Pine Garden Bonsai on page 257.

Pine Garden Pottery

20331 SR 530 N.E.
Arlington (Oso), Washington 98223
☎ *206/435-5995*

Hours *By appointment*
Accessible *No*
Mail Order
Catalog *$2*
FAX *206/435-5995*

Rail-Rider Products

13558 Sunrise Drive N.E.
Bainbridge Island, Washington 98110
☎ *206/842-9827*

Mail Order
Catalog *Free*

Here's an idea that blends the Old World charm of window boxes with the needs of a modern home. This company's hand-crafted solid cedar planters are available with brackets that allow you to hang them from most porch and deck railings. Or, if you want to set the planters directly on the deck, you can order containers with feet that protect the wood. These reasonably priced eight inch-high planting boxes are available in lengths from 24" to 36". Owner Jeannine Mitchell says, "The selection of cedar is strictly supervised; the boxes are assembled with oxidized screws and the brackets are made of galvanized steel." They are available by mail-order, or you can call the workshop between the hours of 9 and 5.

Oregon

Bald Peak Woodworks

24485 S.W. Scholls Ferry Road
[ma] 35566 S.W. Bald Peak Road
Hillsboro, Oregon 97123
☎ *503/628-0894*

Bald Peak makes lovely cedar window boxes, hanging planters and patio containers as well as the furniture listed in the previous chapter. See page 286.

Sally McCready and Mary Vranizan make colorful appliquéd banners for celebrating holidays, announcing party occasions or simply brightening up your garden. They've created several designs for every major event in the year, including padded birthday cakes, valentine hearts, stars and stripes, halloween witches, harvest motifs, an assortment of Santas and a Christmas angel. Another greets guests with the word 'Welcome' and a cheery basket of flowers. University mascots and sports themes are perennially popular. Not only do these talented women catalog sixty-five different symbols, they'll custom-make anything you want. They've encircled monograms with ivy, portrayed a family's beloved beagle and replicated family crests by the dozens. One customer has a collection of some thirty-five different banners that flutter in the landscape throughout the year. The all-weather nylon banners come with a pole, and the company sells adjustable mounting brackets. Standard size is three by five, but they've made thirty-foot-long pennants, as well. You are welcome to visit the workshop by appointment.

Banner Days
Portland, Oregon
☎ 503/292-2298

Hours By appointment only
Mail Order
Catalog Free
Mailing address 7276 S.W. Beaverton-Hillsdale Highway
Portland, Oregon 97225

"Just like people, birds know what they want in a house," says Richard Clarke, who has been making cedar birdhouses and feeders for twenty years. His birdhouses are all handmade, and he builds to suit "every backyard bird and every backyard bird lover." He offers a Wood Duck House, Robin Shelf and many other elegant homes for all kinds of feathered friends. These specially designed little abodes and his exquisite Zen Temple Feeder are available at Portland Nursery and through mail order.

The Bird House
P.O. Box 722
Estacada, Oregon 97023
☎ 503/227-3232

Mail Order
Catalog $1

Carillon Wind Chimes

42425 N.W. Banks Road
Banks, Oregon 97106
☎ *503/324-9460*

Hours *Mon-Fri 9-5, Sat 10-4*
Accessible *No*
Mail Order
Catalog *Free*
FAX *503/324-5813*

This Northwest factory has received national attention. Carillon's electronically tuned wind chimes lend melodic grace to gardens across North America, but there is a wider range of garden ornaments here than the name implies. The company's eight-page color catalog also features hand-painted bells, birdhouses and decorative garden wall plaques designed by Vashon Island sculptor Laura De Groot. The products range in styling from classical to contemporary, and they are offered in several choices of details and finishes. Smart shoppers who stop by the factory in Banks (30 miles west of Portland), take advantage of the factory store's discounted prices (well below retail) and occasionally find very favorably priced "seconds."

Riehl Industries

16076 S.E. Evelyn Street
Clackamus, Oregon 97015
☎ *503/655-7632*

Hours *Mon-Fri 7:30-4*
Accessible *Yes*
Catalog *Free price list and pictures available*
FAX *503/655-7639*

Keith Riehl takes pride in fine metal work. His company makes a line of silhouettes for garden sculpture, creates copper weather vanes and does custom iron work for fences and gates. The team can fabricate in steel, copper, brass or aluminum any item that landscape designers or homeowners might desire. Patterns are made by a computerized machine that uses blasts of hot air to cut intricate designs (even entire scenes) from pieces of sheet metal. Rhiel uses acid for a weathered rust finish, so the items require no maintenance.

Shibumi's catalog features a wide range of Asian garden ornaments, including iron and hand-carved stone lanterns. Their Zenigata granite basin, which is based on the shape of a Chinese coin, features four characters that read, "I learn only to be contented." Their antique hibachis make elegant planters and hand-chiseled granite stepping stones create an inviting path through a moss garden. The bamboo water hammers were designed by ancient garden masters to scare away the deer as the hammer pours water into a pond and slaps back to a resting position. Ask to be added to the company's mailing list to receive periodic sale brochures.

Shibumi Trading Ltd.

P.O.Box 1-F
Eugene, Oregon 97440
☎ 503/744-1832 or 1-800/843-2565

Hours Mon-Fri 8-3:30
Mail Order
Catalog $3, refundable
FAX 503/744-1834

From garden gnomes to cast-concrete copies of classical statuary, pedestals, containers and balustrades, Sol's offers ornaments to suit everyone's taste. They've concrete furniture, fountains and underwater lighting, too. Plus paving and retaining wall materials. The volume is mind-boggling, the prices are right, and the personel is friendly. One of my clients and I persuaded a member of the staff to haul seven huge concrete pots (each weighing over a hundred pounds) into the center of the sales yard so we could decide if they looked well together. Not only did he comply, he cracked jokes! Sol's holds a sale on planters in March and a seasonal close-out in August.

Sol's Garden Decorations

18501 S.E. McLoughlin Blvd.
Milwaukie, Oregon 97267
☎ 503/654-5359

Hours Mon-Fri 8-7, Sat 8-5, Sun 12-5
(April through July);
Mon-Sat 8-5, Sun 12-5
(Aug & Sept and March);
Mon-Sat 8-5 (Oct through Feb)
Accessible Yes

"Statueland offers the largest selection of birdbaths and statuary on the Oregon Coast," say new owners, Jean and George Nichols. "We also have bridges, fountains and fiberglass ponds. The inventory continuously changes. We make some of our own and also purchase from many other dealers." You'll find merchandise marked-down at the end of summer and occasional overstock sales.

Statueland

565 S.W. Highway 101
Lincoln City, Oregon 97367
☎ 503 994 9930

Hours Tues-Sun 9-5:30
Accessible No

Topiary or Not Topiary

21550 N.W. Nicholas Court #E
Hillsboro, Oregon 97124
☎ *503/690-7290 or 1-800/886-7290*

Hours *Mon-Fri 9-4 or by appointment*
Accessible *Yes*
Mail Order
Catalog *Free*
FAX *503/690-7771*

Nansen Pihlaja's topiaries have been featured in numerous magazines, catalogs and on television shows across the country. The studio, which was begun eight years ago, now ships hundreds of pieces throughout the U.S. and Canada each week. They've a wide variety of frames as well as finished herbal, succulent and ivy topiaries. Care and feeding instructions are included, and classes are available. Custom projects are the specialty of the house. "We love visitors, but be prepared to help plant a life-size horse!" says Nan. Her Noah's Ark delighted visitors to the 1993 Northwest Flower and Garden Show.

Retail Sources for Décor & Giftware

Note: Most of the shops listed in this section were founded by gardeners with other discriminating gardeners in mind. They offer a wealth of select garden ornaments, containers and fountains. They usually feature furniture, fine tools, garden apparel and books as well. In some of these stores, you'll find a selection of rare plant materials and/or seeds. These are the kinds of places a serious gardener would detour to visit!

Washington

Bainbridge Gardens

9415 Miller Road
Bainbridge Island, Washington 98110
☎ *206/842-5888*

The indoor area at Bainbridge Gardens is filled with fine furniture, garden ornaments and giftware made by local craftspeople and artisans worldwide. See complete listing on page 340.

City People's Garden Store

2939 E. Madison
Seattle, Washington 98112
☎ *206/324-0737*

City People's Garden Store offers choice pieces for embellishing the garden. See complete listing on page 330.

The inventory varies at this interior design/gift shop, but you'll always find a good selection of large terra cotta pots, plain and decorated, up to 28-inches in diameter. They usually have furniture and sculptural pieces by local artisans suitable for garden rooms.

Fremont Terra Cotta

3411 Fremont N.
Seattle, Washington 98103
☎ 206/547-4657

Hours Mon-Fri 11-6, Sat 10-5, Sun 12-5
Accessible No

Jerry and Marianne Lindquist describe their shop as "a garden catalog come to life." They've concrete, bronze and fiberglass statuary, bird baths, wall hangings, signs, wind chimes, sundials, weathervanes, fountains and ponds. For maintaining the garden there are seeds, tools and watering cans of all sizes; and for inspiration, lots of books. The company is moving to the address listed here in March 1994 from smaller quarters in the same shopping center. This big new store will feature the full line of *Kingsley-Bate* teak garden furniture in addition to the fine garden equipment and decorative accessories that have always attracted customers.

Garden Companions

23808 Bothell Highway S.E.,
Bothell Country Village
Bothell, Washington 98021
☎ 206/486-2530

Hours Mon-Sat 10-6, Sun 11-5;
open until 8 between
Thanksgiving and Christmas
Accessible Yes

"If your circle of friends includes gardeners, remember this store for gifts both decorative and practical," say the owners, Mike Roser and K.C. Sheehan. For those who enjoy walking the yard more than working it, there are beautiful brass sundials, birdhouses and feeders, sonorous wind chimes, Oriental garden lanterns and more. Green-thumbs will appreciate top-quality stainless steel tools, soil thermometers, goatskin gloves or a deluxe garden cart. You'll also find English wildflower seeds and local herb, vegetable and flower seeds. The store's handmade, customized English enamel address signs, decorated with botanical motifs, make a welcoming statement in the landscape. The shop carries a wide selection of fountains and furniture. From I-405, take N.E. 8th exit. Go west to the light. Take a right on 108th Avenue N.E. Look for the first side street on the left.

Garden Works

10632 N.E. 9th Street
Bellevue, Washington 98004
☎ 206/455-0568

Hours Mon-Sat 9-6, Sun 10-4
Accessible Difficult

314 **Great Garden Sources of the Pacific Northwest**

Go Outside

111 Morris
La Conner, Washington 98257
☎ 206/466-4836

Hours Daily 10-6
Accessible No

In the cabin-like, woodsy atmosphere of this store, you'll find lots of containers, birdhouses, bird baths and gazing balls, as well as select pieces of garden furniture. For the working gardener, there are books, apparel, tools and seeds. Watch for their big five-day sale in February.

The Hearts of the Garden

1118 1st Street
Snohomish, Washington 98290
☎ 206/568-0356

Hours Mon-Sat 10-6, Sun 12-5 (closes at 5 p.m. daily in winter)
Accessible No

With its English cottage garden theme, Cindy MacIver's shop features hand painted flower pots, watering cans and garden furniture. She sells books, seeds and tools, containers and lots of decorative accessories to brighten your "country" garden. Her annual sale takes place the first weekend in February. Look for mark-downs after major holidays.

MacBrides Gift & Garden

3236 N.E. 45th
Seattle, Washington 98105
☎ 206/527-2177

Hours Mon-Sat 10-5
Accessible Yes

Laurie MacBride says that you can count on finding Chinese and Indonesian pots, garden furniture, ornaments and lanterns here. And practical things like watering cans, tools, plant supports and gloves. For the birds, there are feeders, houses and baths. Laurie is always on the lookout for garden antiques and collectibles and when she comes across them, "they tend to sell very quickly." She maintains a mailing list to keep interested customers informed as special things come in or items are marked down.

Molbak's

13625 N.E. 175th Street
Woodinville, Washington 98072
☎ 206/483-5000

Few specialty stores carry as large an inventory of ornaments, containers and fountains as you'll find at this big, beautiful garden center. See complete listing on page 335.

Swansons Nursery & Landscape

9701 15th Avenue N.W.
Seattle, Washington 98117
☎ 206/782-2543

Swansons' garden shop delights the most discriminating gardener with a wide range of handsome accessories. See complete listing on page 333.

Oregon

The Arbor is a small shop packed with products that range from "slug pubs" to Winterthur reproduction garden benches. Owners Mary Grace West and Nan Happ place high emphasis on quality products. They carry an attractive selection of ornaments, topiary forms and arbors to decorate the garden, as well as English, Japanese and American tools for maintaining it. They're distributors for *Felco* pruners and *Foldit* carts. They carry *Shepard's* seeds, *Whitney Farms* fertilizers, garden clogs and kneelers. They've gifts for children and adults, including books, cards and bird houses, and they offer gardening and exterior/interior design classes. Attached to the shop is the Arbor Cafe operated by two of their friends.

The Arbor

380 High Street
Salem, Oregon 97301
☎ *503/588-1330*

Hours *Mon-Sat 9:30-5:30;*
Mon-Fri 9:30-8, Sat 9:30-5:30, Sun 12-5
(Christmas season)
Accessible *Yes*

A one-acre garden on the Tualatin River filled with perennials, trees and flowering shrubs is a big draw for this small garden shop that features many one-of-a-kind garden ornaments. You'll find lots of pots, handmade rustic water basins, cedar benches and some antiques and garden sculpture. You'll love the English trugs too. Elizabeth Rocchia offers informal advise on growing the plants you find in her garden and on the placement of decorative items.

The Cottage Garden

957 Willamette Falls Drive
West Linn, Oregon 97068
☎ *503/657-5666*

Hours *March through October, by*
appointment only
Accessible *Yes*

Dragonfly Gardens stocks a wide range of plants and a wide variety of pots to put them in. "Containers are us, says Sarah Lizio."We have one of the largest collections in the Northwest – from Thailand, Malaysia, China and the like." You'll also find bonsai here. See complete listing on page 116.

Dragonfly Gardens

3575 S.E. Division Street
Portland, Oregon 97202
☎ *503/235-9150*

Harry & David's Original Country Store

2836 S. Pacific Highway
Medford, Oregon 97501
☎ *503/776-2277*

Hours *Mon-Sat 9-7, Sun 10-6 (summer);*
Mon-Sat 9-6, Sun 10-5 (winter)
Accessible *Yes*

Most of the merchandise here is overstock from *Harry & David* and *Jackson & Perkins* catalogs. When I visited the store in late summer, I found garden furniture and cushions, such ornaments as wind chimes and bird-houses, baskets and handsome copper containers and lots of garden books! Bare root roses go for rock-bottom prices, and from April through July there's a large outdoor display of bedding plants, bulbs and perennials.

Northwest Garden & Topiary

805 N.W. 23rd Street
Portland, Oregon 97209
☎ *503/222-9939*

Hours *Mon-Sat 10-6; (open until 6:30 during Christmas holidays)*
Accessible *Difficult*

Northwest Garden & Topiary offers a special blend of home and garden accessories. The front room is filled with tropical house plants, French floral stacks and all manner of decorative items for garden rooms. Topiary and containers fill the middle section of this narrow, surprisingly deep storefront space. The topiary frames, many designed by owner Brenda Kelley, include 85 animals, hearts, balls, etc. She sells kitchen herbs and spices here as well. At the rear, you'll find the "Secret Garden" filled with pretty herbs and perennials perfect for condo balconies and the neighborhood's small gardens. Upstairs there are rooms where you can learn the secrets of several popular crafts, including topiary, wreath making, container gardening, herbal baskets, salad baskets, holiday decorations and gifts.

Oregon Garden Store established its reputation by offering carefully selected garden accessories from artisans and manufacturers worldwide. You'll find Italian terra cotta pots, English, German and American garden tools, English teak benches, plus arbors, fountains, wall planters and birdbaths made in the U.S.A. The State Street store carries more one-of-a-kind pieces and features topiary and herbs, plus a small selection of unusual vines, perennials and ground covers. The new Boones Ferry Road location offers a wider selection of landscape plants. Both stores stock garden supplies and such clothing as Wellington boots, garden clogs, aprons and hats.

Oregon Garden Store

333 S. State Street
Lake Oswego, Oregon 97034
☎ *503/697-3635*

15780 S.W. Boones Ferry Road
Lake Oswego, Oregon 97035
☎ *503/636-9341*

Hours Mon-Sat 10-6, Sun 10-5
Accessible Yes
FAX 503/226-2409

This excellent nursery on the Oregon coast offers particularly charming orna-ments, containers, fountains and trelliage. See complete listing on page 375.

Raintree Garden & Gift Center

Highway 101, just north of the
Cannon Beach Junction
Seaside, Oregon 97138
☎ *503/738-6980*

Jim and Dotti Becker's little store doesn't try to duplicate the merchandise offered at large garden centers, but rather offers carefully chosen items, both utilitarian and ornamental, which aren't readily available in the region. They also operate a nationally known mail-order nursery, Goodwin Creek Gardens, which is listed on page 189. As professional nurserymen, they know gardeners' needs and they've stocked this store with an array of high-quality tools, ornaments, books and containers, as well as herbs and everlastings from their garden. "We sell items we use ourselves and like to see in other people's gardens. We are involved in what we sell and we enjoy talking about gardening almost as much as we enjoy gardening itself," They offer several seminars in the spring and crafts classes in the fall.

Secret Garden

154½ Oak Street
Ashland, Oregon 97520
☎ *503/488-3308*

Hours Daily 10-5:30
(April through December);
Mon-Sat 10-5:30 (Feb & March)
Accessible Yes

Yardbirds

2200 N.E. Broadway
Portland, Oregon 97232
☎ *503/288-9985*

Hours Mon-Sat 10-6, Sun 12-5
Accessible Yes

Cathy Pitkin and Connie Vincent set out to create a gift store that caters to people who love their gardens and feathered friends. They've succeeded with a wide range of accessories and decorations that "put the FUN in gardening." You'll discover an array of wind chimes, banners, windsocks and weathervanes, baskets and imported pots, plaques, topiary forms, birdbaths, feeders and houses. In the line of garden apparel, they've umbrellas, hats and gloves. There will probably be some tempting benches and fountains, as well. The merchandise is marked-down after Christmas and again in late summer.

Idaho

Boise Botanical

712 N. Orchard Avenue
Boise, Idaho 87306
☎ *208/343-5900*

Hours Mon-Sat 9-5:30; open Sundays
12-5 (April, May, June & mid-Nov
through Christmas)
Accessible Yes

The specialties here are birdhouses and decorative accent pieces. The store also carries garden clothing and hand tools, specialty seeds, organic supplies and garden books. It's a great place for garden gifts. They've lots of hanging baskets and colorful annuals, herbs and perennials for seasonal displays in containers and an excellent selection of house plants.

British Columbia

Arbutus advertises the best selection in Vancouver for containers – from one inch to three feet in size. The firm buys clay and stoneware pots by the pallet-load. You'll find a huge selection of Mexican and Italian terra cotta pottery here, plus hand-painted Heavenhill containers, California stoneware and Malaysian pots. Decorative items include clay birdbaths, wind chimes and Mexican outdoor fireplaces. There's also a stock of tile and landscape rock. The owners strive to maintain good prices year-round. Something is on sale at all times, and they usually have some "seconds" at very attractive prices.

Arbutus Landscapes

1445 Main Street
North Vancouver, British Columbia
V7J 1C9
☎ *604/988-2880*

Hours Daily 9-6; Tues-Sun 9:30-5:30
(winter)
Accessible Partially

A lovely ambiance surrounds the visitor to the West Van location, an old house converted into a "gardener's toy store." You'll be greeted outside by Rosemary, a stuffed figure clad in gardening attire. Inside, your senses will be delighted by classical music and wonderful fragrances. The place is packed full of wonderful gifts for yourself and others, including ceramic cachepots, fine English tools, trellis work from *English Garden Imports*, weathervanes, books (1,100 titles!) and much, much more. Be sure to explore the attic and the backyard where you'll find, among other things, potted old garden roses and unusual varieties of clematis. The owner, Darlene Sanders, notes that the shop has become a central point of information exchange around B.C. and that customers arrive from points as far as Toronto saying they've heard about the store. Merchandise is marked down in January, mid-summer and late September. The staff conducts pruning and bulb planting demonstrations and are always willing to share gardening advice. You'll find them in Ambleside-by-the Sea, across the Lion's Gate Bridge from Vancouver. The new location in Kitsilano is twice as big and just as nice.

DESTINATION☆
The Avant Gardener

1460 Marine Drive
West Vancouver, British Columbia
V7T 1B7
☎ *604/926-8784*

2235 W. 4th Avenue
Vancouver, British Columbia V6K 1N6
☎ *604/736-0404*

Hours Mon-Fri 10-6, Sat 9:30-5:30,
Sun 12-5
Accessible Yes
FAX 604/926-1427

Courtyards Casual Furniture

2082 West 41st Avenue
Vancouver, British Columbia V6M 1Y8
☎ 604/261-4116

Courtyards' collection of gifts and accessories complement the excellent furniture you'll find here. See page 299 for complete listing.

Dig This

45 Bastion Square
Victoria, British Columbia V8W 1J1
☎ 604/385-3212

3084 Granville Street
Vancouver, British Columbia V6H 3J8
☎ 604/739-1725

Hours Mon-Sat 9:30-5:30, Sun 12-4
Accessible Yes
FAX 604/360-2223

Small but very special shops staffed by very experienced gardeners, Dig This offers seeds (including *Suttons* from England), books, containers, ornaments, benches, trellis work from *English Garden Imports* and an extensive line of unusual garden gifts. They carry bonsai and ikebana supplies, plus tools of all kinds, including a complete line of tools designed for disabled gardeners. They also offer a Christmas catalogue.

☆DESTINATION
Shop in the Garden

6804 S.W. Marine Drive
Vancouver , British Columbia V6T 1Z4
☎ 604/822-4529

Hours Mar through Oct, Daily 10-6;
Winter, Daily 11-5
Accessible Yes
FAX 604/822-2016

This lovely shop is run by Friends of the Garden (support volunteers for the Botanical Garden at the University of British Columbia), who offer a delightful range of garden accessories and plants at a reasonable cost. All profits go back into the garden. Seeds sold here are collected in the garden. It's a popular stop for holiday greenery, dried flower arrangements, garden apparel and tools.

Art in the Landscape

The placement of garden art is an art in itself. It affords the collector an opportunity to be creative with the artist. The idea is to make the piece appear effortless and permanent. It should be used to delight rather than confront the viewer. Remember, too, that garden art will be seen in varying light conditions and changing seasons. Try the piece in several spots within the garden. Dare to experiment.

Garden art is often used to create balance within the garden, although the balance may be asymmetrical. For example, a large contemporary sculpture might be placed at the edge of a wooded area or on a rise within the lawn as a counterweight to the house and its more intensively landscaped environment. Formal gardens, on the other hand, call for symmetrical or rational placement of sculptural elements. A classical piece might be used as a central feature in the garden or placed in a niche at the end of a walkway. A pair of antique urns could set off a doorway or flank the head of a staircase.

☞ **Money-saving tip: Look for craftsmanship and durability in outdoor sculpture.**

Avoid metals that rust and other materials that deteriorate. It is no coincidence that stone and bronze have been the preferred materials of sculptors through the ages. Today, sculptors are also making wonderful works of garden art from aluminum, resins and concrete. Unfortunately, security is another factor you must consider in the placement of art in the landscape. If its weight is not sufficient to deter a would-be thief, consider bolting, welding or mortaring the piece onto a base. (A base may also serve to raise the piece, making it more "important" in the landscape.) Of course, you must also secure the piece if it might fall over and hurt someone.

The sources listed below are a mix of individual artists, art galleries and organizations and a few choice garden shops that seek out the highest-quality products on the market. This is not to say that everything these shops carry is out of the reach of ordinary folks, but that the merchandise is generally "up-scale." 🌿

☞ **Money-saving Tip: One nice piece of garden art may be all you need in the way of ornamentation. If it will last a lifetime, then it's a good investment.**

Sources for Sculpture & Garden Antiques

The Artist's Garden at Hawk Creek Gallery

48460 Highway 101 S.
Neskowin, Oregon 97149
☎ 503/392-3879

Hours Daily 11-5 (July and August);
Thurs-Sun 11- 5 (March through June
and Sept and Oct); or by appointment.
Closed in winter
Accessible No
Catalog Free with SASE

All of the pieces in this shop are designed and made by Oregon artists. Alongside paintings by Michael Schlicting, visitors to the central Oregon coast will find heavy-gauge steel silhouettes of fish and birds by his wife Stephanie. You'll also see Gail Beppu's lovely planters and birdbaths.

Bamboo Gardens of Washington

196th Avenue N.E. at Redmond-Fall City
Road (SR 202)
Redmond, Washington 98053
☎ 206/868-5166

Bamboo Gardens offers handsome hand-carved stone sculpture and "the best bamboo deer scares and water pipes in the U.S.," plus an excellent selection of fountains and garden ornaments. See complete listing on page 164.

Contemporary Crafts Gallery

3934 S.W. Corbett Avenue
Portland, Oregon 97201
☎ 503/223-2654

Hours Tues-Sat 10-5, Sun 1-5
Accessible Yes

This is a terrific resource for garden sculpture, furniture and fine handmade garden ornaments. Founded in 1937, the gallery has achieved leadership by exhibiting innovative work by such notable Northwest artists as Tom Torrens, Marge Hammond-Farness, Lin Cook Harpster, Larry Peterson and Michele VanSlyke. A special garden exhibition in early spring is curated each year by a different artist and features work from across the nation. Exhibits change at regular intervals, so call the gallery for current information. Contemporary Crafts gallery is one of the oldest non-profit art organizations in the country.

"We purchase everything in the south of England and favor the rustic country cottage look," explains Pat Erickson. "We have a varying supply of old garden tools, watering cans and garden accessories and some rustic garden furniture handmade from oak and sweet chestnut. Original Sussex trugs (both old and new), wicker ware grown and hand-woven in Wales and beautiful hand-thrown Victorian-style terra cotta pots. The merchandise is constantly changing, depending on our finds! Visitors enjoy strolling in our large old garden." The shop is located fifteen miles south of Yakima, just off I-82, east of the Yakima River in the heart of the Yakima wine district.

Country Garden Antiques
6451 Yakima Valley Highway
(In the Carriage House of the Old Sawyer Mansion)
Wapato, Washington 98951
☎ *509/877-4644*

Hours By appointment
Accessible Yes

Sculptor John Anderson creates small, self-contained ceramic fountains that can be enjoyed indoors or out. Ranging in height from 12" to 24", these attractive, affordable fountains come in five different finishes with several styles of centerpieces, including a freeform ball, fish or flower form. They've recently introduced a lovely little birdbath and a line of classic pedestals for displaying plants or sculpture. You are welcome to visit the studio by appointment. It's located between Corvallis and Adair Village. From Highway 99W, turn onto Mountain View Drive (only one way to turn), take next left onto Armstrong Way (a dirt road), follow road until you find mail box that says "Anderson". Turn left.

Dancing Waters
300 N.W. Armstrong Way
Corvallis, Oregon 97330
☎ *503/745-7039*

Hours Daily by appointment
Accessible Yes
Mail Order
Catalog Free

Earthrise

2954 West 4th Avenue
Vancouver, British Columbia V6K 1R4
☎ 604/736-8404

Landscape architects Michael Luco and James Bennett take a designer's approach in the containers, ornaments and garden antiques they stock. They've unusual plants, as well, in this cluttered shop, which had no sign in front when I visited. A knowledgeable clientele comes here to find such esoteric items as seeds for English sweet peas, *Peter Beales* old-fashioned roses, rare water plants, old varieties of fruit and nut trees, and unusual bulbs. Many of the plants are kept off-premises. The owners offer much more than merchandise; they bring erudition and years of experience in the field of garden design.

Gardens Antique

3518 Main Street
Vancouver, British Columbia V5V 3N3
☎ 604/876-2311

Hours Mon, Thurs, Fri 12-6, Sat 10-6, Sun 12-5
Accessible Yes

"We are an antiques and nostalgia store that focuses on outdoor living of the past. We are not a garden store, but rather a store where things old and full of character jump out and delight many avid gardeners," says Colin Reid. The inventory varies, but you're likely to find something highly decorative here among the old fountains, fragments of ornamental iron, and antique sculpture. You may even run across old garden books.

Gary Word Gallery 502

1524 30th Avenue
Seattle, Washington 98122
☎ 206/322-5257, 1-800/488-5335

Hours Mon-Fri 10-6
Accessible No
Catalog Yes

Gary Word sculpts free-form in mortar and clay. His figurative pedestals and wall collages and his enigmatic body benches intrigue patrons of the Northwest Flower and Garden Show. Each piece is one-of-a-kind.

George Stastny's hand-carved, one-of-a-kind concrete planters are individually made to customer specification. They're often seen at entrances to buildings and the entry courts of estate properties. Each sculpturally shaped pot is embellished with handsome surface decoration. There is no mold involved; so the company can fabricate custom designs in sizes up to five feet in diameter. These durable containers can be made without drainage holes for use as water features; normally the inside bottom is tapered toward a one-inch opening.

George Stastny Stone Pots
9870 S.W. Bayou Drive
McMinnville, Oregon 97128
☎ *503/472-0160*

Hours Mon-Fri 7:30-5:30
Accessible Yes
Catalog Free brochure

"We produce hand-cast granite garden ornaments that look like carved granite," says Belinda Vos. "Each piece is designed to exact standards and individually hand washed to give a one-of-a-kind appearance." While the company's business is mostly wholesale, retail customers are invited by appointment. Clients are attracted by the quality of work and attention to detail. The company makes five styles of Japanese lanterns that can be ordered with electric wiring. Ornaments include Japanese water basins, signposts and bonsai containers. Their birdbath is simple and elegant.

Granite Impressions
342 Carmen Road
Talent, Oregon 97540
☎ *503/535-6190*

Hours By appointment only
Accessible No
Mail Order
Catalog $1

This Old World-elegant shop is a feast for the eye! It's packed with Italian terra cotta, *Haddenstone* and lead ornaments from England, Victorian wire work, reproduction and antique garden benches and very tasteful contemporary garden sculpture and accessories. Even the tools and apparel are inspirationally displayed. You'll find wonderful garden gifts and lots of lovely books here as well.

DESTINATION ✩
Hobbs

2129 W. 41st Avenue
Vancouver, British Columbia V6M 1Z6
☎ *604/261-5998*

Hours Mon-Sat 9:30-6;
Sun 11-5 (Nov. & Dec.)
Accessible Yes
FAX 604/263-0822

Honeychurch Antiques

1008 James Street
Seattle, Washington 98104
☎ *206/622-1225*

Hours *Mon-Sat 10-6*
Accessible *No*
FAX *206/622-1204*

Honeychurch Antiques specializes in fine Asian antiques, including imported authentic Japanese waterstones, mill stones, sculpture, containers and other elegant garden ornaments from China, Korea, Thailand, Indonesia and India.

Ital'art Co. Inc.

4655 Ridge Drive, N.E.
Salem, Oregon 97303
☎ *503/393-3907*

Hours *Mon-Fri 8-5,*
Sat, by appointment
Accessible *No*
Mail Order
Catalog *$10, refundable*

"At Ital'art we offer the largest variety of handmade pre-cast garden ornaments in the state," says Marco Giulian. "Since we make all our own molds, we can offer unique designs of both European and contemporary garden ornaments." The urns, benches, classical statues, pedestals and fountains this company makes are of exceptional quality. Each piece is potentially a focal point in the garden environment. Much of their business is wholesale, but retail customers will find a good selection at the factory. Take the Salem Parkway exit from I-5 to visit the factory.

Kenton Designs

P.O. Box 262
Redmond , Washington 98073
☎ *206/883-7777*

Hours *By appointment*
Accessible *Yes*

Kenton Pies is one of the Northwest's most versatile sculptors. Working in stone, concrete, masonry, metals and wood, he has created award-winning garden sculpture, architectural ornamentation, fountains, natural streams and waterfalls. "I strive for asymmetrical balance and purity of materials, richness of patina, textures and colors, interesting shapes and interrelationship of elements. Monumental scale is more thrilling to me than delicacy," says the artist. He has hundreds of photographs to share with clients interested in one-of-a-kind garden art.

Neil Kikuchi's one-of-a-kind bells are described as "old visions, new forms." These exquisite pieces are based on ancient designs. Each is distinctively engraved with stylized Japanese characters and signed with the artist's Hanko (chop). Because they are meant to be struck with an accompanying mallet, they can be used as doorbells or simply as art pieces in the garden. The bells and stands are made of steel; they may be coated or left to the elements to take on a look of antiquity.

Kiku Fab Design

13218 4th Avenue N.W.
Seattle, Washington 98177
☎ *206/361-0136*

Hours *By appointment*
Accessible *No*

This non-profit corporation was founded in 1985 to promote stone sculpture in the Northwest and to provide access to professional trade information. The group holds a show each spring at the Sweetbriar Nursery (see page 155) and displays member's works in select garden centers and galleries several times during the year. If you are in the market for fine garden sculpture, write or call the association for a calendar of events or ask to be put in touch with a sculptor whose work might meet your particular needs. You are welcome to write a description of your garden setting and a general description of the type and size of piece you are seeking. They will run your description in the organization's newsletter. Many of the members also work in other media, such as bronze, wood or cast-stone.

Northwest Stone Sculptors Association

Mailing Address *5580 S. Langston Road*
Seattle, Washington 98178-3566
☎ *206/772-6130*

Hours *Daytime hours*

Oak Run Studios

P.O. Box 509
Mosier, Oregon 97040
☎ *1-800/346-3451*

Hours *By appointment*
Mail Order
Catalog *Free*

Artist Arthur Higgins' lyrical sculptures are fabricated of weatherproof, satin-finished aluminum and designed to be mounted on a pipe stand in the ground or attached to a deck post. His background as a jewelry designer is apparent in the delicacy and grace of the designs, yet these pieces are very durable. His kinetic *Wind Petals* move in the slightest breeze. The *Globe Sculptures* feature a 10" gazing ball. And, his whale-form chime adds a musical aspect to the hypnotic rocking and pivoting action of some of the pieces.

Price-Ragen

517 E. Pike
Seattle, Washington 98122
☎ *206/329-8155*
2245 Carillon Point
Kirkland, Washington 98033
☎ *828-6393*

Price-Ragen's two stores are filled with imported Italian terra cotta pots and statuary, *Robinson Iron* garden statuary, gorgeous tropical house plants, and top-of-the-line garden furniture. See complete listing on page 293.

☆DESTINATION
Wildwood Garden Furnishings

7435 S.W. Capitol Highway
Portland, Oregon 97219
☎ *503/452-0301*

Hours *Tues-Sat 10-5*
Accessible *No*

"Wildwood is a concept whose time has come – a garden shop with no plant material," says owner/designer Ron Colvin. What you *will* find are elegant accessories from around the world. Bronze statuary and fountains from Thailand, hand-hammered copper weather vanes, stone carvings from Bali, English garden statuary, Mexican wire work and Italian tiles are but a few of the hand-picked pieces that fill this converted cottage. The adjoining garden displays sculpture and benches and a large collection of hand-crafted ceramic containers not to be duplicated in your average garden store.

Chapter Twelve

One Stop Shopping:
Great Garden Centers

"If a tree dies, plant another in its place."
.....Linnaeus, Philosophia Botanica, 1750

Washington
Seattle Metropolitan Area
Seattle

City People's Garden Store

2939 E. Madison
Seattle, Washington 98112
☎ *206/324-0737*

Hours *Daily 10-5 (April through June);*
Daily 11-5 (July through March)
Accessible *Difficult*

City People's Garden Store offers the urban gardener bountiful resources! You'll find a wide array of indoor foliage and blooming plants in this pretty store. There's hand-crafted twig furniture and locally made cedar garden furniture by *Sarita, Cape Cod Comfys* and others. The containers and ornaments from such companies as *Silvestri* are exceptional. The walls are filled with handsome displays of quality garden tools, drip irrigation equipment, seeds, books, organic soil amendments and environmentally friendly pesticides. Outside, a knowledgeable staff can help you select from an interesting collection of ornamental trees, shrubs, vines and ground covers. Specialty plants include rare and unusual perennials, herbs, ornamental grasses and old garden roses. The design department offers fee-based consultation and maintenance, and the floral department offers delivery and wire service. Inquire about the free workshops and seminars held at City People's several times each year, and, if you're a regular shopper, ask for a spring catalog. You can expect sales on selected items throughout the year and a large nursery stock sale in the fall.

Five Corners Nursery

First Avenue S. at 177th Place
Seattle, Washington 98148
☎ *206/242-2931*

Hours *Mon-Fri 9-7, Sat 9-6, Sun 10-5*
(April through Aug);
Mon-Sat 9-6, Sun 10-5 (Sept & Oct
and Jan through March);
Mon-Fri 9-8, Sat 9-6, Sun 10-5
(Nov & Dec)
Accessible *Yes*
FAX *206/241-2594*

"Customer surveys have shown that our biggest asset is our smiling employees," say Bernice and Fred Konkell. "We pride ourselves on excellent service, and best of all, we all love to garden. You will always find a Washington Certified Nurseryperson available to answer your gardening questions. We hold several seminars throughout the year on everything from herb gardening to installing irrigation systems. Put your name on our mailing list so we can keep you posted

continued on next page--

on events at our store." Call or write this popular Normandy Park garden center for a current calendar; there is always something going on. Be sure to visit the garden gift shop.

Five Corners Nursery
-continued

In addition to their unusual vegetables and herbs and fine array of container plants (see pages 219 and 251, Tomi and Tosh Mano have created an excellent neighborhood nursery on their five acres to serve a full range of landscape needs. They are strong in the standard Northwest palette of shrubs and trees (firs, rhododendrons, magnolias, etc.) and rock garden materials. They're now growing over a hundred varieties of perennials. They offer a free plant list, hold classes, and publish two or three newsletters each year. The vast array of annuals goes on sale during the Fourth of July weekend.

Mano's Earlington Greenhouses
13043 Renton Avenue S.
Seattle, Washington 98178
☎ *206/255-7744*

Hours Mon-Sat 9-6, Sun 10-5
Accessible Yes

Amid the festive atmosphere of the Pike Place Market, this small but wonderful Molbak's satellite store gives out-of-town visitors a taste of Seattle gardening. Locals, especially city dwellers, shop here for their container gardening needs. "Over the years visitors from far and near continue to be amazed by our vast seed collection, which we import from all over the world. Not only will you find seed for a wide array of herbs, annuals and perennials, but also for exotic greenhouse plants, trees, shrubs and wildflowers," says store manager Joyce Kelly. "We offer a lovely selection of bulbs (particularly in the fall), bulk organic amendments, quality garden books and a nice line of garden gifts, ornaments and chimes." Sales on the bedding plants and house plants occur on the same schedule as Molbak's Woodinville store. (See page 335.)

Molbak's Seattle Garden Center
1600 Pike Place
Seattle, Washington 98101
☎ *206/448-0431*

Hours Mon-Sat 9-5:30, Sun 10-5
(mid-March through mid-Oct);
Mon-Sat 9-5:30, Sun 10-4
(mid-Oct until mid-March)

Accessible Yes
FAX 206/441-7282

Sky Nursery & Garden Center

18528 Aurora Avenue N.
Seattle, Washington 98133
☎ *206/546-4851*

Hours *Mon-Sat 9-6, Sun 10-5*
Accessible *Yes*
FAX *206/546-8010*

Sky Nursery has been a growing phenomenon in the last five years. Founded in 1953, it took off in 1985 with an all-new look and organization. "We strive to create an inviting shopping atmosphere with planted displays and ponds complete with koi to stimulate ideas," says Mary Archambault. "Our customers constantly comment on our selection, the vastness of our stock and the courteous and knowledgeable staff that's always willing to help. If we don't have it, nobody does," she adds. This nursery maintains a large stock of everything for the garden, including outdoor lighting, drip irrigation equipment and decorative accessories. Ask to receive *Skylights*, the company's newsletter, and look for free information sheets on pruning, bonsai classes, pools, ponds, perennials, lawn care and more.

Sunflower Greenhouse & Garden Center, Inc.

1900 N.E. 150th Street
Seattle, Washington 98155
☎ *206/367-5440*

Hours *Mon-Sat 10-6, Sun 10-5 (spring & summer); Daily 10-5 (Nov through Feb); closed Christmas through mid-Jan*
Accessible *Yes, except restrooms*

The owners of Sunflower Greenhouses are degree-holding horticulturists who pride themselves on customer service. They maintain a want-list service and will special-order for clients. The stock includes an especially good selection of flowering trees and shrubs and a wide range of roses and water-wise landscape plants. You'll also find bonsai, house plants, fountains, organic supplies and books. The specialty, of course, is container gardening; they grow their own annuals and perennials. At Christmas there are five greenhouses full of poinsettias. A free six-page newsletter, published ten times a year, offers coupon specials and announces upcoming sales.

Swansons' park-like setting, lovely gift shop and espresso bar invite relaxation. Customers are encouraged to browse, and a helpful staff is on hand to "talk plants." The seasonal displays are elegant. Swansons propagates many of the perennials it sells and offers a broad selection of herbs and annuals. Of course, you'll find the usual (and the unusual) complement of Northwest shrubs and trees in great quantity. They've apparel, bonsai, books, bulbs, containers, ferns, fountains and ponds, fruit and nut trees, fruits and berries, furniture, ground covers, house plants, organic supplies, ornaments, paving materials, roses, seeds, vines and wildflowers. The company was established in 1888 in Minneapolis and moved to its present location in 1924. So far out in the country was this store, the staff delivered flowers by bicycle rather than expect customers to traverse the gravel roads! But as Wally Kerwin (the "new owner" for the past fifteen years) says, "We still grow flowers the old-fashioned way." Swansons' design consultants offer complete services to clients who request a site visit.

DESTINATION ☆
Swansons Nursery & Landscape

9701 15th Avenue N.W.
Seattle, Washington 98117
☎ *206/782-2543*

Hours *Daily 9:30-6 (spring & summer);*
Mon-Sat 9:30-5, Sun 11-4:30
(fall & winter)
Accessible *Yes*

A historic schoolhouse in a charming old neighborhood sets a tone that permeates The Wallingford Garden Spot. "We have a great staff of gardeners who love their work. We're always out beating the bushes for new plants or new tools," says Lyn Sherwood, who notes that most of their suppliers are small Northwest growers. They specialize in exotic plants, like Russian hellebores and drought-tolerant perennials, for example, and carry lots of herbs. Expect to find lovely planters, ready to be placed on your patio or made to your specifications. They've organic supplies and a select complement of shrubs, vines and trees. You'll also find excellent selections in garden books, containers, fountains, house plants and gifts. Call for extended hours during the holiday season. Ask to receive *Garden Spot Gazette*.

The Wallingford Garden Spot
& Floral

1815 N. 45th Street
Seattle, Washington 98103
☎ *206/547-5137 or*
1-800/982-2608 (for floral orders only)

Hours *Mon-Fri 9:30-8, Sat 9:30-7,*
Sun 9:30-5

Accessible *Yes*
FAX *206/547-4409*

West Seattle Nursery & Garden Center

5275 California Avenue S.W.
Seattle, Washington 98136
☎ *206/935-9276*

Hours Sun-Thurs 8-7, Fri & Sat 8-9
(April through June);
Daily 9-7 (July through March)
Accessible Partially, with one step up
into the building

"Looks can be deceiving," says Irene Stewart. "We're a small nursery, but we pack a big wallop, especially in our 600 varieties of perennials and our specialty plants. We work hard to carry excellent quality stock for indoors and out." Noting the popular seasonal sales in January and again in August and September, she adds, "Some people just come to see the cat!" If you live in the area, you'll want to receive the quarterly newsletter and get on a mailing list for discount coupons, talks by specialists, and the spring and holiday open houses. Among the decorative and gift items are garden books, furniture and accessories, Christmas decorations and kids' gardening supplies. Call for holiday-season hours.

North Suburban Area

Edmonds Garden Center

610 Fifth Avenue S.
Edmonds, Washington 98020
☎ *206/778-4877*

Hours Mon-Sat 9-6, Sun 10-4
Accessible Yes
FAX 206/771-9539

"We pride our growth on the highest quality nursery stock and garden supplies, and we strive for customer quality in all aspects of our business. Our staff members are continually training and educating themselves in their respective areas of expertise," says Jim Markey. "Customers shop in a comfortable, relaxed environment and leave the nursery with the knowledge and ability to improve their own personal landscapes." In addition to plant materials, the store carries apparel, books, containers and furniture. The Christmas gift shop holds an Open House on the first of December. This locally-owned garden center in downtown Edmonds also sells and services power equipment.

There may not be another garden center in the country comparable to Molbak's in terms of quantity, diversity and sheer spectacle! Under a single roof you'll find every manner of landscape and indoor plant, plus an incredibe selection of garden accessories. The "information gazebo," located in the center of the complex, is a good starting point. Whether you're looking for agapanthus or zantedeschia, the staff will point you in the right direction. More than two-hundred employees grow and care for the plants, create the displays and answer myriad questions. Molbak's supports excellence in design through its spectacular display garden each year at the Northwest Flower & Garden Show. Each month, the company hosts seminars on seasonal gardening and planting design at the nursery. Special events include an October Floral Fairyland for children and a Poinsettia Festival from Thanksgiving into early December. Watch for the January Green Gale on house plants and containers, a Bare Root Sale in February, the Two-for-One sale of annuals in July, and a September special on shrubs, trees and tropical foliage. From I-205, take exit #23 East onto Highway 522. Take the first exit off 522 and turn right on 132nd Avenue N.E. Go two blocks and turn left on N.E. 175th. Molbak's is five blocks on the right.

DESTINATION ☆
Molbak's

13625 N.E. 175th Street
Woodinville, Washington 98072
☎ *206/483-5000*

Hours *Sat-Thurs 9:30-6, Fri 9:30-9*
(winter, summer & fall)
Sat-Thurs 9-8, Fri 9-9 (spring);
Sat, Mon, Tues, Wed & Thurs 9:30-8;
Fri 9:30-9, Sun 9:30-6 (holiday season)
Accessible *Yes*
FAX *206/481-4970*

This 34,000-square-foot store and 3.3-acre nursery site offers amazing selection. The focal point of the store is a lush indoor plant gazebo under glass. This 30-year-old, family-owned business was listed as a National Top 100 nursery by Nursery Retailer magazine. The garden center features a *Sundance Spa* show room and *Brown Jordan* patio furniture, as well as a gift and home decor shop, which offers a constantly changing array of seasonal merchandise. In addition to landscape plants, they sell apparel, books

continued on next page--

DESTINATION ☆
Wight's Garden & Floral

5026 196th S.W.
Lynnwood, Washington 98036-6197
☎ *206/775-3550*

Hours *Mon-Fri 9-0, Sat 9-6, Sun 10-5*
(Jan through beginning of daylight
savings time & again from August until
Thanksgiving); Mon-Fri 9-9, Sat 9-6, Sun
10-6 (mid-April through July);
Mon-Sat 9-9, Sun 10-7 (holiday season)
Accessible *Yes*

Wight's Garden & Floral

-continued

and organic supplies. They've a good selection of water plants, pond supplies and fountains. No Northwest shopping experience would be complete without a latte, so plan a stop at Wight's Cafe Espresso. The special events at Wight's are numerous and well attended! Subjects covered in free classes offered throughout the year include bonsai, pruning, topiary, rose care, orchids and holiday decorating. The gift shop has a children's area, and several events are planned throughout the year for the little ones. Watch for the Rose Sale in March, July Sidewalk Sale, October Red Tag Nursery Sale and After-Christmas Half-price Sale.

Wileywood Nursery & Florist

17414 Bothell Way S.E.
Mill Creek, Washington 98012
☎ 206/481-9768

Hours Mon-Fri 7-6, Sat 8-6, Sun 9-6;
open late in May, June and the
first three weeks of December
Accessible Yes
Mail Order
Catalog $1 (fuchsias)
FAX 206/483-9506

Bob Schmitz writes, "We, the owners and employees at Wileywood, pride ourselves in our customer relationship program. It is important to us to develop a friend. We get to know our customers and cultivate a loyalty that isn't found in many stores." Children are welcome here and happily occupied by a running model train and covered sandbox while parents browse 10,000-square-feet of covered shopping. Wileywood features a full line floral shop (with free wedding planning), U.S. Post Office, fresh fruit stand in season and espresso bar. A complete garden center, Wileywood boasts over 150 varieties of fuchsias, rhodies and roses. You're welcome to get on a mailing list to receive the company's free monthly newsletter. There's a sale on hanging baskets in June, and shrubs are marked-down in October. The nursery is located about a mile south of Millcreek city center.

Eastside

Evans Creek Nursery

Take a brief vacation from urban living at this peaceful nursery just east of Redmond. There's a salmon spawning stream on the property, and the neighbors raise llamas. Eighty-percent of the plants sold at Evans Creek Nursery are grown here. The specialties are flowering shade trees, shrubs and ground covers, but Dan Higgins and Chris Logue also grow lots of herbs, perennials, bulbs, vines and ferns. They've also got the soil amendments and supplies.

20018 N.E. 50th Street
Redmond, Washington 98053
☎ *206/836-4643*

Hours *Thurs-Sat 9-6; Sun-Wed 9-5*
Accessible *Partially*
FAX *206/868-8817*

Furney's Nursery

The wide and wonderful selection of choice nursery stock has always been Furney's best advertisement. Now, the three garden stores in this local chain have added more gift items. Furney's sponsored the Bellevue Gift Show in November 1993 with the new slogan, "Great gardens and gifts begin at Furney's." So, in addition to the house plants, eye-popping seasonal bedding plants and specimen-size trees you've come to expect, look for lots of new garden ornaments, fountains and planters. They've also got extensive displays of tools and gardening supplies. See listings on pages 340 and 348.

13427 N.E. 16th
Bellevue, Washington 98005
☎ *206/747-8282*

Hours *Mon-Sat 9-6; Sun 9-5;*
open until 7 some evenings
in spring and during the
holiday season
Accessible *Yes*

Hayes Nursery

This fine general nursery specializes in unusual, hard-to-find landscape subjects, pond plants and dwarf plants, including bonsai. For inspiration, there's a waterfall garden, butterfly garden, bird sanctuary, grass garden and a rockery. Claire and Larry Hayes hand-pick garden accent pieces for the gift shop. They carry books, handmade pottery and gifts, fountains, bird feeders, English tools and custom-made container gardens. Each staff member is a certified nurseryman. They publish a quarterly newsletter and provide delivery service.

12504 Issaquah-Hobart Road
Issaquah, Washington 98027
☎ *206/391-4166*

Hours *Mon-Sat 9:30-6, Sun 11-5;*
close at 5:30 (Jan through March)
Accessible *Partially*

Kimura Nursery

3860 N.E. Bel-Red Road
Bellevue, Washington 98008
☎ *206/881-6508*

Hours *Daily 9-5; (open until 6:30 in May, June and the holiday season)*
Accessible *Yes*
FAX *206/869-2004*

Kimura's specialties are interior plantscaping, Japanese landscaping, unusual dwarf materials and water gardens. They carry imported Japanese statuary of the highest quality. In business over 30 years, this selective mid-size nursery markets a broad spectrum of materials, from perennials to rocks. See additional listings on pages 234 and 257.

Rosarian Gardens

14520 284th Avenue N.E.
Duvall, Washington 98019
☎ *206/788-8022*

Hours *Wed-Sun 10-8 (spring & summer), Wed-Sun 10-5 (fall & winter); Mon & Tues by appointment*
Accessible *Yes*

"We specialize in roses – old, modern, climbing and miniatures. Our viewing garden features over three hundred roses, which are accented with perennials, landscaped ponds and fountains. We invite you to stroll the paths, smell the fragrance, and catch the colors of each season," say Richard and Ann Klemz. Their friendly neighborhood garden center stocks a full line of plants. "We work with home owners on design and proper planting, and we conduct classes on requested subjects." They've a courtyard with picnic tables and an old-fashioned fire pit that's inviting in winter when the focus turns to the country craft cottage and Holiday Bazaar. Local schoolchildren sing holiday music on weekends and the Klemz family serves homemade treats and beverages. Bargain seekers should know about the company's Bare Root Sales – roses in early spring and trees in December. There's also a mid-summer sale on annuals and perennials and a clearance in September. You'll also enjoy the Craft Show in May.

Squak Mt. Greenhouse & Nursery

7600 Renton-Issaquah Road S.E.
Issaquah, Washington 98027
☎ *206/643-0601*

Hours *Mon-Sat 9-6; (close at 5 in winter)*
Accessible *Difficult*

A lovely stream runs through this nursery, which is situated on ten acres in a pastoral valley between Squak and Cougar Mountains. The biggest draw is seasonal color at grower prices, but this garden center also offers ornaments and furniture, plus good selections in bulbs, ferns, fruit and nut trees, berries, ground covers, herbs, perennials, shrubs, shade

continued on next page--

trees and vines. The nursery's colorful quarterly newsletter, *The Greenthumber*, provides gardening advice and announces specials and special events, such as seminars by Master Gardeners and Master Composters. From I-90, take exit #15. Go one mile south on Renton-Issaquah Road (Highway 900) Look for a big yellow mailbox and sign on the left. Follow the road across the bridge. Also see listing on page 252.

Squak Mt. Greenhouse & Nursery
-continued

Family fun is a high priority here. Stroll the pathways and bridges through the alpine garden and Japanese garden, enjoy the sight and sound of a waterfall garden and savor the fragrances in the herb garden. Then, for a small fee, you can seek entertainment in a nineteen-hole miniature golf garden! Children love picking their own pumpkin in October and coming back in December to choose a living or cut Christmas tree. In summer the greenhouse is filled with annuals and perennials, and the seasonal produce stand is a popular treat. This broad-based nursery carries an extensive array of plant materials and landscape supplies, including components for water-saving irrigation.

Valley Growers
1675 Newport Way
Issaquah, Washington 98027
☎ *206/392-2632*

Hours Mon-Sat 9-6, Sun 10-5; open until 9 during the holiday season
Accessible Yes
Mailing address 960 17th Avenue N.W. Issaquah, Washington 98027

Understated elegance is the phrase that comes to mind when I think of Wells Medina. It's a beautifully organized nursery run by extremely knowledgeable plantsmen. Their specialties are rare conifers, Japanese maples and perennials, and they have an excellent selection of azaleas, rhododendrons and magnolias, plus a number of other trees, shrubs and grasses you won't find in garden-variety (excuse the pun) nurseries. They offer both specimen-size and starter size plants, with excellent selections in each and every department. The colorful annuals, perennials and herbs are exquisitely displayed, and there's a wonderful new perennials border for

DESTINATION ☆
Wells Medina Nursery

8300 N.E. 24th Street
Bellevue, Washington 98004
☎ *206/454-1853*

Hours Mon-Sat 9-6, Sun 10-5 (mid-April through mid-Oct); Mon-Sat 9-5, Sun 10-5 (fall & winter)
Accessible Yes
FAX 206/454-0637

continued on next page--

Wells Medina Nursery
-continued

inspiration. They've books, house plants and bonsai, plus an especially appealing selection of containers, fountains, furniture and ornaments. For practical matters, the nursery stocks garden apparel and organic supplies.

South Suburban Area

Furney's Nursery

21215 Pacific Highway S.
Des Moines, Washington 98198
☎ 206/878-8761

Hours Daily 9:30-6; open until 7 Mon-Sat (spring) and Thurs-Sat (Christmas)
Accessible Yes

With both wholesale and retail operations, Furney's is unique in that it offers plants in such a variety of sizes – seedlings and rooted cuttings to 35-foot-tall specimen trees! Seasonal color is spectacular. They've hundreds of varieties of perennials and ground covers as well as a vast selection of shrubs. It's an excellent source for fruits and berries of all descriptions and wetland and water plants. Like most very large garden centers, landscape plants are but part of Furney's one-stop-shopping approach. The inventory here and in the Bellevue and Bremerton locations includes tropicals, garden accessories, books, tools, soil and soil builders.

Islands in the Sound
Bainbridge Island

☆DESTINATION
Bainbridge Gardens

9415 Miller Road
Bainbridge Island, Washington 98110
☎ 206/842-5888

Hours Mon-Sat 9-5:30, Sun 10-4
Accessible Yes
FAX 206/842-7645

There's a bitter-sweet story here. In 1908, Zenhichi Harui came to Bainbridge Island from Japan and started growing plants and flowers in his small garden. It blossomed into a splendid destination that attracted hundreds of visitors to see the sculpted trees and lily-covered pools. But the gardens were deserted in the early 1940s when Mr. Harui and his family, like thousands of other Japanese-Americans, were forced to leave. Friends tried to maintain it, but the family returned to a nursery in ruins. A few years ago one of Zenhichi's sons, Junkoh Harui, who had his own nursery business for over thirty years, took on the challenge of restoring the property. He is developing a Memorial Garden that features an exquisite old pear tree, several bonsai pines and an old

continued on next page--

wisteria that trails over a bamboo trellis – all treasured plants from his father's garden. He's also creating display gardens for herbs, alpines, ground covers and water plants. A peaceful atmosphere prevails throughout the nursery, which has benches for relaxing with a cup of espresso and an outdoor cafe that serves a delicious lunch. The lovely garden shop features *Woodard* wrought iron furniture, wood furniture by local artisans, tasteful statuary, containers and garden-oriented giftware. The large inventory of plant materials is immaculate. "We try to please, and our clientele knows we care," says Chris Harui. Ask about their classes and two annual Open Houses. From the Seattle Ferry dock, take Highway 305 north to High School Road. Turn left, then take a right on Miller Road.

Bainbridge Gardens
-continued

Vashon Island

"We operate on one of the area's oldest herb and greens farms and sell to the area's better restaurants," explains Vy Biel. "We were one of the early innovators of the wild or gourmet salads, which we offer as Country Salad." Not only does the company grow herbs and perennials (see listing on page 175), but also bulbs, ornamental grasses, ground covers, vines, shrubs and deciduous trees. They have a considerable number of rare and unusual plants, including natives, and they stock fountains, furniture and ornaments, books, general garden supplies, topsoil and natural fiber clothing. They do a number of the fundraising plant show/sales in the area. Selection is best from May through September. You'll find mark-downs in late-August. "We are located on lovely Vashon Island, the closest rural area to Seattle and Tacoma. It's a fun trip to get here; we are serviced by auto or foot ferry and located mid-isle on the main highway," adds Vy.

The Country Store & Farm
20211 Vashon Highway S.W.
Vashon Island, Washington 98070
☎ *206/463-3655*

Hours Mon-Sat 9-6, Sun 12-5
***Accessible** Yes*

Whidbey Island

The Greenhouse
Florist & Nursery, Inc.

9179 900 Avenue W.
Oak Harbor, Washington 98277
☎ *206/675-6668*

Hours *Mon-Sat 9-5:30*
Accessible *Difficult on gravel*

A family business, the Greenhouse Florist and Nursery has been operated by the Vanden Haak family for the past forty years. Their broad knowledge of horticulture provides a sound base from which to grow and propagate over 50 varieties of annuals in most colors, over 40 varieties of perennials and ground covers and over 25 varieties of vegetables and herbs. They offer a large selection of trees, shrubs, seasonal bulbs and garden supplies. Audrey and Henry Vanden Haak invite you to stop by and chat, look at their expanding antique and gift line, and schedule a tour of the greenhouses and design area. They offer weekly specials and an end-of-season sale in July. There's a full-time staff to answer most any question, and seminars are offered at different times of the year.

Northwest Washington

Anacordes

"Greetings from Young's Nursery!" writes Danielle Williams. "We have a great selection of shrubs, trees, annuals, perennials and garden supplies and a fantastic selection of fuchsias (starters and finished baskets) available in spring and summer. We have two Washington certified nursery people, two certified landscapers and a master gardener on staff, so bring us your questions." Dwarf evergreen and large flowering and fruit trees are also featured merchandise. The nursery hosts a Spring Open House Sale and holds three bonsai seminars each year, and they have plans for other topics. They're located off Highway 20, about twenty miles west of I-5. Watch for a big sign on the right.

Young's Nursery

1257 Thompson Road
Anacortes, Washington 98221
☎ *206/293-3120*

Hours Mon-Sat 9-5:30, Sun 10-5
(spring & summer);
Mon-Sat 9-5:30, Sun 10-4 (fall);
by appointment in winter
Accessible *Yes*

Bellingham

Several factors make this nursery special. The plants are grouped by landscape use and exceptionally well-labeled. The containers and baskets, statuary, fountains and gift wares are tastefully selected and displayed. And, the list of free gardening seminars and classes is outstanding. They've a large selection of house plants, a lovely water feature for inspiration, and a surprising number of landscape building materials. Their tag line, "Everything for your gardening needs and a whole lot more," says it all.

Bakerview Nursery, Inc.

945 E. Bakerview Road
Bellingham, Washington 98226
☎ *206/676-0400*

Hours Mon-Sat 9-6, Sun 12-5;
open until 7 on Fri (April through July),
closed Sundays (Jan & Feb)
Accessible *Yes*

The Garden Spot Nursery

900 Alabama
Bellingham, Washington 98225
☎ *206/676-5480*

Hours *Daily 9-6 (Feb & March),*
9-8 (March through Aug),
9-6 (Sept through Nov),
9-9 (holiday season); closed in Jan
Accessible *Yes*
FAX *206/738-4730*

Like its sister store in Seattle, The Garden Spot in Bellingham is staffed by avid gardeners who love their work. Their suppliers are small Northwest growers and the specialties are herbs and unusual perennials. They do not have a floral department at the Bellingham store, but they do carry garden books, gifts, seeds and house plants. They've organic supplies and a select complement of shrubs, vines and trees, plus ornaments, fountains and lots of containers (both planted and unplanted). The ambiance owner Marci Plattner has created is like a French garden house. You'll be comfortable dressed-up or dressed-to-garden in this charming store. The staff offers consultations on the design of perennial borders. Ask about spring and fall classes.

Blaine

Brown's Kalmia & Azalea Nursery

5100 Lincoln Road
Blaine, Washington 98230
☎ *206/371-2489*

Hours *Mon-Sat 9-5 (year-around);*
open Sun 1-4 (spring through fall)
Accessible *Yes*

Barbara Brown is the primary West Coast retail grower of the genus *Kalmia*. By popular demand, she has recently branched into a full-scale garden center that carries books, ornaments and organic gardening supplies, as well as a wide selection of landscape plants. The nursery offers discounts to garden clubs and conducts moss basket classes in May. See listing on page 151.

Everett

Gary McLaughlin says, "We have a very knowledgeable staff that cheerfully answers questions about your garden. We'll help you select plants that fit your special situation. Our bedding plants and perennials are top-quality, and we offer a fine selection of unusual conifers." The company offers free gardening classes, a free quarterly newsletter and in-store consultation. Watch for selected weekly specials and a clearance sale in the fall.

Evergreen Gardens Nursery & Floral

*9407 Evergreen Way
Everett, Washington 98204
☎ 206/355-2441*

Hours *Mon-Sat 9-6, Sun 10-5;
close at 5 (Nov & Jan)*
Accessible *Yes*

Everson

Cloud Mountain Farm & Nursery specializes in fruit trees, but the nursery also grows a nice selection of small garden trees, evergreen and deciduous shrubs, hardy fragrant roses, climbing vines, ground covers and bamboo. You'll find tools and organic supplies available at this seasonal nursery, as well. Look for weekly specials on select trees and shrubs. See page 207 for additional information.

Cloud Mountain Farm & Nursery

*6906 Goodwin Road
Everson, Washington 98247
☎ 206/966-5859*

Hours *Thurs-Mon 10-5, Sun 12-5
(Feb through mid-June);
Thurs-Sat 10-5 (Sept and Oct)*
Accessible *Yes*
Mail Order
Catalog *$1 (fruit trees)*
FAX *206/966-0921*

Ferndale

"We have been told by many of our customers that we have the nicest bedding plants. We grow many of our annuals in our own greenhouses to ensure quality," say Mike and Anita DeLancey. They've perennials and bulbs, shrubs and deciduous trees, fruits and berries, books, apparel and garden ornaments, plus general gardening supplies. Because they are located near the Nooksack River, the DeLanceys hold a pre-flood sale in the fall and shut down for the winter.

DeLanceys' Garden Center

*1951 Main Street
Ferndale, Washington 98248
☎ 206/384-1043*

Hours *Mon-Sat 9-5:30, Sun 11-4
(Feb through Oct)*
Accessible *Yes, except restrooms*

Marysville

Cascade Nursery

8921 55th Avenue N.E.
Marysville, Washington 98270
☎ *206/659-2988*

Hours *Mon-Sat 9:30-6, Sun 10-5*
(spring & summer);
Mon-Sat 9:30-5, Sun 10-4;
closed Wed in winter
Accessible *Yes*

"We're a small (three and a half-acre) retail nursery specializing in roses, perennials and conifers," says Elizabeth Huse. "Service, service, service is what you get here." Besides the above mentioned items, Cascade stocks annuals, bulbs, fruit trees, herbs, ornamental grasses, shrubs, flowering trees and vines. The gift shop features excellent gardening books. At Christmas they carry hand-picked noble and grand firs and have the shop filled with "fun stuff" and wonderful bows. The nursery participates in community education through the Marysville Schools. Take Marysville exit from I-5 and go north on State. Turn east on 88th Avenue N.E., then North on 55th Avenue N.E.

Mt. Vernon

☆DESTINATION
Hart's Nursery

1578 Best Road
Mount Vernon, Washington 98273
☎ *206/466-3821*

Hours *Mon-Sat 9-6, Sun 11-5*
(summer through winter);
Daily 9-6 (spring)
Accessible *Yes*

"Our setting is exceptional, right in the Skagit Valley, near historic La Conner," says John L. Christianson. "We grow many of the plants we sell on our seven acres and have a 60,000-square-foot greenhouse full of bedding plants. Our selection draws people from Seattle to Bellingham. We put special emphasis on roses (including many old fashioned varieties and new David Austin roses) and the rare and unusual perennials. What my wife, Toni, and I are trying to create is a complete 'plant Mecca,' offering every interesting plant available for sale and providing a friendly atmosphere with very knowledgeable plant experts dispensing information." They've a large selection of herbs, and the fruit trees come directly from the Mount Vernon Research Station. In summer, you'll find aquatic plants as well. You may have seen Hart's award-winning display gardens at the Northwest Flower and Garden Show. The business was

continued on next page--

begun by the Hart family as a rhododendron specialty nursery, and their selection of rhodies and azaleas remains excellent. They also feature a large selection of terra cotta pots, twig furniture and birdbaths. Roses are marked down in February; the fruit, flowering and shade trees in March, and the rhododendrons in April. Watch for the Lemon Sale (seconds and overstock) in June, a Two-for-One sale on annuals in July, mark-downs on statuary and fountains in August. In September there's a general plant sale, and in October, mark-downs on ground covers and hedge plants. The semi-monthly gardening newsletter, *The Garden Gazette* keeps you informed.

Note: A popular time to visit is during the Skagit Valley Tulip Festival when you can stroll among colorful flowers, abundant herbs, flowering trees and shrubs and meet the resident llamas and birds. Next door, the Hart family maintains a rustic eleven acre English country garden, **La Conner Flats**, and serves high tea in **The Granary**. (You are welcome to visit the garden; a donation for upkeep is requested. Tea begins at 2 p.m., March through October, and reservations are required. Phone: 206/466-3190.)

The big red barn that you see as you whiz-by between Seattle and B.C. is a friendly neighborhood garden center with all the goodies one would expect, plus a surprising selection of dwarf conifers. They've water plants and basic garden supplies and a terrific stock of garden books. The Christmas lighting is a delight. Ask to be added to the mailing list for half-price sales and special promotions.

Skagit Valley Gardens
1695 Johnson Road
Mt. Vernon, Washington 98273
☎ *206/424-6760*
FAX 206/ 424-5331
Hours *Daily 9-6 (spring, summer & fall);*
9-4:30 (winter); closed between
Christmas and New Year
Accessible *Partially*

Olympic Peninsula

Bremerton

Furney's Nursery

*5261 State Highway 303 N.E.
Bremerton, Washington 98310*
☎ *206/373-8812*

Hours *Daily 9:30-7 (spring);
Mon-Sat 9-6, Sun 10-5 (summer,
fall & winter); extended hours during
the holiday season*

Wherever there's a Furney's, there's everything for the garden under one roof! See listings on pages 337 and 340.

Poulsbo

Valley Nursery

*20882 Bond Road N.E.
Poulsbo, Washington 98370*
☎ *206/779-3806*

Hours *Mon-Fri 9-6, Sat & Sun 9-5
(spring and summer);
close at 5:30 in fall & winter*
Accessible *Yes*

Manager Bob Olcott notes that this general garden center specializes in unusual conifers, perennials and ground covers. They grow their own hanging baskets and offer a big selection of containers, tubs and planters, arbors, statuary and fountains in the gift area, where you'll also find a good collection of books and general garden supplies. Valley Nursery looks like a park. Families come to see the aviaries and enjoy the wooded pastoral landscape with its salmon creek.

Sequim

Dungeness Bay Nursery

*647 Clark Road
Sequim, Washington 98382*
☎ *206/683-2454*

Hours *Mon-Sat 8-5, Sun 10-4
(March through Oct);
Tues-Sat 9-4 (Nov through Feb)*
Accessible *No*

Started in 1989, Dungeness Bay Nursery has developed demonstration gardens and a collection of rare, unusual, dwarf and hard-to-find plants. "To this end," says Don Grant, "we are constantly expanding varieties. The philosophy and goal of Dungeness Bay Nursery is to provide only superior-quality plants." The focus is on ornamental plant materials, and with its acres of landscaped gardens, it is certainly one of the state's prettiest nurseries. You'll also find containers, fountains, soil amendments and garden books. Sales are held throughout the year. They do not have clearance sales except for annuals at the end of their season. Garden tours have become regular events; call about seminars and classes. To get there, follow the Dungeness scenic loop starting at Sequim-Dungeness Way in Sequim. Six miles later, this route comes out on Marine Drive. Proceed along the Bay a quarter-mile to Clark Road. Turn left.

Dungeness Bay Nursery
-continued

Peninsula Nurseries offers plants in sizes both small and large and maintains a sizable inventory year-around. "We attempt to keep in stock the hard-to-find plants, such as empress trees, monkey puzzle trees, Japanese umbrella pines, etc. We are a fun place to visit and shop," says Roger Fell. "We offer pruning seminars, landscape design classes, and such special speakers as Ed Hume and Marianne Bonetti. Watch for the big Anniversary Sale in October. In addition to landscape plants, this downtown garden center carries bonsai, fountains, books, garden furniture and ornaments, house plants, irrigation systems, lighting, organic supplies and paving materials.

Peninsula Nurseries, Inc.
4911 Sequim-Dungeness Way
Sequim, Washington 98382
(206/683-6969

Hours Mon-Sat 8-6; Sun 10-4; closed Sun in winter
Accessible Yes
FAX 206/681-2865

Tacoma Area & Mt. Rainier

Auburn

Annuals, bonsai, bulbs, conifers, ferns, fruits and berries, grasses, ground covers, herbs, house plants, perennials, shrubs and trees and vines (including Northwest natives) are the "softscape" components of owner Wan Song's garden center. Books, containers, fencing materials, soil amendments, tools and organic supplies serve the "hardscape" needs. Selection is best from April through August and markdowns begin in July. The location is at 320th S. and Military Road, a quarter-mile east of Seatac Mall.

ABC Nursery & Greenhouses
32108 39th Avenue S.
Auburn, Washington 98001
☎ 206/952-4114

Hours Daily 9-6
Accessible No
FAX 206/661-0670

Belfair

AG3 Garden Nursery

E2141 Highway 302
Belair, Washington 98528
☎ *206/275-5119*

Hours *Tues-Sat 11-5:30*
Accessible *Yes, except restrooms*

"The goal of AG3 Gardens is to provide an array of garden ideas by way of landscaped planting beds and ever-changing scenic gardens," says Kathy Arnold whose emphasis is on seasonal planting schedules at this full-service garden center. "There will always be something new to see here," she promises. "We grow most of our own stock, so the selection is continually changing." The nursery stocks soils, bark and general garden supplies in addition to a wide range of ornamental plant materials. Watch the Shelton and Bremerton papers for information on scheduled seminars. From Gig Harbor-Purdy, take the Purdy bridge. From Belfair, take Victor Cut-Off Road past High School to the end, then left on Highway 302. Look for the sign on the left-hand-side of road.

Buckley

Buckley Nursery Garden Center

646 North River Avenue
Buckley, Washington 98321
☎ *206/829-1811*

Hours *Daily 9-5*
Accessible *Yes*
Mail Order *(fruit trees)*
Catalog *Free*

"Our biggest business is in fruit trees," says owner Don Marlow. He and his wife Penny try to supply "a little of everything for the home gardener – flowers, ferns, herbs, house plants, shade trees, shrubs, ground covers and vines, soil amendments and tools. The company's fruit catalog lists several species of flowering shrubs available bare-root from February through April. See listing on page 205.

Gig Harbor

With five Washington Certified Nurs-erymen on staff to lend advice and a broad selection of nursery stock, Peninsula Gardens attracts a discriminating clientele from all over the South Sound and Olympic Peninsula. The specialties of the house include roses, perennials, water gardening and Christmas holiday merchandise. On its eight acres, located a mile and a half west of Gig Harbor, you'll discover a shade plant section, a deciduous plant area filled with spring-blooming trees and shrubs and green-houses brimming with annuals and container plants. One full-time staff member does nothing but make fabulous hanging baskets and planted containers. They keep customers well informed with plant lists, a newsletter and periodic seminars. From Highway 16, take the Fox Island exit and travel west a bit over a mile.

Peninsula Gardens

5503 Wollochet Drive N.W.
Gig Harbor, Washington 98335
☎ *206/851-8115 or 1-800/622-8700*
FAX *206/851-8104*
Hours *Mon-Sat 9-6, Sun 10-5*
(spring & summer);
close at 5:30 in winter
Accessible *Yes*

Lakebay

Dale and Claudia Loy tell customers they aren't there for big landscaping projects, but to provide choices other than rhododendrons to make the garden interesting. (Yes, they sell rhodies, too.) Located on the Key Peninsula in the town of Key Center, Sunnycrest is a good source for books, containers and organic supplies in addition to annuals and general landscape plants. "We are always interested in new and different plants, so we seek out many small suppliers. Our main goal is to make our customers successful gardeners. We really enjoy what we do." In September all nursery stock goes on sale.

Sunnycrest Nursery & Florist

9004B Highway K.P.N.
Lakebay, Washington 98349
☎ *206/884-3937*

Hours *Mon-Sat 9-6, Sun 11-4*
(Feb through Dec);
Mon-Sat 9-5 (Jan)
Accessible *Yes*

Puyallup

Alpine Nursery

17518 79th Avenue E.
Puyallup, Washington 98373
☎ *206/847-7078*

Hours *Mon-Fri 9-6, Sat 10-4;*
open Sun 11-4 (April 15 through
July 4 and from Thanksgiving
until Christmas);
(closed Mon in summer & winter)
Accessible *Difficult on gravel*

"We stock conifers, shade trees, fruit trees, ground covers and a good selection of hard-to-find shrubs," say Harlie and Edith Streeter. Noting their bedding plants, hanging baskets and the poinsettias grown for Christmas, they observe, "Our nursery and greenhouses are kept free of weeds and the stock is well-watered during warm weather. We give honest advice and accurate information on planting and maintenance." Selected items go on sale during the summer and fall.

Edgewood Flower Farm

2017 E. Meridian
Puyallup, Washington 98371
☎ *206/927-0817*

Hours *Mon-Sat 9-6, Sun 10-4:30*
(spring & summer); Mon-Sat 9-5,
Sun 10-4:30 (fall & winter)
Accessible *Yes*

Bill and Donna O'Ravez invite visitors who are "seeking quality and the not-so-ordinary" to experience Edgewood Flower Farm. Although they offer a full palette of landscape plants, the specialties here are Victorian moss baskets, custom planted urns and tubs, extraordinary fuchsias and European balcony geraniums. Specimen trees and shrubs abound in this well-kept nursery that features a David Austin English Rose collection along with topiaries, perennials and ground covers. The English-theme garden shop features gift items and books and has an interior/floral designer on staff. They've a large library available for customers' use, and they provide cultural instructions for most plants. Annuals and perennials are marked down in August and September. You'll find Edgewood three miles north of the Western Washington fairgrounds.

Sumner

"We are wholesale growers as well as retailers, specializing in pansies, primroses, fuchsias, annuals and poinsettias. Our special attention to the quality of our own product, as well as an excellent reputation for cleanliness and customer service contribute to the overall success of our business," say managers Joel Adams and Cindy Darland. "Our seminars draw great crowds and rave reviews. We also periodically offer free individual landscape planning sessions with a nationally known author and columnist. A newsletter helps us to keep our customers informed about special events, as well as educating them on a variety of subjects." In addition to a broad range of landscape and indoor plants, the nursery stocks containers, fountains, ornaments, furniture, apparel, books, organic supplies, soil amendments and tools. Selection is best from April through June for fuchsia baskets and annuals. Mark-downs begin in late-June. Special events include classes on bonsai, flower drying and arranging, moss baskets and wreath making, and wintering fuchsias. Ask to receive the nursery's informative newsletter.

Windmill Nursery
5823 160th Avenue E.
Sumner, Washington 98390
☎ *206/863-5843*

Hours *Mon-Fri 9-6, Sat 9-5, Sun 10-5*
Accessible *Yes*
FAX *206/863-8297*

Tacoma

A full service garden center, Evergreen Gardens specializes in herbs and perennials, water gardening and topiary. Within a little over an acre of sales area, Janet Sears has packed-in "fun and unusual plants," garden furniture and accessories, organic supplies, house plants, hard-to-find tools, books and gifts. She offers garden consultation and a complete floral department. "This is a nursery for the love of gardening – whether you're an inexperienced beginner or a seasoned pro, we will counsel

Evergreen Gardens & Gifts
7216 27th Street W.
Tacoma, Washington 98466
☎ *206/565-9369*

Hours *Mon-Sat 9-6, Sun 10-6; extended hours during Christmas season*
Accessible *Yes*
FAX *206/564-5135*

continued on next page--

Evergreen Gardens & Gifts

-continued

your every step in making your garden how you really want it to be." Classes include bonsai, planting, wreath making, floral, general and specific gardening. Call for dates of the Fall Harvest Celebration, and plan to join the Christmas festivities. The nursery is located in University Place in West Pierce County, one block east of Bridgeport Way.

Poole's Nursery Center, Inc.

3518 6th Avenue
Tacoma, Washington 98406
☎ 206/759-3519

Hours Mon-Sat 8:30-5:30, Sun 10-4
Accessible Yes

As Poole's continues into its second century, customers are still greeted by name and delivery service is still available! This company's colorful history began in 1889 when Franklin Poole opened a seed and farm supply store in Tacoma. It remains a family business today, although the names have changed. In 1988 Tony Palermo, grandson of a former partner, bought the venerable company, opting to retain the Poole family name. The founder's granddaughter remains as office manager, a position she has held for forty years! Julie and Tony Palermo describe the nursery as "a blend of the old and the new, with a continued commitment to keeping up to date on the latest horticultural information." They carry the full gamut of ornamentals, including natives, and such specialty plants as alpines, water lilies, bonsai and tropicals. They've landscape supplies, tools, books, garden ornaments and house plants. Watch the *Tacoma News Tribune* for dates of the two big sales in April and for classes and demonstrations on a variety of topics at the nursery.

Choice plant materials, including specimen Japanese maples and bonsai pines, are played against old farm equipment in this pleasant three-acre setting. "We have sale items all year long and are very reasonably priced," owner John Coenen reports. The local Rose Society and Iris Society regularly visit the garden to talk to customers. Garden furniture, containers, tools, apparel and organic supplies serve the gardener, while a wide range of plant materials are there to serve the garden.

Portland Avenue Nursery, Inc.

1409 E. 59th
Tacoma, Washington 98404
☎ 206/473-0194

Hours Mon-Sat 9-5:30, Sun 10-4
Accessible Partially

Olympia Area & Twin Cities

Centralia

During the spring and fall, Rick Schnatterly's Garden Time radio program plays to an eager audience on AM 1470 at 8:30 Wednesday mornings. The rest of the time Rick is minding the store, and what a delightful store it is. "Our large selection of trees and shrubs include unusual varieties. Many of our flower and vegetable bedding plants are grown in our own greenhouses to our high standards," he says. Garden products include bulk mulches, garden tools and "gadgets," plus lots of decorative accessories. Founded in 1927, Pioneer West is the oldest garden center in the area, convenient to Centralia's antique malls and factory outlet stores. The nursery holds an annual Orphan Plant Sale in mid-October and soon after begins decorating for Christmas, with at least ten theme trees loaded with decorations from around the world. Also see listing on page 235.

Pioneer West

710 N. Tower
Centralia, Washington 98531
☎ 206/736-3872

Hours Mon-Sat 8:30-6, Sun 12-5
Accessible Yes

Lacey

College Street Nursery

3613 College Street S.E.
Lacey, Washington 98503
☎ *206/491-1688*

Hours *Mon-Sat 9-6, Sun 11-5*
Accessible *Yes*

"We're a down-home nursery with great customer service," says Bill Pattison. "If we don't have it, we'll find it – at anytime of year. We try to make gardening fun and easy by selling only plants that grow well in our area." There's no category of plant material the company does not keep in stock, from conifers to wildflowers. It also maintains a good selection of non-plant items, such as books, ornaments, fountains, furniture, tools and soil amendments. Aimed at families who want fresh ideas for their gardens, College Street Nursery also serves-up seminars on timely topics.

Olympia

Boulevard Nursery & Greenhouse

2021 Boulevard Road S.E.
Olympia, Washington 98501
☎ *206/352-1728*

Hours *Mon-Fri 9-6, Sat 9-5:30, Sun 10-5 (April through June); Mon-Sat 9-5:30 (July through March)*
Accessible *Yes*

Sue Swanson observes, "Our clientele is attracted by our wide selection of plant material, both in shrubs and trees as well as bedding plants and vegetable plants. We grow our own annuals and vegetables. People also enjoy coming here because of the personal attention we give them." The nursery's weekly sales are advertised in *The Olympian*, and garden advice is free! You'll find lots of poinsettias at Christmas, and such specialty items as bonsai and house plants. Throughout the year, there are containers and fountains, apparel, books, seeds, soil amendments and tools. In summer, the herbs and perennials, ornamental grasses, ground covers and water plants are star attractions, too.

Yelm

"Our garden center offers perhaps the most complete selection of nursery materials in the South Puget Sound Area," says Gordon Kampfer, whose nursery is big business in the little town of Yelm. "We are a reliable source for bare-root fruit, shade and flowering trees, with a stock of 4,000 plants in early February through March." The company inventories 150 different varieties of fruit trees, as well as cane plants. Then 1,000 rhodies, 1,500 azaleas and hundreds of other ornamental shrubs are brought in for the season. Annuals and veggies are displayed 1,000 flats at a time. "But, our specialty is roses – 10,000 bare-root bushes every year (650 varieties), including a wide selection of antique roses," he adds. "Our staff is experienced. Advice and assistance are always available, plus we have a marvelous view of Mt. Rainier!"

Gordon's Garden Center

308 Yelm Avenue E.
Yelm, Washington 98597-0447
☎ *206/458-2481*

Hours *Daily 8-8 (spring & summer)*
9-6 (fall & winter)
Accessible *Yes*
FAX *206/458-8427*

Central Washington

Brewster

The Wilson family specializes in hardy plant materials for the eastern edge of the Cascades. They keep a wide selection in inventory – annuals, ornamental grasses, fruits and berries, herbs, perennials, roses, shrubs, trees and vines. "Mom and Dad are always looking-for and finding new and unusual plants," says Jord Wilson. They've natives and wildflowers along with hardy rhododendrons and azaleas. Inside there's a floral department with house plants, books and gifts. Watch for the September 30%-off Sale.

Wilson Gardens

25891 South Highway 97
Brewster, Washington 98812
☎ *509/689-3606*

Hours *Daily 9-6 (spring); 9-5*
(summer through winter)
Accessible *Yes*

Yakima

Evans Nursery

6612 Tieton Drive
Yakima, Washington 98908
☎ *509/966-0698*

Hours *Mon-Sat 8-6, Sun 9-5*
(Feb through Dec)
Accessible *Yes, except restrooms*
Mail Order
Catalog *Free (alpine fir only)*

"Personal Service, a knowledgeable staff and a clean, well organized, well stocked nursery," are the attributes the owner, Larry Evans, wants customers to associate with his large regional garden center. "We specialize in collected native alpine fir, quaking aspen and vine maple," he says, noting that the company ships alpine fir world-wide. The selection of natives is best in the fall. In addition to a complete range of garden plants, Evans Nursery carries books, bonsai, containers and ornaments, house plants, organic supplies, rocks, topsoil, soil amendments and tools. The staff offers expert garden advice, loans-out tapes on gardening and garden products, and publishes a monthly newsletter. Also see page 256.

Eastern Washington

Othello

Kinder Gardens Nursery and Landscaping

1137 S. Highway 17
Othello, Washington 99344
☎ *509/488-5017*

Hours *Mon-Sat 9-6, Sun 12-5*
(spring & fall); Tues-Sat 9-6 (summer)
Accessible *Yes*

Established in 1985, Kinder Gardens Nursery and Landscaping is located six miles south of Othello. Owned and operated by Dennis and Claudia Kinder, this nursery has grown from four varieties of conifers to an operation that offers over 200 varieties of deciduous and evergreen shrubs and trees. "We supplement our selection with annuals and vegetables, perennials, roses and fruit trees, bark, rock and garden supplies. Our nursery stock is 'eastside' acclimated, and we offer advice on plant needs for proper placement. We take pride in providing quality and quantity, both at an affordable price. Our newly planted 3/4-acre arboretum offers an enjoyable and educational walk through different theme gardens." The Kinders conduct seminars on container gardening and perennial gardens during the season and send plant lists to regular customers. They offer "bare-root specials" in spring.

Pullman

Springtime is especially lovely in the rolling Palouse Hills, when The Pullman Garden Center reopens after a winter break and the whole area becomes an oasis for bird watching. Seven years ago, Suzanne St. Pierre relocated her parent's nursery to an old dairy farm where she remodeled a barn, built a sunroom for house plants and turned the place into a full-service garden center. "We celebrate every season," says manager Theresa Greiner. The Annual Sale is in September. Special events include Pumpkin Patch field trips for kindergarten and first graders and a Christmas Open House the first weekend in December featuring a local classical guitarist and goodies. "We're long on advice," she adds. "Our goal is to make a place that people enjoy coming to. We sell quality plant material and stand behind it. We try to ensure that our customers know what they are getting through signage, service and the use of our small library. We publish a newsletter four times a year." The nursery is located five miles west of Moscow, Idaho and three miles east of Pullman, Washington on State Highway 270.

Pullman Garden Center

Pullman-Moscow Highway
Pullman, Washington 99163
☎ *509/332-5714*

Hours Mon-Sat 8:30-6:30, Sun 12-6 (March through Sept); Mon-Sat 8:30-6, Sun 12-5 (Oct through Dec 23)
Accessible Yes

Spokane

Gibson's carries an unusually wide range of products for your landscaping needs. It's strong in plant materials from annuals to large-caliper trees as well as supplies for the "hardscape." (See page 108.) The extensive collection of nursery stock Is carefully chosen for adaptability in the Eastern Washington/ Idaho area. An experienced staff offers consumer advice and information. The company is also notable for special-ordering and shipping plants and products to clients. It's located two miles south of I-90.

Gibson's Nursery and Landscape Supply

S. 1401 Pines Road
Spokane, Washington 99206
☎ *509/928-0973*

Hours Mon-Sat 8-5:30
Accessible Yes
Mail Order
Catalog Free
FAX 509/926-4352

Mel's Nursery, Floral & Gifts

N. 8800 Division
Spokane, Washington 99218
☎ 509/467-5132

Hours Mon-Sat 9-8, Sun 9-6
(May through July);
Daily 9-6 (off-season);
open until 9 in Nov & Dec
Accessible Partially
FAX 509/467-7476

With its nursery, furniture gallery and gift shop, Sue and Mel Shaw's business covers both interior and exterior design. The nursery division offers a wide range of plant materials, including rock garden plants, bonsai, natives and drought-tolerant species. There are water plants to complement the many fountains available here, and there's a big selection of ornaments, including birdbaths, wind chimes, containers and sundials to adorn the landscape. You'll find furniture for your house and benches and twig furnishings for the garden. Plants are marked-down at the end of the growing season (watch the paper for ads). Then the focus at Mel's turns toward the gift shop and Christmas displays.

Stanek's

E. 2929 27th
Spokane, Washington 99223
☎ 509/535-2939

Hours Mon Sat 9-6, Sun 12-5;
closed Sun in winter
Accessible Yes
FAX 509/534-3050
Mail Order (roses)
Catalog Free

Steve Stanek ships roses all over the country – hybrids, antiques and climbers. But roses are only a small part of the vast array of ornamental landscape plants and specialty plant materials at this large garden center. Stanek's vends many, many varieties of perennials, bog plants and water gardening supplies, a wide selection in containers and ornaments, garden books, tools and much more. This business has been in the family for eighty-one years; they've more than fifty people on staff. Customers drive from far and near for the large selection of plant materials offered here, the seasonal classes and the terrific Christmas displays. Watch for a fall sale and an after-Christmas sale.

Walla Walla

Bordered by two creeks and set off by three acres of lawn, Green Valley is an appealing setting for the plant materials and garden ornaments offered here. An octagonal pagoda-style sales building, which is attached by walkways to large shade houses of the same design, creates a distinctive architectural backdrop for the lovely display gardens. The selection in perennials and annuals is outstanding, and you'll find bonsai and house plants in addition to landscape plants. There are books, garden furnishings and organic supplies. While the owners, John and Yvonne Jaso, occasionally hold a fall sale, they feature on-going specials throughout the gardening season. "Word of mouth has always been our best advertising," say the Jasos. "Each plant is accompanied by a planting guide as well as fertilizer. For those who live in the community, we offer free home visits if the customer is having difficulty with their plant." (I wonder if doctors in Walla Walla still make housecalls...)

Green Valley Nursery

Plaza Way, 1.3 miles south of Bi Mart
Walla Walla, Washington
☎ *509/525-7888*

Hours *Mon-Sat 9-5:30, Sun 12-4*
(March through June);
Mon-Sat 10-5 (July through Sept);
Mon-Sat 10-4:30 (Oct & Nov);
by appointment in winter
Accessible *Yes*
Mailing address *512 E. Alder Street*
Walla Walla, Washington 99362

Southwestern Washington

Kelso

"We stress responsible decision-making in the selection and use of plant materials, as well as proper and conscientious use of pesticides," says Nancy Chennault. She and her husband Jim ask questions and try to match the customer with the plants, supplies and information they need. "We won't sell a plant if customers don't have the proper soil conditions or exposure for it." Ask to receive *The All Seasons Newsery* for coupons and details about classes. Watch for the Longest Day of the Year Sale (weekend of the first week of summer), Annuals Sale (Labor Day+10),

All Season Landscape and Nursery

3829 Pleasant Hill Road
Kelso, Washington 98626
☎ *206/577-7955*

Hours *Mon-Sat 9-6, Sun 12-5*
Accessible *Yes*

continued on next page--

All Season Landscape and Nursery
-continued

Fall Color Sale in October and Inventory Clearance two days after Christmas. The nursery carries everything for the landscape from annuals to trees, plus organic supplies and garden ornaments. From southbound I-5; take exit #46, then turn south on Pleasant Hill Road; from northbound I-5, take exit # 42, follow signs to Pleasant Hill.

Vancouver

Kasch's

13519 Fourth Plain Road
Vancouver, Washington 98682
☎ *206/892-2258*

Hours *Daily 9-5:30*
Accessible *Yes*

The Vancouver branch of this Portland-based garden center chain carries a wide range of landscape plants at competitive prices. See page 366.

White Salmon

Fruit Valley Greenhouse

775 N.W. Loop Road
White Salmon, Washington 98672
☎ *509/493-2894*

Hours *Daily 8-6*
Accessible *Yes*

"Our people really care about other people and meeting their needs," says Fran Cavender. "About 40% of our customers drive over a tall bridge from the Oregon side of the Columbia River to reach our store, paying a 50-cent toll going and coming. We are told by our customers that our shrubs and trees are kept in better shape and our prices are lower than our competitors'. We raise all our own bedding plants in our own greenhouses, which gives us control over our plants from the time they are seeded until they are taken from the store. We pride ourselves in the service we render after the sale." Selection is at its peak the first weekend in May for the annual open house, which includes seminars and special events. After June 15th, all of the annuals are sold at half-price. "Landscape and garden advice is available anytime we have personal contact. We rarely give advice over the phone."

Woodland

"Everything from the Ground Up" is this company's tag line. Circle S not only supplies soils, mulches, decorative rocks, retaining wall materials and other building materials, but also the basic tools, hoses, sprinklers and drip systems to maintain your garden. Also see listing on page 107. The company is a large wholesale/retail garden center, with a sod farm and nursery behind the scene to supply a wide range of plant materials.

Circle S Landscape Supplies, Ltd.

3404 Old Lewis River Road
Woodland, Washington 98674
☎ *206/225-5845*

Hours Mon-Sat 7:30-6, Sun 9-5
***Accessible** Yes*
Mail Order
Catalog Free
FAX 206/225-5845

Ninety-five percent of the customers drive more than twenty miles to Tsugawa's! What draws crowds from the Portland-Vancouver metropolitan area is an "information" approach to gardening. The nursery maintains a library of instructions for gardening projects and offers year-round classes with such titles as *The Principles of Japanese Design*, *Attracting Backyard Wildlife*, *Training and Pruning Fruit Trees*, and *Fall Gardening: The Organic Way*. Although Tsugawa's carries all of the standard Northwest plant materials, there's a decidedly Asian flavor in this five-acre nursery, with over 75 varieties of Japanese maples and large conifer bonsai, for example. Indoors there's an excellent selection of decorative accessories, many by Northwest craftspeople. Bare-root roses, trees of all kinds and small fruits are marked down in March. Annuals go on sale in August. From I-5: take Exit 21. The nursery is on the access road about two blocks northeast of the exit.

DESTINATION ✫
Tsugawa Nursery & Watergardens

410 Scott Avenue
Woodland, Washington 98674
☎ *206/225-8750*

Hours Daily 9-7 (April through Sept);
Daily 9-5:30 (Oct through March)
***Accessible** Yes*
FAX 206/225-5086

Oregon
Portland Metropolitan Area

Portland

Cornell Farm

8212 S.W. Barnes Road
Portland, Oregon 97225
☎ *503/292-9895*

Hours Daily 9-6:30 (spring & summer);
Mon-Sat 9-6, Sun 10-5
Accessible Yes

Cornell Farm grows most of its annuals and perennials, so the quality and selection are excellent here. The nursery is also well-known for hanging baskets and planters. Growers are often on hand to answer cultural questions, and knowledgeable staff members work with customers to find the right shrubs, trees, vines and ground covers for the right spot. You'll find ornaments and furniture, house plants, organic supplies and tools, as well, at this attractive nursery located a half-mile east of St. Vincent's Medical Center.

Dennis' 7 Dees Nursery

6025 S.E. Powell Boulevard
Portland, Oregon 97206
☎ *503/777-1421*
10455 S.W. Butner Road
Portland, Oregon 97225
☎ *503/297-1058*
1090 McVey Avenue
Lake Oswego, Oregon 97034
☎ *503/636-4660*

Hours Daily 10-5 (Jan through mid-Feb);
9-7 (spring); 9-6 (summer & fall);
Daily 8-8 (Christmas season)
Accessible Yes

"One-stop" shopping with a very large selection of quality plants, containers, statuary and most everything related to gardening is what Dennis Snodgrass promises. "If we don't have an item, we will special-order it for a customer. Our staff members are friendly, well-trained nursery professionals. We offer a lifetime guarantee on our plants, and we maintain a huge selection of plant material year-around." Watch for promotional sales from March through June, a huge plant sale in the fall, and clinics in spring and fall. Dennis teaches at Portland Community College. You'll find over a hundred free handouts available at the nurseries.

At the height of the gardening season, Drake's maintains a staff of ten to twelve nurserymen to help people make their selections from a wide array of hardy plants. The garden center has a well-stocked gift shop, and they offer tropical plants, pond supplies and bonsai in addition to landscape plants. "Service to customers is our strong suit," says Marvin Thompson.

Drake's 7 Dees
16519 S.E. Stark
Portland, Oregon 97233
☎ *503/255-9225*

Hours Mon Sat 9-6, Sun 9-5;
Mon-Sat 9-8, Sun 9-5 (May & June)
***Accessible** Yes*
***FAX** 503/256-0865*

Freddy's flagship garden center is a well-kept secret. Its size is deceptive from the street, and the diverse inventory surprised me! It happens to be near my home, so I pop-in often for one thing or another. I expected to find hoses and fertilizer and pansies. I didn't expect to find unusual perennials or such a big selection of house plants at such favorable prices! "We're picky about what we bring in," says the manager, "and we try to have knowledgeable people to serve you." This is not your average chain-store nursery.

Fred Meyer, Raleigh Hills
7700 S.W. Beaverton-Hillsdale Highway
Portland, Oregon 97225
☎ *503/ 292-9154*

Hours Daily 8-10
***Accessible** Yes*

John Georges began this family-operated nursery in 1949. He's still in charge! His nephew, Richard Barhoum, says the focus remains on plant materials and general garden supplies at the one-acre sales yard. "While we do not do landscaping, we help people lay out their landscapes. The season's biggest event is the Annual "Blow Out Sale" in early July.

Georges Garden
8358 S.E. Causey
Portland, Oregon 97266
☎ *503/654-1454*

Hours Daily 9-dark
***Accessible** Yes*

Kasch's

2500 S.E. Tacoma
Portland, Oregon 97202
☎ 503/231-7711
599 A Avenue
Lake Oswego, Oregon 97034
☎ 503/699-9104
675 N.E. 181st Street
Portland, Oregon 972300
☎ 503/661-5020

Hours Daily 9-5:30;
call for extended evening hours in spring
Accessible Yes

"If it has roots, we have it," says George Rogers, who carries on the family business begun in 1949 by his parents Anne and Howard Kasch. It's now a small chain known throughout the Portland area for very competitive prices on a very large selection of landscape plants and hard goods. The original garden store at Tacoma and McLoughlin is presently operating out of a tent while the Highway Department works nearby, but plans call for rebuilding. The Lake Oswego location carries cut flowers in addition to all manner of materials for the garden. Most of the stores have house plants, and all of them stock water plants, rock garden plants and lots of supplies for container gardening.

Langdown Florist & Greenhouses

5645 S. W. Scholls Ferry Road
Portland, Oregon 97225
☎ 503/292-9121 or 1-800/241-ROSE

Hours Mon-Sat 8-6, Sun 11-4;
(closed Sun in Jan, Feb, July & Aug)
Accessible Yes
FAX 503/292-3391

Langdown traces its roots back to greenhouses built in 1948 for growing geraniums and poinsettias. Owner Jim Haslett notes that the company continues to feature container plants, but Langdown has become much, much more. Tucked into a residential neighborhood across from the Portland Golf Club, the newly remodeled store offers a wide range of landscape plants, with an emphasis on unusual annuals and perennials, specimen Japanese maples and other fine trees and shrubs. They've especially nice containers and handsome house plants. You'll find garden sculpture by local artists at times, plus bonsai, alpines and a few water plants. They offer citywide delivery on floral goods. Get on the mailing list for the fall clearance sale in September and a holiday open house just before Thanksgiving.

Oregon Garden Store established its reputation at the State Street store in Lake Oswego by offering select garden furniture and accessories from artisans and manufacturers worldwide. (See listing on page 317.) This new garden center carries many of the same lovely garden furnishings, but it also offers a wide selection of landscape plants. Located on the grounds of the former Gerber Gardens, Oregon Garden Store has renovated the property and brought new enthusiasm for the art of gardening. The staff is knowledgeable, and they're venturing into the less common plant materials. They'll search for anything you're seeking. There's a special emphasis on annuals and perennials. Staff members make custom planters and moss baskets, and they'll even come to your home to design the patio plantings. If you're looking for tools, Italian terra cotta pots or Christmas greens, this is a good place to start. The State Street store will continue to carry more one-of-a-kind accessories and feature topiary and herbs.

Oregon Garden Store
15780 S.W. Boones Ferry Road
Lake Oswego, Oregon 97035
☎ *503/636-9341*

Hours *Mon-Sat 10-6, Sun 10-5*
Accessible *Yes*
FAX *503/226-2409*

The outstanding selection of plant material at these two locations attracts serious gardeners like bees! "We have international suppliers and frequently obtain material that was previously available only from collector's nurseries, mail order or plant society sales," explains Anne Weber. "Our staff is composed of dedicated gardeners, and we really enjoy helping customers develop their own gardens. We go out of our way to supply information and help." The information desk is set up to answer even the toughest questions. Many of the city's garden societies hold their shows and sales at the nursery. Watch *The Oregonian* for details. The Division Street location (formerly known as Portland

DESTINATION☆
Portland Nursery

5050 S.E. Stark Street
Portland, Oregon 97215
☎ *503/231-5050*
9000 S.E. Division Street
Portland, Oregon 97266
☎ *503/788-9000*

Hours *Daily 9-7 (April through Sept);*
9-6 (Oct through March)
Accessible *Yes*
FAX *503/232-0838 or 503/788-9002*

Portland Nursery

-continued

Greenhouse) features fabulous tropicals and water plants and fountains as well as hardy garden plants. Powell's Book Store keeps a wonderful selection of garden books in the Stark Street store. Also see listings on pages 119 and 246.

East Suburban Area

Circle S Landscape Supplies, Ltd.

22420 N.E. Halsey
Troutdale, Oregon 97060
☎ *503/669-6820*

FAX 503/669-0852
Hours *Mon-Sat 7:30-6, Sun 9-5*
Accessible *Yes*

Besides landscape supplies, Circle S is a large wholesale/retail garden center (with a sod farm and nursery behind the scene) that supplies plant materials. See additional listing on page 107.

McGregor's Garden Center

30855 S.E. Ely Road
Estacada, Oregon 97023
☎ *503/630-2390*

Hours *Mon-Sat 9-6, Sun 10-4*
(spring & summer);
Mon-Sat 9-5, Sun 10-3 (fall & winter)
Accessible *Yes*

Don and Phyllis McGregor and their sons, Mark and Chris, have developed quite a company here in the past eight years. In addition to a garden center, there's a lumber yard and wood products shop. All are interrelated. The shop fabricates lots of fancy wood containers for the garden center, and the garden center (the part Mark McGregor enjoys most) makes lots of lovely container gardens. The garden center caters to the needs of eastsiders with a full range of landscape plants and supplies. It sells and delivers mulches and chicken manure and grows its own bedding plants, herbs, vegetable starts and specialty plants in a greenhouse. You can find everything from a one-gallon seedling to an 18-foot silver maple in a 200-pound box on the property. They are in the process of creating a display garden designed as a half-acre maze with fountains, water plants and rock garden materials interwoven in the whole. Sounds like fun.

West Suburban Area

See complete listing for Kasch's on page 366.

Kasch's
3250 S.W. Cedar Hills Boulevard
Beaverton, Oregon 97005
☎ 503/644-1640
2706 S.E. Tualatin Valley Highway
Hillsboro, Oregon 97123
☎ 503/640-9038

A full-service florist and garden center, Means Nursery is the retail outlet for a large wholesale grower with shrubs and trees in production on more than a hundred acres on the Columbia River. The company offers plants at close to wholesale prices, and there are "specials" every week. If you're spending more than $100, there will be an additional discount. They've expanded the inventory to include annuals, perennials, herbs and vegetable starts. The house plants range in size from four-inch to fourteen-inch pots. In addition to plants, you'll find fountains and both terra cotta and cedar containers, plus standard garden supplies. A phone call will get you a free plant list and a subscription to *The Twig*, which is published every other month.

Means Nursery, Inc.
27400 N.W. St. Helens Road
(Highway 30)
Scappoose, Oregon 97056
☎ 503/543-3223 or 1-800/962-3374

Hours Mon-Sat 9-6, Sun 11-5;
open until 7 (May through Aug)
Accessible Yes
FAX 503/543-7422

South Suburban Area

Directly from grower to public, this large garden center is connected with an even larger wholesale nursery. Owner Cindy Lou Pease, says that the company's slogan, "Country Quality That's Affordable," speaks whole truth. Every category of plant material can be found here – annuals, berries, bulbs, conifers, ferns, fruit trees, ground covers, herbs, ornamental grasses, perennials, roses, shrubs, shade trees, vines, water plants and wildflowers. And every category of hard goods – books, containers, fountains, furniture, ornaments,

Evans Farms
22289 S. Molalla Highway 213
Oregon City, Oregon 97045
☎ 503/632-3475

Hours Mon-Sat 8-6, Sun 10-5
Accessible Yes
FAX 503/632-4967

continued on next page--

Evans Farms

-continued

organic supplies, soil amendments and tools. You'll also find bonsai, native plants and seeds. Special events include a fall "Apple Fest" where cider is extracted from a 130-year-old press, and the "fruit tasting" is free. At Christmas the nursery holds an open house, and at the end of each season, a sale. Selection is best from February through June. Garden advice from Oregon Certified Nursery Professionals is yours for the asking.

Kasch's

*15300 S.W. Pacific Highway
Tigard, Oregon 97224*
☎ *639-9841*

Yep, the southern suburbs are also served by Kasch's. See text on page 366.

Loen Nursery Company

*18710 S.W. Pacific Drive
Sherwood, Oregon 97140*
☎ *503/625-6309*

Hours *Daily 9-6 (spring & summer);
9-5 (fall & winter)*
Accessible *Difficult*
FAX *503/625-6793*

Portland-area landscape professionals have been trading with Loen for several years. This large wholesale nursery added a lovely retail garden center in 1991, and in 1992 Thatcher and Brenda Loen bought an additional 43 acres to enable the company to grow all of its own nursery stock. They've developed display gardens that show customers how to combine plants in the landscape. Here you'll make your choices from over 2,000 varieties of 50,000 excellent plants, ranging in size from small to specimen. Hard goods include books, tools, bagged amendments and fertilizers, slug bait (of course), containers, paving stones, birdbaths and statuary. You'll find holiday greenery, cut and live Christmas trees, and spring and fall bulbs, too.

Northwoods Nursery offers gardeners and orchardists a wide selection of hard-to-find, easy-to-grow dwarf fruit trees, nut trees, berries and vines. The retail store is a good source for ornamental grasses, ground covers, native plants and a selection of fragrant shrubs and trees, as well as the fruit-bearing plants for which the company is nationally known. They've tools, organic soil amendments, natural pest and disease controls and books. At Christmas, the nursery sells made-in-Oregon wreaths. See catalog listing on page 208. From Canby, take Highway 170 south toward Marquam about 3 miles, turn right on Gribble Road to the end; turn left on Oglesby and look for the nursery about 100 yards ahead on right.

Northwoods Nursery

27635 S. Oglesby Road
Canby, Oregon 97013
☎ *503/266-5432*

Hours Tues-Sun 10-5 (Jan through May);
closed in summer;
open by appointment during the fall.
Phone or fax orders accepted
Mon-Fri 9-5, Sat 9-noon
(Dec through June)
Accessible *No*
FAX *503/266-5431*

Willamette Valley

Albany

Tom Krupicka says, "Tom's Garden Center is special in that we have, in the same location a gift shop, pet shop and a nursery. Our gift shop includes wicker, statuary and much, much more. Our garden center is small, but we are proud of the locally grown nursery stock we sell. We guarantee our plant materials. We're known here in Albany for our knowledge about insects and diseases (and their controls) and the full line of garden supplies we carry." The nursery has a big house plant section. In spring, they create lots of color bowls and hanging baskets and will customize container plantings. The big Christmas room opens in October; call for the date of the holiday open house.

Tom's Garden Center

410 S. Pacific Boulevard
Albany, Oregon 97321
☎ *503/928-2521*

Hours Mon-Sat 8:30-6, Sun 10-4
Accessible *Yes*
FAX *503/928-2105*

Corvallis

☆DESTINATION
Garland Nursery

5470 N.E. Highway 20
Corvallis, Oregon 97330
☎ 503/753-6601
    541
Hours Mon-Fri 9-6, Sat 9-5, Sun 10-5
Accessible
FAX 503/753-3143
    541

Halfway between Albany and Corvallis on Highway 20, you'll discover Don and Sandra Powell's "five acres of quality plants and a barn-ful of ideas." They take pride in being one of the largest retail landscape and regional nurseries in Oregon, with many Oregon Certified Nursery Professionals on staff. The product line is very diversified, and the couple enjoy providing tours to guests of all ages. They even provide a map. "We aim to have the unusual and hard-to-find plant materials, as well as those commonly used," explain these third-generation nursery people. Don's grandparents founded Garland, and the Powells' children are already actively involved, so it's here to stay! "Because we are a year-around nursery, there are no scheduled mark-downs. Sales occur as supply of specific items are higher than need be. We publish *Garden Path Newsletter* quarterly, offer workshops and classes from October through March, and hold two open houses each year," says Sandra. There's a play area for children and frequent displays of seasonal plants in the barn. The garden shop stocks books, fountains and other decorative accessories, plus an excellent selection of bonsai (Wee Tree Farm, page 259).

Shonnard's Nursery & Florist

6600 S.W. Philomath Boulevard
Corvallis, Oregon 97333
☎ 503/929-3524

Hours Mon-Fri 8:30-6, Sat 9-5, Sun 10-4
Accessible Yes

Lynnette Shonnard says, "Our customer service and willingness to help people find what they are looking for is what makes us special. We carry a full line of nursery stock for all seasons and a year-around Christmas showroom, with all the trimmings. Our shelter for bedding plants is out of the weather and easy to shop." She and her husband, Chris, hold horticulture degrees from OSU. Watch for their annual sale on Father's Day weekend and mark downs in mid-June and October.

Gaston

Annuals, perennials, ground covers, shrubs and trees are available alongside landscape supplies. Larry Williams stocks topsoil, mushroom compost and bark dust, plus containers, fencing materials, paving materials and landscape rocks. The company offers a mailing to all purchasers of firewood and wood pellets.

Williams Fuel
44975 S.W. Seghers Road
Gaston, Oregon 97119
☎ *503/357-6730*

Hours *Mon-Sat 8-6, Sun 8-12;*
(close at 5 in winter)
Accessible *Yes*

Junction City

Bob Hintz offers, "Our nursery is very clean and well-organized to make shopping a pleasant experience. The majority of our stock is hand-selected, and it is maintained by professionals. We have an Oregon Certified Nursery professional at the nursery at all times to assist customers. We treat them like we would like to be treated." Robert's sponsors seminars on Saturday mornings eight to ten times a year and holds a clearance sale in mid-October. You'll also find several week-long sales on specific items during the year. In addition to all manner of landscape plants, the company carries books, containers and fountains.

Robert's Landscape & Nursery
93416 River Road
Junction City, Oregon 97448
☎ *503/998-3056*

Hours *Mon-Sat 9-5:30, Sun 11-4:30*
(closed Sun in January)
Accessible *Yes*

Salem

Guentners Gardens prides itself on having the largest selection and variety of plant materials in the mid-Willamette Valley. It's open year-round – complete with delivery service, gift shop and over three and a half acres of plant materials, displays and gardening supplies. The staff specializes in the sensible usage of chemicals. Michelle Guentner notes that the nursery carries large-size topiary in addition to every category of landscape and indoor plants. You'll find books, apparel, furniture, ornaments, fountains and containers here, too. Watch for the nursery's big sale in the fall.

Guentners Gardens
5780 Commercial Street S.E.
Salem, Oregon 97306
☎ *503/585-7133*

Hours *Daily 9-5*
Accessible *Yes, with exceptions*
FAX *503/581-0217*

Thompson's Garden Store

1298 13th Street S.E.
Salem, Oregon 97302
☎ *503/363-4670*

Hours *Mon-Wed 9-6, Thurs & Fri 9-8,*
Sat 9-6, Sun 12-4 (spring & Christmas);
Mon-Fri 9-6, Sat 9-5, Sun 12-4
(summer, fall & winter)
Accessible *Yes*

Formerly Cascadian Garden Center, Thompson's has expanded under the direction of landscape architect Steve Thompson to include a broad range of plants, with special collections for the more experienced gardener. "Our concept is to make the store a garden of ideas and opportunities, inspiring to our visitors." This small garden center carries lovely furnishings, tools, books and gifts. Classes on bonsai and landscape design are underway, with others to follow. They've bulbs, ferns, fruits and berries, ground covers, herbs, perennials, roses, shrubs, trees and vines, and all the organic supplies needed to keep the plants happy.

Willow Lake Nursery South

4559 Liberty Road S.
Salem, Oregon 97302
☎ *503/363-6783*
Willow Lake Nursery North
5655 Windsor Island Road N.
Keizer, Oregon 97303
☎ *503/390-3032*

Hours *South Store: Mon-Sat 9-6,*
Sun 10-5 (spring and summer);
Mon-Sat 9-5, Sun 10-4 (fall and winter)
North Store: Mon-Sat 9-5:30, Sun 10-5
(both stores closed Sun in Jan)
Accessible *Yes; North location is*
difficult on gravel
FAX *503/364-4473*
(South) 503/393-0732 (North)

The Keizer location is a third-generation family farm started in 1904, where hazelnuts and English walnuts are the featured crops. It includes a full-service garden center with a greenhouse and two acres of landscape plants, complete with ponds, rose garden and perennial garden. The Salem branch is smaller, but it, too, offers a wide range of plants, and it is a distributor for *Henri Studio* garden ornaments. Charlotte Lyman told me, "We built an A-frame in a shopping strip mall and fenced a large area in the parking lot. Business people frequently take a slow stroll through our garden (complete with working fountains and nesting birds). During the holidays, we carry greens and trees, and our gift shop is alive with people enjoying music and food samples." Both stores feature a seasonal Northwest gourmet and gift shop from October through December where among the goodies you'll find the company's own chocolate-covered hazelnuts. They'll pack the food products and mail them to your friends and families.

North Oregon Coast

Wally and Karen Brown operate "a smallish Mom and Pop nursery in the tiny community of Rose Lodge alongside a store or two, a fire hall and a tavern. We carry some of whatever gardeners in our area may need, including fertilizers and chemical supplies, planters, trellises, indoor and landscape plants, and bedding plants in season." The Browns grow their own fuchsias (about 75 varieties – a few old and a few obscure) and have a collection of over 40 varieties of orchid cactus, with inexpensive starters available. They offer occasional classes, a weekly newspaper column and unsolicited bits of wisdom. "Its casual," they explain. "We allow time to browse. You may have to hunt for us. We can probably be found at a propagating bench. The cat on the counter doesn't answer questions or give out change. Everyone else does."

Brown's Rose Lodge Nursery

5211 Salmon River Highway
Otis, Oregon 97368
☎ *503/994-2953*

Hours *Daily 9-6 (March through Aug);*
Mon-Sat 9-6 (Sept through mid-Oct);
Mon-Sat 9-5 (Oct 15 through Feb)
Accessible *Yes, with a few exceptions*

To me, visiting this beautiful garden center is part of the joy of going to the North Oregon Coast. Mary Lee Saulsbury's good taste is evidenced in her wonderful selection of decorative accessories for gardens and garden rooms. She now stocks a Canadian line of arbors, trellis work and benches that Portlanders and Californians have begun taking home in great quantities. You'll find *Henri Studio* statuary, containers, ponds, fountains and water plants, too. Out back, there's a display area with a terrific array of plant materials selected for maritime environments. The owners are very sensitive to preserving the quality of the coast's palette of indigenous and adapted species. They carry lots of plants suitable for rock gardens and are working with a local group to promote interest in bonsai.

DESTINATION ☆
Raintree Garden & Gift Center

Highway 101, just north of the
Cannon Beach Junction
Seaside, Oregon 97138
☎ *503/738-6980*

Hours *Daily 9-5:30*
Accessible *Yes*
Mailing address *Hamlet Route, Box 304*
Seaside, Oregon 97138
FAX *503/738-4045*

Eugene Area & South Oregon Coast

Eugene

☆DESTINATION
Down To Earth

532 Olive
Eugene, Oregon 97401
☎ *503/342-6820*

Hours *Mon-Sat 9-6, Sun 11-5*
Accessible *Yes*
FAX *503/342-2261*

Located in historic Farmer's Union Marketplace, this company occupies a wonderful piece of architecture. The all-wood structure, built in the 1920s, is the only grain elevator remaining in downtown Eugene. This environmentally-conscious establishment offers quality tools, organic fertilizers, certified organic seed and natural pest controls, including predatory insects. For sale in the nursery area are trees, shrubs, water plants and everything wonderful for the flower garden. The spirit of the past is alive in the gardening workshops on such topics as herbs, grafting, pruning and perennials. On Mother's Day, to kick-off Historic Preservation Week, the company hosts an Annual Farm Heritage Festival where such old-time crafts as sheep shearing, horseshoeing, tool forging, spinning and weaving are demonstrated. Included are pony rides, hayrides and a petting zoo for children.

Duckworth's Nursery

84846 S. Willamette
Eugene, Oregon 97405
☎ *503/345-5408*

Hours *Daily 9-6;*
after-hours by appointment
Accessible *Yes*

"We stock trees up to four-inches in caliper and full-grown shrubs, including rhododendrons six-feet tall and over," says Peggy Duckworth. The nursery carries a large selection of evergreen trees year-around and living Christmas trees during the holiday season. They've also a large selection of flowering vines, such as wisteria, jasmine, clematis and passion vine. Plants are the Duckworths' primary business. They sell some tools and garden ornaments, but no chemicals or soil amendments. "We have many one-of-a-kind plants, and we try to locate any tree or shrub needed. For example, we have found replacement plants to match full grown landscaped settings. We plant and deliver all over Oregon and into Washington. Plants are marked-

continued on next page--

down four times a year. We send our regular customers extra discounts not offered to the general public. Garden advice is given anytime, and, for a small fee, we'll come to your home to provide on-site help." The nursery is located two and one-half miles outside the city limits of Eugene. Drive to the end of Willamette St. and look for the large sign.

Duckworth's Nursery
--continued

Andy Amort says, "Glenwood Nursery stocks a very wide range of plants including unusual and hard-to-find trees, perennials and Northwest natives." A full-service garden center, it offers classes on a variety of subjects and a quarterly newsletter. It's a good source for books, ornaments and containers, fountains, furniture, organic supplies and house plants, as well.

Glenwood Nursery, Inc.

4006 Franklin Boulevard
Eugene , Oregon 97403
☎ *503/741-4100*

Hours Mon-Sat 9-7, Sun 11-5 (spring);
Mon-Sat 9-5, Sun 11-5
(summer, fall & winter)
Accessible Yes
FAX 503/747-9339

G. Brent Whitley, the general manager, explained to me that Gray's, which began in 1940, has developed a reputation for quality. "It is viewed as the information center for the local region for gardening and problem solving (pests, diseases, etc.). It is the area's largest outlet for vegetables and lawn seed. Most all of our regular staff are Oregon Certified Nursery Professionals or working toward certification. We have our own extensive training program." The nurseries hold four major sales each year and numerous seminars on topics ranging from rose pruning to landscape design. They stock soil amendments, organic supplies, tools, fencing materials, drip irrigation systems, low-voltage lighting, paving materials, containers, fountains and ornaments, books, furniture and house plants. "Our phones require full-time staff to provide garden advice."

Gray's Garden Centers

737 W. 6th Avenue
Eugene, Oregon 97402
☎ *503/345-1569*
160 Oakway Road
Eugene, Oregon 97402
☎ *503/343-3117*
4441 Main Street
Springfield, Oregon 97477
503/747-2301

Hours Mon-Sat 8-7, Sun 9-5 (spring);
Mon-Sat 8-6, Sun 9-5
(summer, fall & winter)
Accessible Yes
FAX 503/345-1231

Southern Oregon

Ashland

Valley View Nursery

1675 N. Valley View Road
Ashland, Oregon 97520
☎ *503/488-2450*

Hours *Mon-Sat 8-6, Sun 10-4;*
(closes at 5 in winter)
Accessible *Yes, but on gravel*
FAX *503-488-2454*

Although this "growers outlet" does not sell "hard goods," customers come from all over Southern Oregon and Northern California for great selection and prices. Eric Baron, one of the owners, took a great deal of time explaining the company's system to me. "It's a meat and potatoes place," he said. "What we grow are the plants (over 1,000 different varieties) most commonly used in landscapes in the Northwest." Because Valley View sells to mass-merchandisers, the nursery has developed a computer system that has revolutionized plant tags and speeded-up the check-out. If you loose a receipt, they can tell you a year later what you bought and how to care for it! Color pictures of mature plants are displayed in the sales yard, and the company publishes a delightful newsletter ten times a year. They offer volume discounts and deliver throughout the Rogue Valley. "We were originally a wholesale-only operation, but ladies from the garden clubs threatened to burn us down if we didn't sell to them," said Eric.

Medford

Bonsai Gardens

2968 Jacksonville Highway
Medford, Oregon 97501
☎ *503/776-3401*

Hours *Mon-Sat 9-5, Sun 10-4*
(closed Sun in winter)
Accessible *Yes*

This well-kept nursery offers house plants, bonsai and water plants as well as every imaginable shrub, tree, ground cover or herbaceous plant for the landscape. Owner Esther Lee says that the focus of attention here is on pond and rock installation. They've fountains from four different sources, lovely rocks and lots of rock garden plants. Bonsai Gardens also offers one-on-one instruction in the art of bonsai, so it's not surprising that the plants in stock include interestingly shaped dwarf conifers. You'll discover annuals, ferns, fruit trees, roses, vines and very special perennials here, as well.

Wally Minnick says, "Our setting allows us interesting options." The shrubs, trees, ground covers, annuals, perennials, herbs and vines here appear to belong in the pastoral landscape. Visitors relax inside a glass greenhouse in the coffee house/bakery or admire the wide selection of indoor specimen plants, including over 200 cymbidium orchids. The gift shop features a selection of locally made pottery and baskets, some filled with local jams and jellies. In summer they sell farm produce, mostly organically grown, from Stagecoach and other nearby farms. The company maintains a mailing list to announce January and June sales and other activities of interest. Call for information about seminars on the care of house plants. Stagecoach Farms is located a little over a mile east of the charming town of Jacksonville.

Stagecoach Farms Nursery

*3900 South Stage Road
Medford, Oregon 97501*
☎ *619/776-3544*

Hours *Daily 9-6*
Accessible *Yes*

Winston

Wildwood Nursery is another of Oregon's hidden treasures. "It was founded in 1921 by Clarence Moyer, a friend of Luther Burbank and innovator of the first rank, for whom Moyer's Red Nandina and the Moyer prune were named. He also developed numerous varieties of camellias and daffodils," explains Carl Riggs. The nursery has been in continuous operation since its founding and is included on the National Register of Historic Sites. New owners Paula and Carl Riggs are restoring the eighteen peaceful acres of grand old trees that front the Umpqua River. The Moyer family's first log cabin is still standing, and the Riggs have restored a Sears catalog barn that was for many years the Moyer's home. Yet to be restored is the 600 gallon redwood water tank, one of the few remaining in the country. You can admire the cork oak

DESTINATION ☆
Wildwood Nursery

*8374 Old Highway 99 S.
Winston, Oregon 97496*
☎ *503/679-4006*

Hours *Daily 9-6;
(closes at dusk in winter)*
Accessible *Yes*
Mail Order *(Christmas trees)*
Catalog *Free*

continued on next page--

Wildwood Nursery

-continued

planted by Luther Burbank, a graceful stand of cedars of Lebanon and many other spectacular trees remaining from the Moyer era. In spring you'll marvel at the waterfall of wisteria cascading from the tops of old myrtle trees. The Riggs are taking cuttings from old camellias and hollies on the place to include within the nursery stock at this garden center. I almost forgot to mention that this is also a good place to buy plants, soil amendments, garden books and accessories!

Central Oregon

Bend

Landsystems Nursery

21336 Highway 20 E.
Bend, Oregon 97701
☎ *503/389-5926*

Hours Daily 9-5:30
Accessible Yes
FAX 503/389-5982

Landsystems' challenge is to provide plant material that can thrive in hot dry summers and in cold winters. "We provide our customers with native plants, including juniper, manzanita, sage and snowberry, but many are surprised at the large variety of perennials, shrubs and trees that do well in our harsh climate," says the owner. Located on seventeen acres east of town on an old homestead, this big, friendly full-service nursery is set among mature trees and a pond that is home to wild ducks. "Many of our customers like to take a stroll before they get down to the business of picking out plants. Landsystems truly has something for everyone, and our retail shop is no exception. We not only carry basic garden accessories; our shelves also include bonsai plants and tools, bird feeders, baskets, books and holiday decorations. You might have to step over the nursery's dog to get in the shop or move a sleepy cat off the counter, but that's the preferred atmosphere: casual, yet professional. Judging from customers' feedback, they like our style too." The nursery holds seminars on such subjects as landscaping and irrigation, and items are marked-down on a continual basis.

Eastern Oregon

Hermiston

Jari and Sheila Boettcher love the small town atmosphere of their nursery, where the plants are displayed in railroad-tie beds under large old shade trees and the walkways are paved with fresh bark. "We have a lot of birds that nest and dine in the nursery," Sheila observes. Perhaps they, like the human visitors, enjoy the lily pond, waterfalls and little stream bed. Inventory includes the gamut of landscape plants, plus garden ornaments, furniture and books. General supplies include irrigation equipment and edging materials. In April the nursery has an "Anniversary by Auction" that has proved very popular. Customers select items they want auctioned. Westwinds is south of Hermiston. You can see it from I-84. Take the Exit 182 interchange. The company is a mail-order source for hybrid poplars; see page 147.

Westwinds Nursery,
Turf & Landscape

Col. Jordan Road
Hermiston, Oregon 97838
☎ *503/567-7235*

Hours Mon-Sat 8-6; 8-4:30 (winter)
Accessible Yes
Mail Order (hybrid poplars only)
Mailing address Rt. 1, Box 1920
Hermiston, Oregon 97838

Idaho

Southwestern Idaho

Boise

☆DESTINATION
Sterling Nursery

9707 Fairview Avenue
Boise, Idaho 83704
☎ *208/376-3737*

Hours *Mon-Fri 9-7, Sat 9-5:30,*
Sun 10-5 (spring & summer);
Mon-Fri 9-6, Sat 9-5:30, Sun 12-5
(fall & winter)
Accessible *Yes*
FAX *208/322-4515*

"Sterling Nursery presents its merchandise in a creative manner to help our customers visualize the plant combinations as they would appear in their yard," says manager Judi Bettys. "Our staff is extremely knowledgeable. They love plants, and they're eager to help each customer select the right shrub or tree or perennial. We carry a complete inventory from March through November. Then the nursery is put to bed for the winter, and all activity is centered in the botanically-oriented gift shop. Sterling's Christmas Shop is regarded as the best in the area. Our customers drive from surrounding states to visit and see the animated displays and the train that runs around the inside roof of the building." Several classes are held during the winter months. The gift shop offers seeds and annuals that can take the cold, as well as the usual complement of *Meadowcraft* wrought iron garden furniture, teak benches, tropical foliage and lovely accessories. When spring comes, the nursery will once again be packed with high-quality landscape plants. End-of-season sales take place in late- June, at Labor Day, and again in mid-October. Seasonal promotions are both entertaining and informative. A pianist performs Easter and Mothers Day weekends, a bluegrass band is on hand for the Fall Festival in early October, and the sound of a harp adds magic to the Christmas Open House. Free clinics are conducted each Saturday from March to June. Newsletters are mailed-out several times each year, and advice is given on an individual basis.

"We attract serious gardeners and farmers, who look to us for information on soil, insects and disease problems," says Karen France, manager of the main store on Orchard Ave. "In addition to general garden supplies, we're a well-rounded garden center, offering such decorative accessories as fountains, statuary and containers. We have a large selection of perennials, some of which we grow ourselves." Union Farm & Garden carries water plants, has good sources for native plants (like sages and grasses), and supplies a wide range of ornamentals suitable for Boise's high mountain desert climate. Sign-up for the mailing list to receive the newsletter and information on free seminars.

Union Farm & Garden

250 N. Orchard Avenue
Boise, Idaho 83706
☎ 208/375-0185
2141 Broadway
Boise, Idaho 83706
☎ 208/345-3540

Hours Mon-Sat 9-6, Sun 11-5;
open until 8 mid-April
through mid-July
Accessible Yes, except some rock areas

Nampa

Mike and Marilyn Blickenstaff are real plants people. Not only do they carry all the familiar landscape plants, but also they promote the use of natives. Indigenous trees, shrubs, grasses and perennials are given a special place in the nursery. The Blickenstaffs publish "ever-evolving" descriptive lists of such decorative or food-producing plants as lilacs, viburnums, fruit trees, grapes and berries and of the best shade trees for Southwest Idaho. They specialize in perennials, claiming the largest selection in the area, and they offer a wide selection of rock garden plants. Indoors, you'll find tropicals, bonsai, fine furniture and decorative accessories for the garden. They sponsor occasional classes and hold a Harvest Festival in mid-October. The major sale is at Labor Day.

Greenhurst Nursery & Garden Center

3209 S. Happy Valley Road
Nampa, Idaho 83686
☎ 208/466-5783

Hours Mon-Sat 9-6, Sun 11-5
(March through Oct);
Mon-Sat 9-5:30 (winter)
Accessible Yes
FAX 208/466-8896

Northern Idaho

Coeur d'Alene

Duncan's Garden Center & Nursery
1920 N. 4th Street
Coeur d'Alene, Idaho 83814
☎ *208/664-5005*

Hours *Daily 9-7 (spring); 9-5:30*
(summer, fall & winter)
Accessible *Yes*

Summer is festive in Coeur d'Alene, and Duncan's colorful perennials, water garden plants and rock garden subjects accompany mood. The nursery is equally sensitive to the region's severe winters. Not only does owner Steve Badraun stock a worldwide range of plants that thrive in cold climates, but also he carries a well-labeled section of natives. When it's frigid outdoors, Duncan's features beautiful house plants and bonsai to make the indoor environment cheery. There's a floral department staffed by seven designers in this 12,000-square-foot garden center. There's a Christmas shop and a gift gallery with ornaments and containers, garden supplies, tools and books to discover, too. Get on the mailing list to keep informed about classes and "specials."

Moscow

Hillside Nursery
2120 Robinson Park Road
Moscow, Idaho 83843
☎ *208/882-4956*

Hours *Mon-Sat 9-6*
(March through Dec. 24);
by appointment on Sunday
Accessible *No*

"We are a small Mom & Pop operation, started out of a love of gardening," say Barbara and Keith Johnson. "We try to have a wide variety of plants, many of which we grow from seeds or cuttings. We freely offer advice or seek help for customers." The Johnsons offer discounts for quantity sales. Their stock includes annuals, bulbs, conifers, ferns, fruit and nut trees, fruits and berries, ground covers, herbs, perennials, shrubs trees and vines. In addition to garden greenery, they've house plants, organic supplies and tools. From Mountainview Road, turn east on Joseph. Follow road to Robinson Lake Park. At the park, turn right, follow the road one mile.

Orofino

Michael and Joan Mount pack a lot of plant material into their small store. They provide a free plant-list on which you'll find some pretty unusual offerings. Perennials include gaura, hardy gloxinia, 'Flashing Lights' dianthus, 'Golden Showers' coreopsis and apricot-colored iris. They've Japanese maples, hardy rhododendrons and dogwoods, plus rugosa and woodsii roses grown on their own roots. The name "Green Things" also means house plants. The nursery mixes its own soils and maintains good selections in pots, ornaments, bark dust, fertilizers and pest controls.

Green Things
13910 Highway 12
Orofino, Idaho 83544
☎ *208/476-3022*

Hours *Mon-Sat 8:30-5:30;*
open Sun, same hours
(March through July)
Accessible *Yes*
Mailing address *P.O. Box 2167*
Orofino, Idaho 83544

Sandpoint

Lee's Nursery buys varieties that are specific to the Northern Idaho climate. A full-line garden center, it introduces new varieties each year and has increased stock threefold in the past three seasons. Diane Boling says, "If our customers want a variety that we do not have, we make every attempt to locate it. At Lee's our employees are totally customer-oriented; they are trained to provide advice. We specialize in organic grow-ing products and help customers under-stand how to use them. Our trees and shrubs are fully guaranteed for the season. We're well-known for our large and varied selection of house plants." Visitors will find books and good selec-tions in benches, containers, ornaments and fountains. Beyond the decorative items, there are tools, stepping stones, irrigation systems, soil amendments and mulches. Price-reductions begin in July.

Lee's Nursery
1650 Highway 200 E.
Sandpoint, Idaho 83864
☎ *208/263-1411*

Hours *Mon-Sat 9-7, Sun 10-5 (April*
through July); Mon-Sat 9-7 (Aug through
March)
Accessible *No*

Central Idaho

Bellevue & Ketchum

Webb Nursery

162 Glendale Road
Bellevue, Idaho 83313

891 Washington Avenue
Ketchum Idaho 83340
☎ *208/726-4927 (both locations)*

Hours *Daily 8-5:30 (April through Sept);*
Mon-Fri 8-4:30 (Oct through March);
Daily 8-5:30 (holidays)
Accessible *Yes*
Mail Order
Catalog *Free to public within state; $4*
outside Idaho
Mailing address *P.O. Box 744*
Ketchum, Idaho 83340
FAX *208/788-2633*

Doug Webb explains that he founded his nursery as an adjunct to his landscaping business because he was unable to find plants suitable for the high, dry climate of Idaho's ski country. In the thirteen years since, he has become more and more involved with the nursery. His stock is composed of improved varieties (both indigenous and non-native) that thrive above 6,000 feet. "People want finished-looking landscapes filled with dependable plants," he states. "We won't sell a plant until we've had it over a year and are sure it is acclimatized." The company grows quaking Aspen trees, which are available in all sizes, and a wide range of other cold-hardy shrubs, trees and perennials. It carries organic supplies, garden books, containers, fountains and ornaments, plus a line of locally made cedar log furniture. Look for monthly sales from April through September and ask to receive a monthly newsletter brimming with garden advice.

Twin Falls

Kimberly Nurseries, Inc.

2862 Addison Avenue East
Twin Falls, Idaho 83301
☎ *208/733-2717*

Hours *Mon-Sat 8-6, Sun 10-5*
Accessible *Yes*
FAX *208/733-0043*

Jeff Robinson, son-in-law of Jack Wright, the owner of Kimberly Nurseries, notes that Kimberly's has been Idaho's most progressive nursery since 1907, when the original owners sold trees door-to-door. This large regional nursery serves as "nature's gallery," encouraging people to develop low-maintenance gardens with clean borders and color accents. It promotes the use of ground covers above and beyond junipers and encourages low-water-use landscape with new emphasis on native plants. Kimberly has a landscape architect on staff and serves a wide geographical area with landscape services. The four garden centers in this local chain (two are in Utah) carry an extensive

continued on next page--

range of non-plant items as well – books, containers, fencing, fountains, furniture, irrigation systems, lighting, organic supplies, ornaments, paving materials, retaining walls, rocks, soil amendments and tools. Jack Wright has designed and patented an exciting new mobile garden center to better-serve remote areas. Call for information.

Kimberly Nurseries, Inc.
--continued

Eastern Idaho

Chubbock

"We have years of experience in unique plant materials and old-fashioned service," says local owner Laurie Shouse. In addition to a full line of regionally adapted plants (bought in quantity along with the other Kimberly Nurseries), the company offers garden supplies for the do-it-yourself crowd and maintenance services for those who want it. The gift department has an excellent selection of horticultural gifts, and the garden center carries benches, statuary and fountains. There's a large Christmas gift shop, too. "Come in and see what we have that no-one else has," she promises. "We hold festivals throughout the summer and to inaugurate the holiday season, we sponsor a huge fireworks show in the cold winter skies and collect gifts for needy children." Plants usually go on sale in the fall.

Kimberly Nurseries East
212 E. Chubbuck Road
Chubbuck, Idaho 83202
☎ *208/238-1000*

Hours *Mon-Sat 8-6, Sun 11-4*
Accessible *Yes*
FAX *208/237-4871*

Idaho Falls

In business since 1964 providing "climate tested" plants and seeds for Eastern Idaho and surrounding areas, Town & Country's nursery stock is displayed among landscaped beds and curving brick walkways. John Crook says, "We carry a large selection of shrub roses and hardy rhododendrons and azaleas adapted to our cold, dry climate (Zones 2 to 4). We also have a complete

Town & Country Gardens, Inc.
5800 S. Yellowstone Highway
Idaho Falls, Idaho 83402
☎ *208/522-5247*

Hours *Mon-Fri 9-7, Sat 8-6*
(April through June); Mon-Sat 9-6
(July through March)
Accessible *Yes*
FAX *208/523-4508*

continued on next page--

Town & Country Gardens, Inc.
-continued

line of water garden supplies, including plants, pond liners, pumps, etc. Visit our display garden, which showcases a wide variety of perennials, played against ponds and waterfalls. We offer the largest selection of perennials in Eastern Idaho." With a landscape architect on staff, the nursery provides design and installation for landscapes and irrigation systems throughout the region. The nursery holds sales on Arbor Day and Earth Day, a bare-root fruit and shade tree sale in early April and a Fall Planting sale in September. Garden seminars are conducted each Saturday during February, March and September. In late fall, you'll find a complete Christmas specialty shop.

British Columbia

Vancouver Metropolitan Area

Vancouver

Ford's Flowers & Nursery

4445 W. 10th Avenue
Vancouver, British Columbia V6R 2H8
☎ 604/224-1341

Hours Mon-Sat 9-5:30, Sun 11-5
(April through Sept)
Accessible Yes
FAX 604/224-1467

Located near the gates to UBC and suppliers to an urban trade, Ford's specializes in patio and balcony plantings, garden gifts, seeds, bulbs and tropical plants. In the courtyard nursery, you'll find a pleasant selection of shrubs, trees, ground covers and vines suitable for the small garden and lots of annuals and unusual perennials. They've organically grown herbs, organic supplies and nice containers and ornaments. The floral business is the focus throughout the winter months.

Southlands is the sophisticated plant enthusiast's dream. Thomas Hobbs and Brent Beattie's elegant new garden centre features an outstanding collection of plants. Included are such rare garden treasures as hardy euphorbias, variegated aralia, Japanese Jack-in-the pulpit, pineapple scented broom, Oriental trillium and cape fuchsias (which are not fuchsias at all, but rather are related to pentemons). You'll find species clematis, sasanquas and lots of Mr. Hobbs' favourite gray-leafed plants, including *Salvia argentea* and Russian sage. In winter the large greenhouse showroom is brimming with exotic tropicals and blooming plants for gift-giving and dressing-up one's own indoor environment. A "customer hang-out" with comfy wicker chairs and French bistro tables is just one of the charming aspects of this nursery. Although you'll find an even larger selection of garden accessories at Hobbs on West 41st (see page 325), don't miss the handsome locally made standing birdhouses and trellis work from English Garden Imports on display here. Get on the mailing list to receive a chatty, informative newsletter that announces the nursery's popular classes and describes terrific plants! For the sake of safety, cross S.W. Marine Drive at the light on Blenheim and turn left on 49th to Balaclava.

DESTINATION ✰
Southlands Nursery Ltd.

6550 Balaclava Street
Vancouver, British Columbia V6N 1L9
☎ *604/261-6411*

Hours Daily 9-6
Accessible Yes
FAX 604/261-6429

North Suburban Area

West Vancouver

"Because our indoor space is less than a thousand square feet and the outdoor area only three times that, we've mastered the art of packing more product into minimal space yet still look open and airy," says owner Rob Harrington. "Our hard goods have a permanent home, so regular customers know exactly where to look, but our seasonal colour changes every ten to

continued on next page--

West Van Florist & Garden Centre

1821 Marine Drive
West Vancouver, British Columbia V7V 1J7
☎ *604/922-4171*

Hours Mon-Sat 9-6, Sun 10-5
Accessible Yes
FAX 604/922-9735

West Van Florist & Garden Centre
-continued

fourteen days for a continual visual treat". The book buyer keeps a wonderful selection in stock, and the gift wares are exceptional too. Call to find out about class schedules. Staffmembers have begun teaching others how to make the perennial moss baskets, ivy balls and sedum wreaths their customers have come to love. You'll find them one mile west of Lyon Gate Bridge.

East Suburban Area

Burnaby

Knapp's Gardenworks

6250 Lougheed Highway
Burnaby, British Columbia V5B 2Z9
☎ 604/ 299-0621

Hours Mon & Tues 9-6, Wed-Fri 9-9, Sat & Sun 9-5; open until 9 on weekdays and until 6 on Sat & Sun
(April through June & in Dec)
Accessible Yes
FAX 604/299-4403

With its sixty employees, this big, bright Burnaby store is the flagship garden centre of the Art Knapp chain. You'll find an information desk staffed by experienced people in each of the sales areas. The manager, Mr. Zaplatynski, tells his staff, "If you wouldn't plant it yourself, don't sell it to someone else." Watch for customer appreciation days six times a year (merchandise is marked 15%-off) and seasonal promotions in spring, early summer, fall and again in December. Knapp's offers quarterly newsletters and conducts seminars on Sunday afternoons in spring and fall.

☆DESTINATION
Mandeville Gardens

4746 S.E. Marine Drive
Burnaby, British Columbia V5J 3G6
☎ 604/434-4111

Hours Sat-Thurs 9-6, Friday 9-9; Sat-Thurs 9-8, Fri 9-9 (early-April through mid-June & all of Dec)
Accessible Yes
FAX 604/434-0240

Mandeville has provided high-quality products and services to three generations of Lower Mainland gardeners. Customer information services include help with diagnosing garden problems, free weekly seminars, insurance estimates and delivery services. Staff members will order and reserve special plants, make custom colour bowls and moss hanging baskets, and even arrange the rental of spreader and lawn roller equipment. The tropical plants, alpines, rare perennials and water garden plants compare favourably with the offerings of the best of the specialty nurseries. "We welcome questions about our nursery

continued on next page--

stock and help clients fulfill landscape visions by pulling plants for their landscape plans," says the manager, who adds that the company offers a "no quibble" guarantee on trees and shrubs. Annual events include exhibition weekends that celebrate spring bulbs, rhododendrons, roses and other plant materials. They've a nice selection of trellis work from English Garden Imports and marvelous decorative accessories. Get on the mailing list to receive an excellent bi-monthly newsletter that announces frequent seminar dates and offers growing tips. There's a geranium sale the first week in April, a "two-for-one" bedding plant sale in early-July, and a mid-October perennial sale.

Mandeville Gardens
-continued

Coquitlam

"We are a neighborhood garden centre specializing in colour, quality and unusual varieties," says Bill Pastorek. Bedding plants are marked down at the end of June and shrubs go on sale in November. You'll find everything from annuals to conifers, plus such garden necessities as soil amendments, containers, organic supplies and tools. They've bonsai, bulbs, house plants and garden ornaments, too.

Como Lake Garden Centre
1649 Como Lake Avenue
Coquitlam, British Columbia V3J 3P7
☎ *604/939-0539*

Hours Daily 9-6; open until 9
(spring and Christmas holiday season);
closed from Christmas day through Jan
Accessible Yes

Port Coquitlam

David Hunter offers great choices in perennials and water plants, and he maintains one of the largest selections of Jackson & Perkins roses in the Lower Mainland. The centre carries a very complete line of such products as pesticides, fertilizers and organic supplies. Call for information about the annual sale in late fall and night classes offered through the local school district.

David Hunter Landscape
Nurseries Ltd.

1525 Lougheed Highway
Port Coquitlam, British Columbia
V3D 1A5
☎ *604/942-4616*

Hours Daily 9-9 (spring & summer);
9-5:30 (fall and winter)
Accessible Yes

South Suburban Area

Delta

J's Plants 'n' More Garden Centre Ltd.

11941 80th Avenue
Delta, British Columbia V4C 1Y1
☎ 604/590-3606

Hours Mon-Sat 9-6, Sun 9-5;
open until 8 Mon-Fri (spring) and until 9
(the three weeks before Christmas)
Accessible Yes
FAX 604/590-1170

"We pride ourselves on quality products, particularly our house brands," says the owner, adding that the centre's prices are competitive and its staff is friendly. You'll discover a broad spectrum of ornamentals for the landscape and tropicals for interior use, plus garden lighting, organic supplies, tools, topsoil, ornaments and books. Call for information about periodic seminars.

Richmond

Jones Nurseries Limited

16880 Westminister Highway
Richmond, British Columbia V6V 1A8
☎ 604/278-8671

Hours Daily 9-5:30
Accessible Yes
FAX 604/273-0650

This retail nursery is backed by a large wholesale operation. The staff "chauffeurs" customers to the 100-acre site down the road where plant materials from ground covers to specimen trees are kept. The nursery also sells a wide selection of the all the usual supplies that attract customers to a garden centre. There are "specials" year-around and a very popular quarterly newsletter with gardening tips, "feature plants" and even staff gossip. Jones Nurseries offers seminars on pruning, bulbs, fall colour, flower arranging and wreath making. The wholesale division is the exclusive North American supplier of specimen Tasmanian tree ferns (*Dicksonia antarctica*). "Even the Queen has one, you know," says Sabrina Jones.

Fraser Valley

Abbotsford

Cannor Nurseries

34261 Marshall Road
Abbotsford, British Columbia V2S 1L8
☎ 604/854-1616

Hours Daily 9-5:30
Accessible Yes
FAX 604/854-3336

With 400 acres in production, Cannor Nurseries is respected in the green industry for its high-quality shrubs and trees. As a neighborhood garden centre, it supplies everything a homeowner could need. In addition to landscape plants, there are tools and organic supplies. The Abbotsford and Victoria stores have floral shops, bonsai collections and especially good selections of perennials. Call for extended hours in spring and during the holiday season. Also see listing on page 149.

Cannor Nurseries

-continued

Chilliwack

The waterfall garden that accompanies the house plant section here creates a relaxing mood as you enter. The selection of garden plants is excellent. See the previous listing for additional information.

Cannor Nurseries

48291 Chilliwack Central Road
Chilliwack, British Columbia V2P 6H3
☎ *604/795-5914*

FAX 604/795-6148

Big plans are underway on the eighteen acres at this new location! In addition to greenhouses filled with tropical plants and wide, wonderful choices for the garden, Brian Minter is constructing a lagoon and nature preserve on the property. Gardeners from Northwest Washington to the Vancouver metropolitan area and the Gulf Islands trust Brian's good advice on Star FM CKSR and CBC radio. His taste and experience are evidenced in this wonderful garden centre. He observes, "We value customers and love to share our excitement about new and unusual plants. We do not specialize in any one area, but pride ourselves on a very wide range of indoor and outdoor plants. We like to be first with new introductions and get feedback from our customers on their success with them. We love to explore innovative ways of gardening." The seasonal seminars here provide additional opportunities for gardeners to learn about such diverse topics as pruning, starting seeds, water gardening and floral design. In addition to excellent selections in plants, you'll find locally

DESTINATION ☆
Country Garden Ltd.

10015 Young Street N.
Chilliwack, British Columbia V2P 4V4
☎ *604/792-6612*

Hours *Daily 8:30-5:30*
Accessible *Yes*
FAX 604/792-8893

continued on next page--

Country Garden Ltd.

-continued

made twig trellises, benches and bird houses, garden books, fountains and tools and all kinds of garden supplies. At Christmas, the greenhouses are ablaze with acres of poinsettias. Call for the dates of the big Hanging Basket Sale and the annual Dawn 'til Dusk Sale.

Country Garden World

45675 Knight Road
Sardis, British Columbia
☎ *604/858-6162*

Hours *Daily 8:30-5:30*
Accessible *Yes*

Brian Minter's Country Garden World, located behind the Chilliwack Mall, carries smaller quantities of the same fine stock you'll find at the parent store.

Vancouver Island

Comox

Anderton Nursery

2012 Anderton Road
Comox, British Columbia V9N 8B5
☎ *604/339-4726*

Hours *Daily 9-5*
(March through mid-Nov)
Accessible *Yes*

George and Wendy Prothero grow their own bedding plants and perennials, both standard and unusual varieties. "We have a large perennial display garden with plants labeled, and we welcome visitors." In addition to a full range of landscape plants, they carry soil amendments, organic and chemical supplies, fountains and water plants. Customers look forward to summer months when this friendly neighborhood garden center offers U-pick strawberries.

Duncan

B. Dinter Nursery Ltd.

2205 Phipps Road, RR 7
Duncan, British Columbia V9L 4W4
☎ *604/748-2023*

Hours *Daily 8-6 (spring & summer);*
9-5 (fall & winter)
Accessible *Yes*
FAX *604/748-0586*

Bernie Dinter notes, "In August 1992, we completed a major renovation and now offer a well-laid-out sales yard, shade house and tropical greenhouse. Six acres at the nursery are dedicated to growing, and we offer many uncommon plants. You are always welcome at our information centre for advice and design services." The nursery, which is located three miles south of Duncan across from Whippletree Junction, publishes plant lists for roses and perennials. It has a well-rounded stock in landscape plants, water plants, organic

Ganges

This design-build landscape firm opens its nursery sales yard to the public by appointment, providing access to a wide range of professional-quality plant materials and landscape supplies.

Hallman Landscape Associates

245 Old Divide Road, RR2
Ganges, British Columbia V0S 1E0
☎ *604/537-9316*

Hours By appointment only
Accessible Yes
FAX 604/537-9343

Nanaimo

"We grow 80% of our own material," says Bill Saunderson. "Lots of people come to our garden centre because we have a 45-acre container nursery (wholesale) from which to select larger specimen materials. We collect rare and unusual plants and carry everything from liners to large-caliper trees. Our rhododendron selection is very extensive, with over 200 varieties. The display garden is set up to give customers ideas on layout and eventual sizes. Competent staff members are here to help customers 363 days a year." From fall into early spring, Green Thumb carries a good selection of house plants, and in late summer you'll find reduced prices on general landscape materials.

Green Thumb Garden Centre

6261 Hammond Bay Road
Nanaimo, British Columbia V9T 5M4
☎ *604/758-0944*

Hours Daily 8:30-5:30;
call for extended hours in summer
Accessible Yes
FAX 604/758-1987

Victoria Metropolitan Area

Manager Mark Hile says, "We carry just about everything you would find in a large garden centre, including rare perennials, grafted conifers and ornamentals. Our clientele comes to us for quality merchandise, personal service and our convenient location."

Big Barn Garden Centre

1286 McKenzie Avenue
Victoria, British Columbia V8P 2L9
☎ *604/477-4435*

Hours Mon-Fri 8-9, Sat & Sun 8-6
(spring and summer);
Daily 8-5:30 (fall & winter)
Accessible Yes
FAX 604/477-0012

Cannor Nurseries

4660 Elk Lake Road
Victoria, British Columbia V8Z 5M1
☎ *604/658-5415*

FAX 604/658-5052

Unusual perennials are a specialty at the Victoria branch of this excellent company. See complete listing on page 392.

Cedar Hill Nursery & Garden Centre

1550 Church Avenue
Victoria, British Columbia V8P 2H1
☎ *604 477-2658*

Hours *Mon-Sat 9-5:30,*
Sun & holidays 10-5
Accessible *Yes*
FAX 604/477-2809

The only full-line garden centre within the Victoria city core, Cedar Hill prides itself on "old favourites and new introductions." Although the company operates from a fairly small location, it carries house plants and brings in a wide and varied selection of landscape plants daily from an acreage property in central Saanich. "We pursue the unusual," says Elaine Wallner, adding that her knowledgeable staff offers friendly service and "lots of advice." Look for weekly features and specials. They've books, containers, organic supplies, soil amendments and tools in addition to nursery stock.

Elk Lake Garden Centre

5450 Pat Bay Highway
Victoria, British Columbia V8Y 1T1
☎ *604/658-8812*

Hours *Daily 9-5:30*
Accessible *Yes*
FAX 604/658-8466

What attracts most of the customers to this garden centre is the multitude of perennials grown from North American, English and European seeds. John Derrick estimates that the company offers between eight-hundred and a thousand varieties over the course of a year. He stocks a full range of landscape plants, house plants and specialized materials for water gardens and rock gardens. Tools and supplies complete the inventory. While Elk Lake does not have regular sales, it is committed to "quality and reasonable prices at all times."

In business since 1945, this wholesale/ retail nursery tries to keep its prices low and its selection large. Marigold offers lots of colour and a friendly staff eager to help. It's one of the biggest garden centres on the island. Customers shop with wagons, and although the management has provided a covered shopping area, customers still venture out into the six acres of landscape plants to make their selections. The company is famous for thousands of poinsettias and geraniums in season, and it's also well-known for seasonal colour gardens in containers. The nursery carries house plants, garden ornaments, fountains and lots of lovely plants for the rock garden, too. Ask about the 20%-off coupons in February and July.

Marigold Nurseries Ltd.

7874 Lochside Drive, RR#1
Saanichton, British Columbia V0S 1M0
☎ *604/652-3312*

Hours *Daily 8-5:30;*
closes at 5 P.M.Dec through Feb
Accessible *Yes*
FAX *604/652-1330*

"Millstream Nurseries carries top quality nursery stock in a beautifully laid-out, rural setting. Our clients love the extra care we take to keep the garden centre clean and the plants healthy. We grow winter heather, rhododendrons, cedar hedging, junipers and many other shrubs. Combined with other hand-selected nursery stock, perennials, bedding plants and roses, we truly offer our clients distinctive plants for a beautiful garden," says Annette Milbradt. She notes that the nursery holds sales on overstock and that garden advice is available from owner John Zoetemilk, who has over forty years of landscaping experience. "He is pleased to help anyone with plant or landscaping questions," she notes. Millstream is located .5 Km north of the Trans Canada Highway. The nursery does not carry garden supplies.

Millstream Nurseries & Garden Centre Ltd.

2412 Millstream Road
Victoria, British Columbia V9B 3R3
☎ *604/478-2412*

Hours *Daily 9-6*
(March through April &
Aug through Nov);
9-8 (May & June);
Sat-Wed 9-6, Thurs-Fri 9-8 (July)
Accessible *Yes*

Van Isle Bricklok Surfacing and Landscape Supplies

893 Van Isle Way
Victoria, British Columbia V9B 5R8
☎ *604/478-5012*

Hours *Wed-Fri 8-7, Sat-Tues 8-5:30;*
open Sun 8-5 in spring
Accessible *Partially;*
building not accessible,
but orders will be brought outside
FAX *604/478-8512*

Van Isle is a one-stop landscape centre with a large selection of shrubs, trees, ground covers and bedding plants in addition to landscape supplies. (See listing on page 54.) "It's a lovely place to wander around, and our staff tries to make customers feel comfortable and welcome," says the manager.

The Okanagan

Kelowna

Burnett & Sons Nurseries, Ltd.

2180 Ethel Street
Kelowna, British Columbia V1Y 3A1
☎ *604/762-3512*

Hours *Mon-Fri 8:30-8,*
Sat & Sun 8:30-5 (spring & summer);
Daily 8:30-5 (fall & winter)
Accessible *Yes*
FAX *604/861-5184*

You'll find everything for the garden from annuals to conifers here, plus books, containers, ornaments and fountains, house plants, organic supplies, seeds and tools. "We've been a family-owned business since 1922," says Don Burnett. "Now, the third generation offers service, quality and guaranteed products to our many fine customers. We grow most of our own annuals and perennials, and we have a reputation for being one of the finest in the Okanagan Valley." For over ten years, Don has broadcast the Burnett Garden Show to a listening audience of more than 7,000 on radio station CKOU. Merchandise at the nursery is marked down in June and October. Call for information about the four-session gardening course conducted through Okanagan College each spring and the date of the Burnetts' Christmas Open House.

"We're one of the largest nursery/ landscapers in the interior of British Columbia," says Brent Mac Donald. "Our primary business is the design, supply and installation of residential and commercial landscapes. We offer some of our nursery production through our retail centre in order to meet the needs of home gardeners and small landscapers. We carry one of the biggest selections of large-caliper trees in central British Columbia." Watch for the annual two-for-one sale in September. Although you won't find decorative accessories here, the company does stock chemicals, paving materials, retaining wall materials, seeds, soil amendments, tools and topsoil.

West-Wind Nurseries Ltd.

2169 Benvoulin Road
Kelowna, British Columbia V1W 2C7
☎ *604/860-0025*

Hours *Mon-Fri 8-6, Sat 9-5 Sun 10-4*
(April through June);
Mon-Sat 9-5 (July & August);
Mon-Fri 8-6, Sat 9-5
(Sept through mid-Oct);
Mon-Fri 8-5
(mid-Oct until mid-Dec,
weather permitting);
closed in winter
Accessible *Yes*
FAX *604/862-8065*

Keremeos

"We grow varieties of plants that are suited for our hot, dry climate and follow with after-market service and advice – all with a small-town friendly smile," say Don and Anna Bartlett. Located 4 Km west of Keremeos at the historic red bridge, their garden center keeps a horticulturist on staff to give expert advice. They publish planting guides for the annuals, bulbs, conifers, fruit and nut trees, fruits and berries, ground covers, herbs, perennials, roses, shrubs and trees they stock. The Bartletts also supply containers and soil amendments.

Don and Anna's Greenhouses and Garden Centre

RR #1
Keremeos, British Columbia, V0X 1N0
☎ *604/499-5785*

Hours *Daily 9-8*
(April through mid-June);
call for hours after June 15
Accessible *Yes*
Catalog *Free*
FAX *604/499-5785*

The Kooteneys

Cranbrook

Top Crop's Nurseryland Feed & Pet Food Centre

2001 10th St. N.
Cranbrook, British Columbia V1C 5M2
☎ *604/489-4555*

FAX 604/426-4280
Hours *Daily 8:30-8 (spring);*
Mon-Sat 8:30-5:30
(summer, fall & winter)
Accessible *Most areas*

Originally suppliers to a rural trade, Top Crop has attracted a lot of urban customers who enjoy a store where seed is sold by the ton and items as diverse as hayscrapers are available. The garden centre, which offers house plants and everything for the landscape, has become a large part of the business. Staffmembers provide in-store consultations and advice on the radio. "Our appreciation for things that are alive and growing has helped us continually broaden our store," says Greg Fisher. "We try to specialize in the areas we jump into!"

The Cariboo

Kamloops

Agri Supply Ltd.

1935 East Trans Canada Highway
Kamloops, British Columbia V2C 4A1
☎ *604/372-7446*

Hours *Daily 9-5:30 (April through June);*
Mon-Sat 9-5:30, Sun 9:30-5
(July through March)
Accessible *Yes*
FAX 604/372-1607

Within a twenty minute drive from this nursery, gardeners encounter USDA Zones 2 through 6! The displays here are designed to show shrubs, trees and perennials in complementary arrangements, and an expert horticultural staff is on hand to assist both beginners and advanced gardeners. "We specialize in hardy perennials. We grow many ourselves and inventory over 200 species," says Jay Ross. Noting that the company offers every item a gardener would need, he adds, "We personalize the sale to the customer's needs. The last Saturday of August you'll find a season-ending 50% reduction on all nursery-stock.

Appendixes & Indexes

Regional Index:

Summary of Money-saving Tips

Free Information

Visit public gardens for inspiration.

Window-shop at nurseries. Read books. Ask questions. Learn everything you can.

Ask your local public library about "inter-library loans," through which you can obtain almost any book in print.

Tap into Cooperative Extension Services. These gold mines of information are funded by your tax dollars!

Garden Design

Start with a Master Plan. It's cheaper to erase pencil marks than to tear out a misplaced walkway.

Make outdoor "living rooms" large enough to really use. A few extra bricks or pieces of lumber are small investments in the future.

Seek professional help with the design and construction of such complicated site work as circular driveways, freestanding masonry walls and retaining walls.

Check local building codes before designing any landscape amenity.

Garden Construction

Remember that the lowest bid is not necessarily the best bid.

Before signing a contract, ask to see samples of a company's work.

Locate sewer, water, gas and any buried electrical cable lines.

Protect existing plants from the onslaught of the construction crew.

Cover-over an unattractive old concrete walk or patio with a handsome paving material; it's one of the least-expensive ways to "dress up" a home and garden.

Always place a PVC pipe sleeve underneath new walls, walkways or driveways for future electrical and/or irrigation lines.

If you're handy with a hammer, have a fence company set the posts and construct the face of the fence yourself.

Light only the areas you use at night; try various lighting schemes before you decide on permanent placement.

Garden Conservation

Before even thinking about establishing a new landscape or beginning a garden renovation, test and amend the soil. It's a total waste to put good plants in poor soil!

Cut back on your use of "store-bought" fertilizers.

Make your own fertilizer/mulch from garden and kitchen wastes.

Stock-up on bagged soil and soil amendments when they are marked down at garden centers and mass-market home improvement stores.

Ask questions about the source of any bulk soil you're bringing-in – you may be buying weeds.

Conserve water. (See page 112 for water-wise tips.)

Know when it's time to remove a tree.

Hire a qualified arborist to evaluate and treat your existing trees or to remove a tree, if necessary.

Use selective pruning to remodel an old garden; replace "hopelessly overgrown" plants.

Add years of life to your landscape by learning proper pruning practices.

Don't waste money on "pruning paint."

Buy high-quality tools; they're more economical in the long run.

Rent expensive, seldom-used equipment. Split the cost with a neighbor.

Plants

Select the right plant for the right place.

Avoid impulse buying.

Stick to your Master Plan.

Shop around.

Learn how to select healthy plants.

Remember that "bargain plants" are usually no bargain.

If you're investing money in roses (or any other plant that requires a lot of maintenance), invest time in education before making varietal selections.

Plant trees to reduce the cost of heating in winter and provide cooling effects in summer.

If you can't afford mature shrubs, don't buy a lot of little plants. Fill in with annuals until the shrubs fill-out.

Don't go to plant sales expecting to find bargains, but rather to find rare and unusual plants.

Learn proper planting techniques. The major cause of plant loss is due to improper planting!

Propagate new plants from seeds and cuttings.

When you divide perennials and bulbs, trade plants with a fellow gardener.

Grow annuals and vegetables from seed. Seeds are cheap. Don't be afraid of failure; for every seed that doesn't germinate, three others will.

Inspect house plants carefully before making your purchase.

Protect your investments with good maintenance techniques.

Garden Furnishings

Buy garden furniture and accessories off-season.

Mail-order Shopping

"**O**ur store is 10½ inches tall, 8½ inches wide and 48 pages deep. It has no crowded parking lots, long check out lines or hidden rest rooms," write Charley and Carol Yaw, owners of Charley's Greenhouse Supply, in the letter that accompanies their catalog. There's a lot to be said for that kind of store! Today's busy life-styles have made catalog shopping more popular than ever. I never dreamed when I began writing this book how many marvelous garden products are as close as my phone, fax or mail box! Before you place an order, however, here are 25 tips that could save you some grief. 🐞

Mail-order Shopping Tips

1. Be sure you're ordering from a catalog that is current.

2. Read catalog descriptions carefully.

3. If you're ordering a plant, make sure that it is suitable for your climate and growing conditions.

4. Consider whether it is of sufficient size to give you the kind of garden results you expect in your lifetime.

5. Read between the lines, and don't be misled by hype. The word "vigorous" may be a euphemism for a vine that can smother your fence in a single season. Assume that inexpensive "collections" are the most common plants the company grows. A collection may contain a hodgepodge of hues that won't complement your color scheme.

6. Be sure the shipping and handling charges aren't excessive in relation to the order.

7. Order early in the season.

8. Specify exactly what you are ordering; list the name of the item, item number, flower color, size of pot, etc.

9. If you require a specific delivery date, state it clearly.

10. If you don't want a substitute, say so.

11. Be careful about timing when the products are to shipped. While most companies are attentive to the proper time for shipment, the company may not be aware of temperature extremes in your area and certainly can't be expected to know when you'll be away on vacation.

12. If there's a toll-free number, don't hesitate to use it, but be sure you communicate all pertinent information (see previous tips).

13. If the order blank is too small for you to write all the information you wish to convey, photocopy the blank on a larger sheet of paper and use the bottom to write additional information. If the blank is too small to write legibly, look for a copier with enlarging capability.

14. Provide clear, complete shipping instructions. Include your phone number, even if it's not requested. Remember that private shipping companies such as UPS cannot deliver to a post office box.

15. Don't send cash through the mail. Paying by credit card gives you some recourse. Otherwise; send a check or money order.

16. Read the catalog to be sure your preferred method of payment is acceptable to the company.

17. Don't forget to add in shipping, handling and taxes if applicable.

18. Keep a copy of your order. If you're ordering by phone, make notes.

19. Check for and understand the company's guarantee policy to see if they replace plants that die in shipment or fail to thrive in your garden.

20. Open and inspect the package as soon as it arrives.

21. If you have ordered live plants, get them in the ground as soon as possible. If any item fails to thrive, notify the nursery.

22. If you find items missing, notify the company at once.

23. If you need to return or exchange an item, do it immediately.

24. If you put the order on your credit card, check to make sure you were billed the correct amount. If the company offered to refund the price of the catalog with the first order, be sure that amount was actually deducted.

25. Save a tree. Don't order a catalog you don't need. Catalogs are costly to produce. If you regularly receive a catalog that doesn't meet your gardening needs, ask to be dropped from the list. 🌺

Border Protocol

A "Permit to Import" is required for the importation of plants (including seeds) into Canada from the United States and all other countries. Arrangements must be made in advance through the Plant Protection Division of Agriculture Canada in Ottawa. Information about import permits and required phytosanitary certificates on plant materials brought from Canada to the United States can be obtained from the U.S. Department of Agriculture.

The bottom line is that it's a difficult process. **Do not** attempt to buy plant materials to carry across the border in your car! Some nurseries have all the necessary permits and can arrange shipping. Tourists should ask to speak to the nursery manager if they wish something shipped. Most catalogs specify whether the company is set-up to ship between borders. If you're not sure, ask!

With the new North American Free Trade Agreement, it may become less costly to import hard goods. As this book goes to press, it is still wise to inquire about duty fees if you're planning to make any major purchases in a country other than your own. 🌺

Geographical Index

Note: I've listed as ☆DESTINATIONS the places I think are most unusual in terms of visual appeal, personalities and/or historical interest. These are the gardens, nurseries and shops I'd detour to visit on vacation. They are marked in this index with a star. It's all subjective. I believe every source listed in this book has merit. You may have your favorites, and if you disagree with my picks, let me know. My hope is that you'll tuck this book into your glove box when you travel and find it helpful. Please do not drop-in at any place that is "by appointment only." If you're traveling some distance, it's best to confirm days and hours of operation. One more tip: map out your route in advance. Places of interest in the Seattle Metropolitan Area, for example, may be further apart than Spokane, Washington is from Coeur d'Alene, Idaho. Certainly, the travel time will be greater. *NBS*

Washington

Seattle Metropolitan Area

Seattle

Books
Center for Urban Horticulture Library, 26
Flora and Fauna Books, 34

Decorative Accessories
Bruning Pottery, 304
D.E. Dodroe & Co., 304
Fremont Terra Cotta, 313
Gary Word Gallery, 324
Honeychurch Antiques, 326
Kiku Fab Design, 327
Luciano Arts, 305
MacBrides Gift & Garden, 314
Oriental Furniture Warehouse, 306
Price-Ragen ☆, 293

Furniture
Cape Cod Comfys, Inc., 286
Don Willis Furniture, 291
J.F. Henry, 292
Price-Ragen, 293
Yard Leisure, 291

Garden Centers
City People's Garden Store, 330
Five Corners Nursery, 330
Mano's Earlington Greenhouses, 331
Molbak's Seattle Garden Center, 331
Sky Nursery & Garden Center, 332
Sunflower Greenhouse & Garden Center, Inc., 333
Swansons Nursery & Landscape ☆, 333
The Wallingford Garden Spot & Floral, 333
West Seattle Nursery & Garden Center, 334

Hardscape Materials
Lighting Supply, 76
Pratt & Larson, 51
Seattle Lighting Fixture Company, 77
Seattle Sun Systems, 67
Sunglo Solar Greenhouses, 68

Plant Materials
Enchanted Garden, 242
The Garden Shed, 219
Good Shepherd Gardens and Nursery, 132
Indoor Sun Shoppe, 243
Madrona Nursery, 173
Oasis Water Gardens, 235
Sea-Tac Dahlia Gardens, 201
Star Nursery and Landscaping, 143

Soil Builders, Pest Controls & Tools
The Garden Shed, 219
Growers and Associates, 84
Sawdust Supply Company, 87
Woodland Park Zoo, 88

Viewing Gardens
Center for Urban Horticulture ☆, 26
Children's Hospital and Medical Center ☆, 26
Japanese Garden in Washington Park Arboretum ☆, 27
Kubota Garden ☆, 27
Seattle Tilth Association Demonstration Gardens ☆, 27
Volunteer Park Conservatory ☆, 27
Washington Park Arboretum, ☆, 27
Waterfall Garden in Pioneer Square ☆, 27

North Suburban Area

Edmonds

Decorative Accessories
Aw Pottery, 303

Garden Center
Edmonds Garden Center, 334

Lake Forest Park

Plant Materials
Heathwood Cottage Nursery, 154

Lynnwood

Furniture
Rich's Stoves, Spas and Patio, 293

Hardscape Materials
Seattle Lighting Fixture Company, 77

Garden Center
Wight's Garden & Floral ✭, 335

Mill Creek

Garden Center
Wileywood Nursery & Florist, 336

Eastside

Bellevue

Furniture
Al's Easy Livin', 291
Garden Works, 313
Rattan Interiors, 293

Decorative Accessories
Garden Works, 313

Garden Centers
Furney's Nursery, 337
Kimura Nursery, 338
Wells Medina Nursery ✭, 339

Hardscape Materials
ABC Campbell's Children USA, 71
Mutual Materials Co., 49
Seattle Lighting Fixture Company, 77
Terrazzo and Stone Supply Company, 55

Plant Materials
Foliage Gardens, 168
Interlake Plant Store, 251

Viewing Garden
Bellevue Botanical Garden ✭, 26

Bothell

Decorative Accessories
Garden Companions, 313

Furniture
Garden Companions, 294

Hardscape Materials
Backyard Adventures, 72

Plant Materials
Barfod's Hardy Ferns ✭, 167

Soil Builders, Pest Controls & Tools
Pacific Topsoil, Inc., 86

Duvall

Garden Center
Rosarian Gardens, 338

Fall City

Plant Materials
Fall City Greenhouse and Nursery, 250
The Herbfarm ✭, 213

Issaquah

Garden Centers
Hayes Nursery, 337
Squak Mt. Greenhouse & Nursery, 338
Valley Growers, 339

Hardscape Materials
Marenakos Rock Center, 55

Kirkland

Plant Materials & Decorative Accessories
The Sweetbriar, 155

Soil Builders, Pest Controls & Tools
Northwest Landscape Supply, 108

North Bend

Plant Materials
Mt. Si Bonsai, 251

Redmond

Decorative Accessories
Bamboo Gardens of Washington ★, 164
Kenton Designs, 326

Furniture
Elco Fireplace & Patio, 292

Garden Center
Evans Creek Nursery, 337

Plant Materials
Bamboo Gardens of Washington, 164
Hillcroft Nursery, Inc., 173

Woodinville
Note: also see Snohomish, if you're in the area.
Many of the locations are near Woodinville.

Garden Center
Molbak's ★, 335

Plant Materials
Baker & Chantry Orchids, Inc., 242
Bassetti's Crooked Arbor Gardens ★, 229
Cottage Creek Nursery, 172
Olympic Nursery, 142
Pat's Perennials ★, 174

South Suburban Area

Des Moines

Garden Center
Furney's Nursery, 340

Kent

Plant Materials
Pearson's Nursery, 252

Maple Valley

Hardscape Materials
The Playground Store, 72

Soil Builders, Pest Controls & Tools
Cedar Grove Compost Co., 86

Renton

Plant Materials
Alpine Nursery, Inc., 141
Hazelwood Gardens Rhododendron Nursery,
  152
Soos Creek Gardens, 236
Tropical Foliage Unlimited, 244

Tukwila

Furniture
Rattan Interiors, 293

Hardscape Materials
Seattle Lighting Fixture Company, 77

Plant Materials
Bonsai Northwest, 256

Islands in the Sound

Bainbridge Island

Decorative Accessories
Rail-Rider Products, 308

Garden Center
Bainbridge Gardens ★, 340

Plant Materials
Agate Nursery, 174
Harbor Crest Bonsai, 257

Viewing Garden
The Bloedel Reserve ★, 26

Vashon Island

Garden Center
The Country Store & Farm ★, 175

Plant Materials
Colvos Creek Farm ★, 262
Puget Garden Resources, 175

Whidbey Island

Clinton

Plant Materials
Cultus Bay Nursery, 175

Lake Stevens

Plant Materials
Silver Sun Nursery, 154

Lynden

Hardscape Materials
Garden Cedar Inc., 61

Marysville

Garden Center
Cascade Nursery, 346

Monroe

Plant Materials
West Coast Wholesale Nursery, 144

Mount Vernon

Garden Centers
Hart's Nursery ✮, 346
Skagit Valley Gardens, 347

Hardscape Materials
Charley's Greenhouse Supply, 66

Plant Materials
Roozengaarde ✮, 195
Wells Nursery, 143

Sedro Wooley

Plant Materials
Fruitdale Nursery, 250
Thompson's Greenhouse, 178

Snohomish

Decorative Accessories
The Hearts of the Garden, 314
Nichols Bros. Stoneworks, 305

Plant Materials
A&D Peony and Perennial Nursery ✮, 176
Cricklewood ✮, 177
Flower World ✮, 250
Kattenhorn Gardens, 154
Mollgaard Floral, 251
Shinoda Floral, 244
Walsterway Iris Gardens, 198
Willow Creek Farm & Nursery, 179

Stanwood

Plant Materials
The Gathering Garden ✮, 178
Stanwood Nursery, 120
Waverly Gardens ✮, 179

Olympic Peninsula

Bremerton

Garden Center
Furney's Nursery, 348

Plant Materials
Silver Bay Herb Farm, 214

Brinnon

Plant Materials
Whitney Gardens & Nursery ✮, 155

Humptulips

Furniture
Humptulips Cedar Furniture, 288

Plant Materials
Hollyvale Farm, 142

Kingston

Plant Materials
Heronswood Nursery ✮, 265
Pacific Wetlands Nursery, 129

Port Angeles

Plant Materials
A&R Propagating, 151
Pacific Plant Company, 118

Port Orchard

Soil Builders, Pest Controls & Tools
West Sound Landscaping Supplies, 108

Port Townsend

Plant Materials
B&D Lilies, 199

Sumner

Garden Center
Windmill Nursery, 353

Tacoma

Decorative Accessories
Old Main Street, 77

Furniture
Rattan Interiors, 294

Garden Centers
Evergreen Gardens & Gifts, 353
Poole's Nursery Center, Inc., 354
Portland Ave. Nursery, Inc., 355

Hardscape Materials
Old Main Street, 77
Seattle Lighting Fixture Company, 77

Plant Materials
Connell's Dahlias, 200
Chieri Orchids, 242

Viewing Garden
Lakewold ✭, 28
W.W. Seymour Botanical Conservatory ✭, 29

Olympia Area & Twin Cities

Centralia

Garden Center
Pioneer West, 355

Chehalis

Plant Materials
Chehalis Rare Plant Nursery, 229

Eatonville

Plant Materials
James Rhododendron Nursery, 153

Elma

Plant Materials
Heather Acres, 153

Lacey

Garden Center
College Street Nursery, 156

Morton

Plant Materials
Raintree Nursery, 375

Mossyrock

Plant Materials
Natives Northwest, 117

Olympia

Garden Center
Boulevard Nursery & Greenhouse, 356

Plant Materials
Black Lake Organic Farms and Garden Store, 218
The Lily Pad, 200

Onalaska

Plant Materials
Burnt Ridge Nursery & Orchards, 206

Tumwater

Plant Materials
Fairie Herbe Gardens, 212

Yelm

Garden Center
Gordon's Garden Center, 357

Central Washington

Brewster

Garden Center
Wilson Gardens, 357

Yakima

Garden Center
Evans Nursery, 358

Plant Materials
Loo Wit Gardens, 183

Vancouver

Furniture
Sparks Home Furnishings, 295

Garden Center
Kasch's, 362

Hardscape Materials
Builders Lighting, 78

Plant Materials
Aitken's Salmon Creek Garden, 196
Legato's Garden, 251
Lilies and More, 199
Robyn's Nest Nursery, 184

Viewing Garden
Hudson's Bay Gardens ★, 29

White Salmon

Garden Center
Fruit Valley Greenhouse, 362

Woodland

Garden Centers
Circle S Landscape Supplies, Ltd., 363
Tsugawa Nursery & Watergardens ★, 363

Plant Materials
Lewis River Reforestation, Inc., 129

Oregon

Portland Metropolitan Area

Portland

Decorative Accessories
Backyard Bird Shop, 123
Contemporary Crafts Gallery, 322
Northwest Garden & Topiary, 316
Oregon Garden Store, 317
Wildwood Garden Furnishings ★, 328
Yardbirds, 318

Furniture
Fishel's ★, 296
Ludeman's, Inc., 296
Oregon Garden Store, 296
Wildwood Garden Furnishings, 297

Garden Centers
Cornell Farm, 364
Dennis' 7 Dees Nursery, 364
Drake's 7 Dees, 365
Fred Meyer, Raleigh Hills, 365
Georges Garden, 365
Kasch's, 366
Langdown Florist & Greenhouses, 366
Oregon Garden Store, 367
Portland Nursery ★, 367

Hardscape Materials
A-1 Quality Pickett Fence, 60
Creative Play Structures, Inc., 73
Heartland Industries, 69
Gazebos 'N' Gardens, 62
Ludeman's, Inc., 73
Moore/Lawrence Greenhouse Mfg., Inc., 67
Pratt & Larson, 53
Rain or Shine, 110
Sturdi-built Greenhouse Mfg. Co., 67
Wildwood Playgrounds, 71

Plant Materials
Bonsai Artworks, 258
Bovees Nursery ★, 156
Dragonfly Gardens, 116
Emerald Hydro-Turf, Inc., 125
The Plant Peddler, 245

Soil Builders, Pest Controls & Tools
Metro Washington Park Zoo, 89
North American Soils, 89
Rain or Shine, 110

Viewing Gardens
Berry Botanic Garden ★, 30
Elk Rock/ The Bishop's Close ★, 30
Fir Acres/ Lewis and Clark College ★, 30
Hoyt Arboretum ★, 30
Japanese Garden in Washington Park ★, 30
Leach Botanical Garden ★, 30

East Suburban Area

Clackamas

*Decorative Accessories & Hardscape
  Materials*
Riehl Industries, 310

Plant Materials
The Plantsmen Nursery, 147

Corbett

Plant Materials
Bonnie Brae Gardens, 193
Columbia Gorge Daffodil & Tree Farm, 193
Oregon Trail Daffodils, 194

Eagle Creek

Plant Materials
American Ornamental Perennials, 132
Goose Creek Nursery, 254

Estacada

Garden Center
McGregor's Garden Center, 368

Plant Materials
Brentwood Park Organics, 220
Squaw Mountain Gardens, 232

Soil Builders & Pest Controls
Brentwood Park Organics, 220

Gresham

Decorative Accessories
Backyard Bird Shop, 123

Plant Materials
Kasch Nursery, 369
Sandy Nursery, 147

Milwaukie

Decorative Accessories
Sol's Garden Decorations, 311

Plant Materials
Rare Plant Research, 246

Soil Builders, Pest Controls & Tools
McFarland's Bark, Inc., 89

Sandy

Plant Materials
Dover Nursery, 156
Porterhowse Farms, 231

Troutdale

Garden Center
Circle S Landscape Supplies, Ltd., 368

Columbia Gorge

Hood River

Plant Materials
Rasmussen Farms, 255

Parkdale

Plant Materials
Wood's Native Plants, 121

West Suburban Area

Aloha

Hardscape & Plant Materials
Clearwater Fish & Pond Supply, Inc. ★, 237

Viewing Garden
Jenkins Estate ★, 30

Banks

Decorative Accessories
Carillon Wind Chimes, 310

Furniture & Hardscape Materials
Swings by Jandon, 289

Beaverton

Decorative Accessories
Backyard Bird Shop, 123

Garden Center
Kasch's, 369

Hardscape Materials
Oregon Decorative Rock Co., 56

Plant Materials
Oregon Miniature Roses, 162

Cornelius

Plant Materials
Big Trees Today of Oregon, Inc., 144

Forest Grove

Plant Materials
Dutchmill Herb Farm, 215
Five Star Gardens, 145

Hillsboro

Decorative Accessories
Bald Peak Woodworks, 308
Topiary or Not Topiary, 312

Furniture
Bald Peak Woodworks, 286

Garden Center
Kasch's, 369

Plant Materials
Chehalem Mountain Nursery, Inc., 145

North Plains

Plant Materials
Blossom Creek Greenhouse, 245

Scappose

Garden Center
Means Nursery, Inc., 369

South Suburban Area

Canby

Garden Center
Northwoods Nursery, 371

Plant Materials
Hazel Dell Gardens, 146
Swan Island Dahlias, 202

Oregon City

Garden Center
Evans Farms, 369

Sherwood

Garden Center
Loen Nursery Company, 370

Plant Materials
Caprice Farm Nursery ★, 184
Red's Rhodies, 246

Tigard

Garden Center
Kasch's, 370

Tualatin

Hardscape Materials
Builders Lighting, Inc., 78
Interstate Rock Products, Inc., 56
E.F. Hughes Water Gardens, 237

Soil Builders, Pest Controls & Tools
Grimm's Fuel Company, 89

West Linn

Decorative Accessories
The Cottage Garden, 315

Plant Materials
Boske Dell Natives, 115
Stubbs Shrubs, 157

Wilsonville

Plant Materials
Barn Owl Nursery, 215
Edmunds' Roses, 160
Justice Miniature Roses, 162

Willamette Valley

Albany

Garden Center
Tom's Garden Center, 371

Plant Materials
Nichols Garden Nursery, 216
Stone Crop Gardens, 232

Aurora

Plant Materials
Bonsai Village, 258
Phil Parker, 118

Corvallis

Decorative Accessories
Dancing Waters, 323

Garden Centers
Garland Nursery & Wee Tree Farm ★, 372
Shonnard's Nursery & Florist, 372

North Oregon Coast

Cloverdale

Plant Materials
Loucks Nursery, 146

Eddyville

Plant Materials
Qualitree Inc., 130

Lincoln City

Decorative Accessories
Statueland, 311

Neskowin

Decorative Accessories
The Artist's Garden at Hawk Creek Gallery, 322

Newport

Plant Materials
Yaquina Nursery and Greenhouses, Inc., 247

Rose Lodge

Garden Center
Brown's Rose Lodge Nursery, 375

Seaside

Garden Center
Raintree Garden & Gift Center ✮, 375

South Beach

Plant Materials
Ferris Nursery, 116
Wisteria Herbs and Flowers, 187

Waldport

Plant Materials
Willard Thompson Nursery, 157

Eugene & South Oregon Coast

Bandon

Plant Materials
Growth Unlimited Nursery, Inc., 129

Coos Bay

Viewing Garden
Shore Acres Botanic Garden ✮, 31

Cottage Grove

Plant Materials
Territorial Seed Company, 221

Drain

Plant Materials
Kelleygreen Rhododendron Nursery, 157

Eugene

Furniture
Emerald Pool & Patio, 297

Garden Centers
Down To Earth ✮, 376
Duckworth's Nursery, 376
Glenwood Nursery, Inc., 377
Gray's Garden Centers, 377

Plant Materials
Greer Gardens ✮, 264
Lorane Hills Farm & Nursery, 188

Soil Builders, Pest Controls & Tools
Down To Earth, 84
International Reforestation Suppliers, 109
Mallory Growers and Landscape Supply, 110

Hardscape Materials
Oregon Timberframe, 63

Lorane

Plant Materials
Balance Restoration Nursery, 128

Springfield

Garden Center
Gray's Garden Centers, 377

Plant Materials
Gossler Farm's Nursery ☆, 264

Southern Oregon

Ashland

Decorative Accessories
Secret Garden, 317

Plant Materials
Valley View Nursery, 378

Grants Pass

Hardscape Materials
Cascade Block, 52

Medford

Decorative Accessories
Harry & David's Original Country Store, 316

Furniture
Pool & Patio Place, 297
Rogue River Rustics, 288

Garden Centers
Bonsai Gardens, 378
Stagecoach Farms Nursery, 379

Hardscape Materials
Cascade Block, 52
Interstate Stone, 56

Plant Materials
Harry & David's Original Country Store, 316
Ponderings Plus, 238
Siskiyou Rare Plant Nursery ☆, 265

Viewing Garden
Jackson & Perkins ☆, 162

Rogue River

Plant Materials
Sunrise Water Gardens, 238

Talent

Decorative Accessories
Granite Impressions, 325

Williams

Plant Materials
Forestfarm ☆, 263

Winston

Garden Center
Wildwood Nursery ☆, 379

Central Oregon

Bend

Furniture
Fireside Spa and Patio, 297
The Lift, 298

Garden Center
Landsystems Nursery, 380

Hardscape Materials
Central Oregon Tile, 52

Plant Materials
Joyce's Garden, 189

Northeast Oregon

Hermiston

Garden Center
Westwinds Nursery, Turf and Landscape, 381

Idaho

Southwest Idaho

Boise

Decorative Accessories
Boise Botanical, 318

Furniture
Michael's Furniture Showplace, 298

Garden Centers
Sterling Nursery ☆, 382
Union Farm & Garden, 383

Hardscape Materials
Rocktile Specialty Products, 50
Boise Stone, 57

Plant Materials
Edward's Greenhouse, 190
Franz Witte Landscape Company, 148

Viewing Garden
Idaho Botanical Garden ★, 31

Nampa
Garden Center
Greenhurst Nursery & Garden Center, 383

Northern Idaho

Coeur d'Alene

Garden Center
Duncan's Garden Center & Nursery, 384

Moscow

Garden Center
Hillside Nursery, 384

Orofino

Garden Center
Green Things, 385

Sandpoint

Garden Center
Lee's Nursery, 385

Plant Materials
Mountain Springs Nursery, 148
The Peaceable Kingdom, 216

Central Idaho

Bellevue

Garden Center
Webb Nursery, 386

Ketchum

Garden Center
Webb Nursery, 386

Twin Falls

Garden Center
Kimberly Nurseries, Inc., 386

Southeast Idaho

Chubbock

Garden Center
Kimberly Nurseries East, 387

Idaho Falls

Garden Center
Town & Country Gardens, Inc., 387

Pocatello

Hardscape Materials
Mountain Tile Distributers, 53

Plant Materials
Pocatello Sod & Trees, 148

British Columbia

Vancouver Metropolitan Area

Vancouver

Decorative Accessories
The Avant Gardener, 319
Dig This, 320
Gardens Antique, 324
Earthrise, 324
Hobbs ★, 325
Shop in the Garden ★, 320

Furniture
Courtyards Casual Furniture, 299

Garden Centres
Ford's Flowers & Nursery, 388
Southlands Nursery Ltd. ★, 389

Hardscape Materials
Adera Natural Stone Supply Ltd., 57
Robinson Lighting, 78
Tile Town, 54

Plant Materials
Japan Bonsai, 260
Shop in the Garden, 320
Takamatsu Bonsai Design, 260

Chilliwack

Garden Centres
Cannor Nurseries, 393
Country Garden Ltd. ☆, 393

Langley

Plant Materials
Lindel Lilies, 200
Trees Unlimited, 149

Maple Ridge

Plant Materials
Rainforest Gardens, 191

Mission

Furniture
Great Canadian Basket Company, 287

Plant Materials
Ferncliff Gardens, 201

Rosedale

Viewing Garden
Minter Gardens ☆, 33

Sardis

Garden Centre
Country Garden World, 394

Howe Sound Area

Gibsons

Furniture
Timothy Clement, 289

Squamish

Soil Builders, Pest Controls & Tools
Coast Mountain Beauty Bark Ltd., 90

Peace River

Prince George

Plant Materials

Home Grown Plants & Hydroponics, 248

Vancouver Island

Bowser

Plant Materials
All Season Nursery, 259

Comox

Garden Centre
Anderton Nursery, 394

Duncan

Garden Centre
B. Dinter Nursery Ltd., 394

Soil Builders, Pest Controls & Tools
Neiser's Forest & Garden, Ltd., 111

Fanny Bay

Plant Materials
Island Sun Greenhouses, 256

Ganges

Garden Centre
Hallman Landscape Associates, 395

Plant Materials
Fraser's Thimble Farms, 117

Nanaimo

Garden Centre
Green Thumb Garden Centre, 395

Port Alberni

Furniture
Sarita Furniture Ltd., 288

Index of Sources

Bold page numbers indicate main listing.

Nomination Form

Based upon my personal experience, I wish to nominate the following garden source for inclusion in the next edition of Great Garden Sources of the Pacific Nothwest. Please include the sources name, address, phone number and your comments or observations in the space provided below, on a photocopy of this page, or on a separate sheet of paper. Mail or FAX forms to the publisher.

_____

Source Name

_____

Address

_____

_____

City, State/Province & ZIP/Postal Code

_____

Phone

Comments & Observations

_____

_____

_____

_____

_____

_____

_____

_____

To be considered, please include your name, address and phone number below.

_____

Your Name

_____

Address

_____

City, State/Province & ZIP/Postal Code

_____

Your Phone

May we telephone you for more information about your nominee?

❑ YES

❑ NO

Please mail or FAX your nomination to:

The **Authors** Communication Team
Post Office Box 25211
Portland, Oregon 97225 U.S.A.
Facsimile 503/297-0873

First Printing February, 1994